FEDERAL STATISTICS

report
of
the
President's
Commission

Volume II
1971

For sale by the Superintendent of Documents, U.S. Government Printing Office
Washington, D.C. 20402 - Price $4 per set of 2 volumes; sold in sets only
Stock Number 4000-0269

TABLE OF CONTENTS

VOLUME II

i

VOLUME I

TABLE OF CONTENTS

iii

THE ROLE AND FEASIBILITY OF A NATIONAL DATA BANK, BASED ON MATCHED RECORDS AND ALTERNATIVES

By

Morris H. Hansen

THE ROLE AND FEASIBILITY OF A NATIONAL DATA BANK, BASED ON MATCHED RECORDS AND ALTERNATIVES

TABLE OF CONTENTS

SUMMARY

The creation of a national statistical data bank has been proposed to be accomplished by the comprehensive matching of individual federal records such as Census returns, federal tax and Social Security records and others. The purpose is to provide statistical information that interrelates the various items available in the different record systems. An important goal is to facilitate the retrieval of statistical summaries of micro data in various forms to serve specific needs as they arise. The confidentiality of the individual records would be preserved — the proposed system would be such that only statistical summaries could be retrieved.

This paper examines the role of such a national data bank, problems it raises, and possible alternatives. It makes the following principal points:

1. The comprehensive linking of massive files is a simple operation and relatively inexpensive when the records to be linked contain standard identifiers on which the files can be ordered and compared. When the files do not contain standard identifiers, and in addition when they do not have identical time references and

do not observe the same conventions in the recording of identifying information, the automatic linking of files is feasible, but the process is far more costly, matching errors are substantially increased, and manual intervention may be necessary to resolve many problems. Standard identifiers are not included in some of the important and essential files proposed to be linked, and even where they exist the units identified may not be comparable over time or between record systems.

2. The proposals for a comprehensive linking of files have been the source of much concern and criticism from the Congress, the press, and others because of the potential for invasion of individual privacy. The expressed concern has been strong despite assurances given that the confidentiality of the individual records would be preserved.

3. In my judgment the additional statistical results that can be achieved by comprehensive linking of federal records would be far less than seems to be anticipated by many who advocate this major development. While the records available to be matched do contain many important items of information, they frequently lack information that is essential to a particular study. Moreover, the desired integration of information can often be more readily accomplished by a sample survey or from the Census, or by record linking as needed for a small sample, or by a combination of these.

4. Much can be accomplished by linking the particular records as they are needed and when required, without a comprehensive and continuing record integration system. Some studies involving comprehensive integration of two or more sets of records, and a considerable number of relatively small sample studies have been done. Relatively small sample studies that integrate information from two or more record systems do not provide the basis for and have not aroused general concern and criticism about invasion of privacy. Presumably many additional needs can be reasonably served by such studies, designed to be responsive to particular problems. In such sample projects needed supplemental information often can be provided by direct data collection. Moreover, I believe that the Congress and the public will support such sample studies without arousing serious concern and criticism about the potential for invasion of privacy.

5. It may be desirable, in addition, to develop a small general-purpose sample study, involving record linking and perhaps also supplemental data collection, that can be immediately responsive to many additional needs for information without awaiting the design and completion of such studies.

6. Such alternative approaches should be examined before embarking on a massive record-matching project, involving hundreds of millions of records, with new or updated records becoming available each year.

7. Even if such a massive integrated record system were created, there are disclosure problems that have not received adequate attention and that might defeat the purposes for which the system was established.

INTRODUCTION

This paper examines the role of a national data bank based on individual matched federal records, the problems involved in matching and in assuring confidentiality of individual records, and alternative means for obtaining needed information.

The proposals for a federal data center developed out of a series of reports. The initial report was prepared by a committee of the Social Science Research Council, under the chairmanship of Richard Ruggles, on the preservation and use of economic data. This report emphasized the need for and the great capability of the computer to extract information in forms as needed. It also emphasized the need for preservation of data tapes after they had served their initial purposes, instead of allowing their loss, as was common practice in the statistical and administrative agencies. It recommended the creation of a federal data center to accomplish the preservation of records and to provide storage facilities and retrieval and related services. It also recommended taking steps to facilitate the integration of data from different sources.

Subsequently, the Office of Statistical Standards of the Bureau of the Budget arranged with Edgar S. Dunn, Jr., acting as a consultant, to examine the Ruggles Committee report and make recommendations concerning its implementation. Dunn, with support from some additional federal staff reports, placed strong emphasis on the interrelationship of records. He stated that "the greatest

7

deficiency in the existing federal statistical system is its failure to provide access to data in a way that permits the association of the elements of data sets in order to identify and measure the relationship among independent activities." He recommended the establishment of a National Data Service Center whose primary mission would be to provide services to users of federal statistical data both inside and outside of the government. He examined alternative organizational approaches for solving some of the problems and for accomplishing the recommended program developments.

As these reports became available and discussions progressed, great concern was expressed in the Congress and in the press concerning the implications for invasion of privacy. Extensive hearings were held, and the Special Subcommittee on Invasion of Privacy of the Committee on Government Operations, under the chairmanship of Congressman Cornelius E. Gallagher, prepared a report.

In the meantime the Bureau of the Budget appointed a committee on the storage of and access to government statistics, under the chairmanship of Carl Kaysen. In completing its assignment, this committee re-examined how the federal statistical system could be organized and operated so as to serve the needs of users more effectively. It viewed with concern the consequences of the increasing trends toward decentralization of statistics, and the increasing difficulty, in this setting, of achieving the goals of providing access to and integration of information for statistical purposes.

Again, the Kaysen Committee placed strong emphasis on the need for integrating information from various record systems, and for finding means for increasing access to micro data of both individual and integrated records. It recognized the need to preserve the confidentiality of the data and thereby to avoid the invasion of privacy. Its recommendations incorporate and extend those of the earlier reports, as follows:

> "The Federal Statistical System has three basic functions; namely, (1) collection, (2) integration and storage in accessible form, and (3) analysis, tabulation, and publication. It is reorganizing the second that offers the most promise. This function is now

8

the least well-performed of the three, and it is the one which is most easily separated out from the present organizational structure. However, it must be done on a substantial scale, and in such a way as to recognize the interaction of this function with the other two. Further, the new organization must not be confined to a merely archival function. If it is defined along the lines suggested below, it offers the best promise, in the judgment of the Committee, for starting the development of the Federal Statistical System toward a more integrated and efficient form.

Accordingly, the Committee proposes the creation of a National Data Center. *This Center would be given the responsibility for: (1)assembling in a single facility all large-scale systematic bodies of demographic, economic, and social data generated by the present data-collection or administrative processes of the Federal Government, (2) integrating the data to the maximum feasible extent, and in such a way as to preserve as much as possible of the original information content of the whole body of records, and (3) providing ready access to the information, within the laws governing disclosure, to all users in the Government and, where appropriate, to qualified users outside the Government on suitably compensatory terms. The Center would be further charged with cooperation with state and local government agencies to assist in providing uniformity in their data bases, and to receive from them, integrated into the federally generated data stock, store, and make accessible, the further information these agencies generate. The funding and staffing of the Center should recognize both these functions.*

In more detail, the functions of the Center would be:

1. *To establish and maintain an inventory of all available data in the relevant categories in the Federal System.*

2. To set and enforce uniform disclosure standards so that the legal requirement of confidentiality can be met with no unnecessary sacrifice of analytically useful information.
3. Similarly, in cooperation with the state and local government units, to perform similar tasks for information generated at those levels of government.
4. To assemble centrally the data from all these sources, integrate it to the maximum feasible extent, and preserve it in usable and accessible form. This will involve:

The maximum ability to exhibit the interrelations of various kinds of data.

The preservation of detail in basic records, and the avoidance of the loss of information in the storage, manipulation and retrieval of information.

The ability to produce the full measure of inherent information which is computable from the basic records.

5. In cooperation with users in and out of government and collection agencies, to set the standards for further collection efforts, so as to make maximum use of administrative information and provide maximum cross-linking of different bodies of data.
6. To provide facilities — from working space to linked input-output consoles — for major users within government to facilitate their access to the data and improve their ability to work with it.
7. To develop software and hardware, especially input and output devices.
8. To define the regulations and compensation arrangements under which non-government users would have access to data in the Center. In general, subject to disclosure restrictions, standard

tabulations and tapes could be made available at cost to private users for research and analytical purposes. However, the Center should not become a service bureau or data-processing agency selling special order analyses to private users in competition with firms and individuals in the information processing industry."

The Kaysen Committee proposed establishing a Director of the Federal Statistical System in the Office of the President, transferring the Office of Statistical Standards and the Bureau of the Census to this office, as separate units, and creating within it the National Data Center as a parallel unit. It would work in close cooperation with and in physical proximity to the Bureau of the Census. Also recommended was the creation of a Federal Statistical Council representing the major data-producing and -using agencies in the system. It would report to the Director of the Federal Statistical System.

The Committee anticipated that this approach not only would provide data center facilities and services, but also would be a force toward increasing use of the central statistical agencies rather than encouraging increased decentralization of the federal statistical system.

The Kaysen Committee emphasized strongly the importance of and the potential for use of micro information. This need and emphasis relate to access to micro records (subject to disclosure limitations) of individual record systems, and also to interrelated micro information from the files of the various agencies. Its recommendations were strongly directed toward achieving this goal.

Some Preliminary Comments

Considerable progress on improved access to statistical information has been achieved in the past several years. Nevertheless, I believe that much remains to be done, that emphasis on the means for improved access to information is needed and is important, and that additional steps should be taken to preserve important records. Additional centralization of the federal system along the lines recommended by the Kaysen Committee should be a major advance in achieving these and other goals, and as a part of this development, a somewhat less ambitious federal data center

11

should be established along the general lines recommended.

Nevertheless, it is my judgment, based on the evidence and arguments in the subsequent discussion, that the great emphasis on the feasibility and the importance to data users of a massive program of integrating to the fullest extent feasible the various federal statistical records on a micro record basis does not hold the promise in effective use that is implied in these recommendations, at least in the near future. Much of what can usefully be done in this regard can be done better and at lower cost on a sample basis, with *ad hoc* record-matching as needed. A considerable amount has been done. Also, a continuing integrated record study on a very small sample scale is feasible, and I believe it is desirable.

Much of the discussion of a data center seems to imply that once it is in existence and operating, extensive and very low-cost information of greatly increased utility will become massively available. Such impressions, if they exist, seem to me to be mistaken and they have drawn attention away from more limited worthwhile developments in integrated records to meet identified needs, and from a systematic approach to improving the federal statistical system and data preservation and access that is highly desirable and feasible.

I should add that the great and I believe unnecessary emphasis on integrating and matching micro records on a massive basis and to the fullest extent feasible has been the cause of concern in the Congress and elsewhere about invasion of privacy. While I do not believe that a properly protected statistical data system with integrated records would result in all of the problems in preserving confidentiality and preventing invasion of privacy that the critics assert, nevertheless the mere discussion of integration of records on such a massive scale has created a continuing obstacle, and, in my opinion, an unnecessary one, for achieving worthwhile statistical goals. With the far more modest approach of integrating records to serve identified statistical needs, and ordinarily using only relatively small samples in studies that integrate records for people, I believe that most of this criticism will disappear, and such a program will go forward unhandicapped.

In the discussion that follows, I shall attempt to make clear the basis for the views I have expressed.

THE PRINCIPLES AND PROBLEMS OF
MATCHING RECORDS, WITH ILLUSTRATIONS

Some Principles

A considerable amount has been done on the theory, methods, and practice of matching or "linking" records from two or more record systems. Some of the relevant literature is cited at the end of this paper which describes methods, theory, and results, and here I shall briefly mention only a few principles.

The terminology that has gained some acceptance will be useful. We say that a "match" of records is the true correspondence of the records, and that the records are "linked" in an operation when they are treated as though they match. Thus, there are two kinds of errors in a system or procedure for linking records. The first is linking records that do not match, and the second is failing to link records that do match. One may be able to assess the costs of controlling errors at various levels, the cost of each type of error, the costs of alternative methods, and arrive at a reasonably close approximation to optimum methods and rules for linking records.

It is desirable, if the purposes of a record-linking study are to be accomplished, to keep both kinds of errors at a reasonably low level, although in some situations it is a more serious problem to erroneously link records that do not match than it is to fail to link records that do match, and *vice versa*. To avoid the erroneous linking of records that do not match calls for the use of "tight" linking rules, *i.e.* the linking of only those records for which the evidence is strong that a match in fact exists. Thus, in cashing a check a bank ordinarily prefers to have "tight" linking rules and thereby reduce the risk of errors of the first type. In some statistical studies it may be preferable to have a low linking rate, and reasonable assurance that the linked records are in fact a match, than the alternative, but if this leads to the exclusion of a large fraction of the records it may not be a very satisfactory solution. The second situation, where it is preferable to link records in error rather than fail to link records that do match, may result in linking many records that do not match and often calls for the multiple

13

linking of the same records where the tentative links are to be investigated more fully to establish the final record linkages for the study, presumably based on more effort and evidence, and considerably tighter linking rules.

By enough care and effort, or with the proper identification aids, it may be possible to hold both kinds of errors to a reasonably low level. In statistical inquiries it is ordinarily highly desirable, but may not be feasible, to achieve the desired low level of errors, depending on the information available for use, the rules followed in linking, and the effort expended on potential problems.

The linking of two files of any size is relatively straightforward even if one or both of the files is very large provided there is a unique identifier for each record and each of the files can be ordered on the basis of this identifier for record-by-record comparison and linking. However, when there is no such unique identifier system, and when many of the records have errors in the identifiers, differences in the way the name and address is recorded, differences in time references, and differences in other information, it may be necessary to compare several or many different records in one file as potential matches with several or many different records in the other file. It is then difficult to put them in an order to limit the number of comparisons and at the same time insure that in fact a sufficiently high proportion of matching records have a high probability of being linked. In such circumstances the amount of work per record linked and the potential for error increases substantially as the size of the file increases.

Record Linkage on the Basis of Name, Address, and Certain Other Characteristics

The kinds of information used and useful in linking records depend on the nature of the units involved. If we are trying to link records for individual people perhaps the most common items to be used, in the absence of an identifying numbering system, are name and address. Comparability of addresses is a common problem, especially because of the extensive movement of the population. Names, also, may appear differently in different files. Other

14

factors are sometimes used as identifiers, if available in the record sources, including age, sex, place of birth, and other items. The greater the number of items used as linking criteria the greater the chance of assuring that a link is in fact a match, and at the same time, the greater the chance of making errors of the second type and not linking records that are in fact matches. This can arise with tight matching rules because of differences between the two records for various reasons, in the source information as well as because of differences in the conventions observed in recording the information.

The problems of computer linking of two or more very large record files on the basis of name, address, and other information, where the files are not identical with respect to the time references of the addresses, spelling, or the conventions in recording names and other information, and in the absence of an adequate and comprehensive identification numbering or other symbol system, are becoming more widely recognized. Computers, with the present state of understanding and software development, have difficulty in using such information with anything like the flexibility that a human being can bring to the task. Differences in addresses are a special problem. Differences in spacing, spelling, punctuation, abbreviation, and various conventions can, with tight linking rules, cause great reductions in the proportion of matched records that are in fact linked. Looser rules can cause the linking of large numbers of unmatched records. Much progress has been made in increasing the flexibility of software to deal with such problems, but the best automated approaches today are still *far* short, in applying needed reason and imagination to the many problems encountered in record-linking, of what can be accomplished by a human being.

In practice, a procedure found to be effective in linking records that do not contain unique and comprehensive identification systems for each member of the population is to take full advantage of automated matching, separately identify the links that have a very high probability of being matches, and then identify tentatively one or more links for those records which have some apparent potential for becoming a match. Human beings then intervene and apply far greater flexibility and judgment in making determinations on the marginal cases. This system has been reasonably successful in a number of applications. Problems of the quality of the product achieved, and of the cost, or both may be involved. In practice, priority rules for weighing the evidence are established based on prior experience and studies, often with a scoring system such that pairs of records with scores above a certain level are linked, and those below are not. Sometimes, in a statistical study, an intermediate class is tabulated separately, consisting of records that are dubiously linked.

Without standardized record formats or an adequate identifying numbering system, the problems of achieving high linkage, with low matching errors, are still very great in situations where there are tens of millions, or even hundreds of millions of records in one or both of the files being linked, and the files are not controlled and completely comparable on names, addresses, and the time references for addresses. These observations have taken no account of the added problems of name changes, especially for women when they marry. Procedures for dealing with this problem need to be included in a record-linking system.

As a consequence of these problems, computer linking of large files of records that do not have a controlled identification system is fraught with difficulty, and, in practice, extensive human intervention and manual work are required to achieve satisfactory linking of records without high levels of errors, or, alternatively, the record-linking fails to match many and a high proportion of records that should match.

Increasingly sophisticated rules, weighting systems based on different types of evidence, and record-linking algorithms for linking records on computers have been created and are under development. Substantial progress has been made. But very much remains to be accomplished. In the absence of an adequate identification system that is in essentially full use in any large record system to be linked, we are far from being able to regard the problems of the automated record-linking system as reasonably solved. The tremendous power of the computer is still insufficient to meet at low cost the logical and other problems that remain.

The linking of records for families, households, or business establishments on the basis of name or names, address, and possibly other supplemental information poses an even more difficult situation. A person is a uniquely defined entity. He exists, and in theory at least, is uniquely identifiable, and a person is the same entity at one point in time as another. There may be errors in identifying him. However, there is no conceptual problem — just an operating one. This is not at all true with respect to the units such as business establishments, business concerns, families, households, and many other such artificially defined units. Consequently, the efforts to match such units involve substantial additional hazards, and in practical record-linking operations these hazards are found to be real and cause great difficulty. For such units a tight matching rule is not sufficient to identify the same unit in two different records or especially at two points in time. The identifying characteristics may be complete and identical in the two record systems, but the unit, such as the business establishment, may not be comparable in a useful sense. There may have been a consolidation of two establishments, or other major change, and this change may not be reflected at all in the identifying characteristics but may be of real substance and cause difficulties in statistical interpretations. As another example, the persons reported in an individual tax return, taxpayers and dependents, often will be different from the family or the household members at the same address even when such identifying characteristics as name and address, and even Social Security numbers for the taxpayer or taxpayers agree.

Record Linkage on the Basis of a Comprehensive and Adequate Number Identification System, With Stable Units

The situation is very different if an adequate, comprehensive, and standardized numbering or other identification system is in effective use in two or more record systems that are to be linked, and if the units to be matched are stable entities, such as people, and not constantly going through changes and transformations that affect the basic entity, as with families, business establishments, and many other social and economic units.

A comprehensive numbering system with stable units would exist if we were to establish a system embracing the population, assign numbers to all persons at birth, not allow duplicates and carry the numbers into the relevant record systems. This is the situation that currently exists in the Scandinavian countries, and a few others. Numbers are assigned at birth that follow persons throughout their lives and are included in their records. This system is being used to develop massive record-linkage systems with the computer. I am not fully informed on where it stands today, but it was in the developmental stage four years ago, and presumably still is, because even in this situation there are problems. Nevertheless, we have many demonstrations that, with the power of the modern computer, large record systems can be effectively linked under such circumstances.

In the United States, we have large files that can be interrelated automatically both between record systems or for records within a system for different points or intervals of time, and produce statistically valid results, at least to the extent that the data relate to the persons assigned the numbers (and not, for example, to groups of persons such as a taxpayer or taxpayers plus dependents). These files relate to those persons that are identified within the Social Security and Internal Revenue Service record systems. In both of these the Social Security number has been adopted, is used consistently, and is comparably recorded in both systems. There is some problem in getting the numbers correctly recorded in any updating. Once this is done, record-matching is reasonably straightforward for these files for the sub-set of the population that is covered. I see no problem in interrelating these records in additional ways for statistical purposes, beyond what may be done for administrative purposes, if the confidentiality restraints are solved and if the costs are justified by the statistical results achieved. They often are.

Increasing use of the Social Security number in various record systems is taking place, with substantial progress, so that additional accomplishments may be feasible in this area. However, extensions in the use of the Social Security number will cause concern over possible invasions of privacy and this problem needs additional attention. Another possible problem in large-scale extensions is that the Social Security number reported by a person sometimes will be in error, inadvertently or by design. I understand that the Social Security Administration does not accept the responsibility of validating numbers on request. There is still another problem in the present system that arises from the fact that one person may have two or more Social Security numbers. These are legally allowed in the system, and exist to some degree. Recently estimates have become available that suggest that the number of assigned in excess of one to each person may be of the order of 3 or 4 percent of all numbers assigned. [1] Many of these multiple number assignments are identified and can be brought together by the Social Security Administration for the persons involved. Presumably such multiple numbers cannot be so identified in other record systems that use the Social Security number.

If the numbering system is ever extended to cover all persons, or even all persons 16 years of age or older, with all of them covered in at least one reasonably current and comprehensive record system for the population, its utility would be greatly increased.

Record Linkage on the Basis of Number Identification Systems That Relate to Unstable Units

A comprehensive number identification system that relates to unstable units is the Employer Identification number used on a comparable basis both by the Internal Revenue Service and the Social Security Administration, and used also by the Bureau of the Census in its censuses of business and manufacturers and many current surveys, and perhaps by others. The identification number relates to those legal entities that are employers in industries covered by the Social Security system. Such employers are responsible for making direct FICA contributions for each employee, and also for making deductions from the employee's personal earnings, and transmitting the money to the Internal Revenue Service. The records are also transmitted to the Social Security Administration, which keeps an account for each employee. For covered employers the file is essentially comprehensive. Some studies have shown very little undercoverage of employers in the system, and these generally by small or marginal employers. Studies by the Census Bureau two decades ago led to the decision to use the system for

---

1   From Report to the Commissioner by the Social Security Number Task Force, Social Security Administration, May, 1971.

taking the Census of Business and Manufactures by mail instead of making field canvasses to locate the establishments.

Some serious problems arise when the units identified by the Employer Identification (EI) numbers are used for statistical purposes because the EI number relates to the legal entity, which is a corporation (in the case of an incorporated enterprise), a partnership, a sole proprietorship, and other legal entity. In the case of many large manufacturing companies such as General Motors, companies that operate chain stores, and a great many other large business concerns, the legal entity covers many different establishments operating in varying kinds of business and in differing geographic locations. For many statistical purposes these establishments need to be and are separately identified.

The Social Security Administration does attempt to obtain the cooperation of companies, on a voluntary basis, in identifying "reporting units" below the company level for large multi-unit-companies. The reporting units are individual establishments within the manufacturing sector. For other kinds of business the reporting unit presumably includes all establishments in the same kind of business within a county. Voluntary cooperation in this reporting unit program is substantial but not complete, and the units are inadequate to serve some important statistical purposes. For example, such units are not adequate to produce statistics for cities, or for areas within counties or cities.

In order to take the Census of Business and Manufactures by mail, the Bureau of the Census obtains the mailing addresses by EI numbers from the Internal Revenue Service, and obtains measures of size and industrial codes from the Social Security Administration records plus its own sources for the multi-unit establishments. The confidentiality of the information is assured in its use by the Census Bureau. The EI number is the control unit for much of the work, and the integration of the Internal Revenue Service, Social Security Administration, and Census records by EI number with the computer is a straightforward and highly effective operation. But without supplemental surveys by the Social Security Administration and the Bureau of the Census to identify the establishments within the EI numbers, the statistical purpose would not be reasonably served.

The principal point to be noted is the unstable character of the units covered by the EI number. In a legal sense the units are highly stable. A legal entity has an EI number, retains it as long as the entity exists, and if the legal entity changes, presumably (and it is generally true in practice) the EI number changes. But from an economic, social, and statistical point of view these units are highly unstable over time. A corporate (or other) entity at one point in time may consist of ten business establishments. At another time it may have taken over 16 more establishments from another legal entity, perhaps in other industries; at still another point in time it may have acquired complete control over a subsidiary, another corporation. Moreover, the fact that in this latter case two separate legal entities exist carries no implication that they are not totally integrated units in any real sense, in that they have common ownership and control. Knowledge of and measurement of such situations may be of the greatest importance in a particular statistical study, but any statistical system that associates information over time with the EI number, which it is feasible to accomplish in an automatic linking of records, meanwhile neglecting to go behind the record with intensive supplemental studies, is likely to arrive at statistical measures and conclusions that involve the grossest kinds of misinterpretation or errors.

As a further problem for record-matching, the unit that is covered by income tax reports to the Internal Revenue Service is not necessarily, and in fact often is not, this same legal entity. Frequently, the tax reports are consolidated returns for two or more entities, and there are other problems of noncomparability. The EI number is carried in the IRS files for the units covered (or at least for the principal or reporting entity). However, because of consolidated tax reporting and other differences in the units covered, it is not possible to link the Social Security or Census records automatically, on a computer, with the corporate tax returns without supplemental professional staff intervention in order to achieve reasonably comparable information. It is true that for the great bulk of the companies there will be comparability. The lack of comparability exists especially in a relatively small proportion (but a large number) of large enterprises that account for a very high fraction of the business activity of the nation.

Because of the importance of facilitating the use and comparison of the substantial information in the tabulations made from the corporate income tax returns with the Census results and other sources of information, and the problems of noncomparability between the Census establishment statistics, the Census enterprise statistics, and the Internal Revenue Service statistics, the Bureau of the Census now makes a link study every five years, undertaking to match the Census returns against the Internal Revenue Service returns. The published results show the establishment and industrial content of the industry statistics as developed by the Internal Revenue Service. (Of course, in this process the confidenality of each set of records is maintained.) This study does take advantage of the EI number in automatic matching. But if it were done as an automatic job without extensive manual intervention and judgment the results would be very different and misleading. In practice it involves large amounts of professional work and judgment in arriving at decisions on the relations between the data in the Internal Revenue Service tax returns and the Census questionnaires prior to tabulation.

The problem with unstable units is far greater in longitudinal studies than in the cross-sectional studies discussed above. In longitudinal studies the match on EI number, even if one is willing to do analyses in terms of the aggregates of establishments covered by the EI number, is likely to yield noncomparable results as to changes that are occurring. Suppose, for example, that one wants to study the impact of R & D, or of capital expenditures, on the performance or growth of a company, and tries to use R & D as an independent variable for comparisons with growth over time. The changes observed in a company as covered by the EI number over time will involve such a complex of other factors that there is no comparability. The EI number match alone provides no reasonable basis for conducting such a study. Intensive intervention and judgments are required to accomplish exclusions and inclusions that may make it feasible to more nearly achieve the goals of such a study.

I say this as though intensive study and personal intervention can assure reasonable comparability. Actually, the complexities caused by unstable units are substantial. A case in point is the effort made by the Bureau of the Census to develop a time series for individual manufacturing plants.[2] A major effort was made to assemble comparable data for individual plants over time, beginning with 1954, for 25 selected industries. Some of the studies contemplated would examine such topics as investment functions, the efficiency of new plants as compared with older plants in the same industry, the impact of capital expenditures on changing inputs, economics of scale, optimum scale, factors affecting services, etc. A discussion of the study is beyond the scope of this paper. However, the paper prepared in 1964 and reporting the results for the period 1954-1959 indicates many difficulties in developing the record and finding the most effective means of using it. Also, the problems in assembling reasonably comparable data over time for establishments have proved very substantial. Because of the pressures of other projects, the difficulties in successfully pursuing this one and the consequent lower priorities it has received, the project is currently dormant, in spite of extensive interest in it. Hopefully, it will be revived and continued, for it may fulfill some promising goals. I cite it as an illustration of the difficulties and complexities of achieving comparability of information over time for unstable units. In this case no general numbering system was involved, but the Bureau of the Census had created its own numbering system for automated processing using but going beyond what can be accomplished with the EI number, and identifying with their own numbering systems the establishments within multi-unit companies.

I can only indicate that there are substantial problems in such studies and cannot begin to convey the nature of all of them. This much extensive experience teaches. The important point is that in such studies automated matching is perfectly feasible at very low cost and at high speed. However, if it is used without extensive professional study and intervention in an effort to correct or adjust sources of noncomparability, it will often lead to unsatisfactory and grossly misleading results.

---

2 See Maxwell R. Conklin, "Time Series for Individual Plants from the Annual Survey of Manufactures and Related Data," *1964 Proceedings of the Business and Economics Statistics Section, American Statistical Association,* pp. 404-410.

448-559 O - 71 - 3

EXAMINATION OF THE ROLE, POTENTIAL STATISTICAL GAINS, AND PROBLEMS OF A COMPREHENSIVE DATA BANK BASED ON LINKED FEDERAL RECORDS

Alternatives

We have seen the problems of linking automatically for statistical purposes records that do not relate to stable units, or that are not covered by adequate identification systems. Now let us examine what can be accomplished in the way of substantive statistical results on the basis of matched records, taking joint account of the content of the records and the potential for adequate linking of the relevant records.

In this discussion we shall again limit consideration to records for people and groups of people such as households or the groups of people represented in an individual tax form, or to business concerns and establishments and related units (not including farms). These are units and populations of great statistical importance, about which there has been extensive discussion and concern for accomplishing record linkage.

Record-linking studies generally serve one or two rather different purposes, although both purposes often are served in a single study. One purpose is the evaluation or improved understanding of the reliability and accuracy of the statistical information that is obtained separately from the unlinked records. For this purpose the same or related types of information are sometimes brought together, record by record, for analysis of differences. A second purpose is to interrelate different items of information from two record systems in order to obtain such information at lower cost (or sometimes of higher quality) than could be accomplished through other means, or that might not be feasibly obtained by other means. For either purpose one may be concerned with cross-sectional studies, or with longitudinal studies.

Evaluation Studies for the Same or Similar Items of Information

Extensive use has been made of record-matching studies based on small samples to serve the first of the above two purposes, that

24

is, for evaluation and improved understanding of the statistical reliability and accuracy of information collected in censuses and surveys, and in the administrative records. Such studies reflect the impact of conceptual differences, although these often are confounded with differences in response. They are frequently based on comparisons record by record and item by item, and skill and judgment are often necessary and applied in resolving problems that arise. As the product of such studies, cross-tabulations are mostly made by comparing the two sets of reports for the same or similar items of data. Because of the great care needed there seems to be consensus that such studies are best done for relatively small samples. Moreover, the purpose of the studies eliminates the need of large samples, and it would be a great waste to conduct them on the millions of cases contained in the files, even if it were practicable. The only potential gain from comprehensive record-matching, as distinguished from the use of relatively small samples, is cross-tabulation in massive detail, or tabulations by small geographic areas, and these are not the principal needs of such studies.

A number of illustrations of such evaluative studies are given in the listing below of some record-matching studies that have been conducted.

Studies to Interrelate Different Items of Information

The second major role mentioned above for record-matching was to interrelate different items of information, by linking two sets of records, thus providing correlated information on a record by record basis at lower cost or of greater validity than could be obtained through a direct data-collection operation or by other procedures, or that could not reasonably be provided by other means. The desirability and necessity of interrelating different items of information is so basic and important that it is beyond any question or dispute. It is a standard and essential technique of analysis. However, there are various ways of obtaining interrelationships of information of which record-matching is one.

A principal means of interrelating various types of information is to collect the items of information to be interrelated in a census or sample survey, or to ask for at the source and record additional relevant items of information in an administrative record, although

25

this may be difficult to accomplish in a large record system.

The collection of such interrelatable data is one of the prime purposes of the major censuses and sample surveys. In general, censuses and surveys are highly useful and effective means for achieving such results. However, a problem arises in obtaining such information from a census or survey if one wishes to obtain information for longitudinal studies, that involves extensive recall over long periods of time. To the extent that one is considering stable units, such information can sometimes be obtained through repeated surveys of identical units — locating and obtaining information from the same units in successive surveys designed to provide current information at the time of each survey. This is being done increasingly for longitudinal studies through surveys, and with considerable effectiveness in locating the people. Information from records may also be added.

Another alternative method is to obtain certain common items of information in each of two or more record systems, and sort and tabulate other items in each record system on such common items of information without record-matching. Among the more common items for interrelating information for people are demographic characteristics such as age, sex, race, and geographic location. Over the decades and in many countries information from censuses and vital records have been interrelated by collecting these basic and relatively simple items of information in each data system. Thus, age-sex specific death rates are computed by tabulating the death statistics for a specific time interval by age and sex and by tabulating the census counts by these same characteristics. An age-sex specific death rate is computed by dividing the deaths in the specific age-sex group by the population in the same age-sex group, and without any record-matching. There are problems beyond the scope of this paper in such studies, but the approach has been widely and successfully applied.

The same approach is applied in business establishment statistics by using a common industrial classification and common size codes in tabulating information from two different sources, and then interrelating them for the subclasses. The problems with establishment statistics are more difficult, because of difficulties in comparability of classification, even with a common classification system. There are two current types of proposals for dealing with this problem — and both involve difficulties. One proposal is to establish and maintain a classified industrial directory that identifies and makes available the same classifications to each statistical agency. Another is to integrate such data-collection operations in a single agency. There are no easy solutions, but we have also seen that large-scale automatic record-matching does not provide an easy or necessarily even a workable solution.

The use of samples to link records for needed and worthwhile studies instead of linking large files on a comprehensive basis is such an obvious means of obtaining needed results that I will not comment on it further here except to say that much can be done with relatively small samples, and the burden of proof ought to be on the person who says that comprehensive record linkage is needed. Such an approach frequently will totally serve the need. A relatively small sample of a large file can still produce a large sample in absolute size, large enough to provide fairly detailed tabulations. Thus, a sample of .1% of a file of 80,000,000 produces a sample of 80,000, and 1 percent produces 800,000. Of course, the sample size needs to be adapted to the purposes to be served. The advantage of relatively small samples is especially great when it is recognized that an automatic linking of records without manual intervention will, with a few important exceptions, be likely to produce misleading and unsatisfactory results, and that where such problems exist the intensive work necessary to achieve reasonably satisfactory results ordinarily can be effectively done only on relatively small samples.

There are a number of worthwhile results to be accomplished by interrelating different items of information on a comprehensive basis in various large-scale federal records. However, much has already been done along this line, and I believe it is easy to overrate what can be accomplished beyond what is already being done, and to underrate the problems. Recently there is a tendency to overlook or underrate what can be accomplished by some of the other means, as described above.

What Are the Important Federal Records (for People and Business Units) Available to be Linked?

The principal records that are available on a reasonably comprehensive basis in the federal administrative or statistical agencies as candidates for record-linkage efforts are listed below. In addition, some relevant records based on national samples are also listed.

I. *Records for people, or personal groups such as families or groups of people reported on individual tax returns).*

  A. Comprehensive files (*i.e.*, files with essentially complete coverage of the defined population and where the defined population is a substantial part of the total population).

    1. Internal Revenue Service individual income tax returns (annual).

    2. Supporting records for the individual tax returns

      a. Reports on wages and tax deductions
      b. Reports on dividend and interest payments

    3. The accumulated-over-time individual tax files maintained by Internal Revenue Service, with accumulated records retained for the individual taxpayer.

    4. The Social Security Administration accumulated individual accounts on earnings under the maximum taxable earnings base.

    5. The Social Security Administration records on beneficiaries, under OASDI and persons enrolled under Medicare.

    6. The decennial Census of Population (and Housing) returns. (The name and address are not recorded in machine readable form).

    7. Vital records — registered births and deaths. These are essentially state records, and their use in record linkage may involve treating them as state instead of federal records. (The registration area for marriage and divorce is not yet extended to all states.)

  B. Sample files (these are too numerous to list except for certain major ones that have special relevance to this discussion).

1. The Social Security Administration one percent Continuous Work History Sample (CWHS), showing accumulated records for a one percent sample of Social Security account numbers, with richer statistical detail than is retained in the accumulated individual accounts on covered earnings for all individuals (item 4 above).

2. The Current Population Survey sample, and related sample studies.

3. Decennial Census evaluation study samples.

II. *Records for companies, business establishments, and related units.*

A. Comprehensive files

1. Internal Revenue Service income tax returns — corporate, partnership, and proprietorship (annual).

2. Social Security Administration records on wage deductions filed by employers (quarterly).

3. The Census of Business and Manufactures returns (quinquennial).

4. Various records for special but important business subpopulations such as those of Securities and Exchange Commission, Federal Reserve Board, Federal Communications Commission, and others.

B. Sample files (only certain samples of special relevance to this discussion are listed).

1. The Bureau of the Census Annual Survey of Manufactures sample.

2. The Bureau of the Census samples of wholesale trade, retail trade, and selected services (monthly).

3. The Bureau of Labor Statistics employment and payroll samples (monthly)

4. The Securities and Exchange Commission-Federal Trade Commission quarterly financial survey.

A comment should be made on the linking of sample records. It is feasible and common to link records from a sample against a complete file, and can be done with more or less success depending on the other problems involved. However, except for very large samples, the linking of two independent samples is not a practical and useful exercise. Thus, the CPS sample each month contains a probability sample of something of the order of one person, or one family in 1,000 (a sample of about 50,000 households or 80,000 people in the labor force). The work history sample of the Social Security Administration is a 1/100 sample, or something of the order of 800,000 persons currently in the labor force (although the coverage is not quite comprehensive). They are independent samples. Consequently, the linking of these two records, if all matches could be linked, would produce successfully linked records for an expected (1/100) (1/1,000) = 1/100,000 of the Social Security file, or for about 800 persons. This could be increased with the rotation of the CPS sample, but in any event a great deal of linking produces a relatively small payoff in expected linked records. The actual payoff will be lower because of the matching problems. The work history sample is a very large one. Two small independent samples would have almost no overlap.

In examining the potential role of a national data center to achieve the comprehensive linking of federal records we need to explore not only the records available for linking but what already has been accomplished, and what additional worthwhile objectives might be achieved by creating such a large-scale approach to record-linking. These will be discussed in the next two sections.

Some Record-Linking Studies That Have Been Done or Are Under Way.[3]

Following is a partial list of record-linking studies that have been done, or are being done, with some supplemental comments on them. Some are continuing or repetitive studies. While this list is not comprehensive, I believe it covers many of the important record-linking projects and is illustrative of others.

---

3 It should be emphasized again that in these studies the confidentiality of the various administrative or survey records is assured in the same way as for the census records. The methods used to assure confidentiality are an interesting topic in their own right.

Record-linking studies for people, households, and individual tax return units.

1. A series of studies has been made linking Census returns, or Current Population Survey returns, or both, with Internal Revenue Service individual income tax returns.

   a. The first such study was for a sample of about 15,000 households from the 1950 Census matched against Internal Revenue Service records. This study also included the results of the intensive re-interview evaluative sample taken by the Census Bureau as a part of the post-enumerative survey following the 1950 Census. The primary purpose of the study was to evaluate the quality of the statistics in the Census, based jointly on the intensive re-interview survey results and the tax returns, and to improve the quality of various income distribution estimates. The matching was done using name and address and certain characteristics information.

   b. A similar study was made following the 1960 Census but with a sample of Internal Revenue Service returns matched against the Census results. This study was made to evaluate income reporting and also to help the Office of Business Economics improve the annual estimates of income distributions based on the tax returns.

   c. A similar study is under way for the 1970 Census but involving the Current Population Survey sample, the corresponding linked 1970 Census returns, and the individual Internal Revenue Service tax returns. This one benefits, in the record-linkage phases of the study, from the decision to collect the Social Security number in the Current Population Survey sample. This by no means makes the linking automatic. There are problems of failures to report Social Security numbers in the Current Population Survey, and reporting errors.

2. Closely related is an ongoing study linking a sub-sample of the Current Population Survey sample, the accumulated longitudinal information on wage deductions in the Social Security Administration records, and the individual Internal

Revenue Service tax returns. This study makes use of the Social Security number for linking the Internal Revenue Service and Social Security Administration records, and benefits from the reporting of Social Security number in the Current Population Survey returns, but, again, the problems in reporting are such that the linking with Current Population Survey, especially, is far from a simple automatic computer operation. It was found advantageous to do the record-linking manually even though Social Security number was used in the linkage.[4]

The goals of the study are both to improve the quality and interpretation of the information, and to obtain supplemental information unavailable without such a record-linking study. Also sought is the ability to interpret more adequately the information in the Social Security Administration longitudinal wage records and, with the added information from the record linkage, to be able to evaluate more adequately the consequences of alternative Social Security programs.

This study has placed a strong emphasis on obtaining "best" information, and on calibrating income information, and has not put a high priority on creating an output that interrelates different items of information. It holds promise of useful results in the future. Its slowness in producing results stems especially from the differences in the units being linked, priorities, and the need to identify and minimize the effect of matching problems, significant errors or differences in the data reported, and other factors.

3. Studies linking the Current Population Survey sample with the Census returns were conducted in 1950, again in 1960, and a study is being conducted for 1970. These have been useful evaluative studies, comparing and evaluating Census and Current Population Survey information. The record-linking has been done on the basis of geographic information, name, address, and other characteristics.

4 See Joseph Steinberg (Social Security Administration), *Interacting Data Systems and the Measurement of Income Size Distributions,* prepared for Conference on Income and Wealth, University of Pennsylvania, March 24-25, 1967 (unpublished).

4. A large-scale matching study involving the linking of 1960 Census returns with death certificates for deaths occurring during a four-month period following the 1960 Census was conducted by the Population Research and Training Center, University of Chicago, with the cooperation of the National Center for Health Statistics and the Bureau of the Census. The record matching was done at the Bureau of the Census in order to preserve confidentiality. The primary goal of the study was to produce statistics on death rates by socio-economic groups, but it has also served as a basis for evaluative studies on reported data. One publication relates to educational differentials in mortality by cause of death, and additional reports will be forthcoming. Between 75 and 80 percent of the records were linked, and this low rate causes problems in the analysis and interpretation of results.

5. A birth registration-Census matching study was made for a sample of births occurring prior to the 1950 Census with infants covered in the 1950 Census, and *vice versa*. This was an effort to evaluate the completeness of coverage of infants in the Census, as well as the completeness of birth registrations. (A similar study had been conducted in connection with the 1940 Census, but the war interfered and it was not completed.)

6. A series of record-linking studies was made to evaluate the completeness of the 1960 Census, as distinguished from comparing data reported in two records, although data comparisons were also involved in some instances. Record-linking studies to evaluate the completeness of a census put greater stringencies on the accuracy and completeness of the matching. Erroneous matches or erroneous non-matches of the order of 3 to 10 percent are regarded as very low matching error rates in the studies mentioned above. However, such an error rate in matching studies designed to measure undercoverage of the Census greatly reduces the value of the study. The undercoverage rate itself is presumed to be of the order of 3 percent. The studies that have been conducted include:

a. A match of a sample of persons covered in the 1950

Census against the 1960 Census returns.

b. A match of a sample of birth registrations between 1950 and 1960 against the 1960 Census returns.

c. A match of a sample of immigrants (from the alien registration) between 1950 and 1960 against the 1960 Census returns.

d. A match of a small sample of persons identified as missed in the 1950 Census (from a post-enumeration sample survey taken in 1950) against the 1960 Census returns.

e. A match of a sample of Social Security Administration records for Old Age and Survivorship beneficiaries against the 1960 Census returns.

f. A match of a sample of Selective Service records against the 1960 Census returns. (This study could not be completed because Selective Service would not permit direct contact with the people involved to resolve problems.)

7. Some record-linking studies for the 1950 Census were conducted, but the matching problems were so serious that adequate resources were not provided to cope with them. The principal results were not published but provided guides to improving the studies for 1960.

8. Record-linking studies for the 1970 Census coverage evaluation program include:

a. Linking of a sample of persons enrolled for Medicare against the 1970 Census returns.

b. A pilot study in the District of Columbia involving the matching of drivers' licenses for males in the young and middle adult age groups against the Census.

c. A sample of infants drawn from the 1970 Census returns, to match against the birth registrations, and provide an updated measure of the completeness of birth registration. This study aims not only at evaluating completeness of birth registration, but also through the improved correction of birth figures at evaluating the completeness of Census enumeration of infants.

d. The Internal Revenue Service-Census match discussed under (1) above.

Studies involving record-linking for business concerns or establishments.

1. The linking of Internal Revenue Service, Social Security Administration and Census records by the Census Bureau, as a means of developing mailing lists for the quinquennial Censuses of Business and Manufactures, and the linking project with corporate tax returns were discussed above. There are other important projects linking these records with additional data results. Some of these projects include:

a. *County Business Patterns* is an annual publication prepared by the Bureau of the Census based on the linking of Social Security employer records on wage items, number of employees, wages paid, and industrial codes with Census records on establishments and industrial codes, and with the results of supplemental surveys to obtain updated information on reporting units for large multi-establishment companies. The publication reports employment and payrolls by industry for counties and aggregates of counties.

b. By matching Internal Revenue Service and Social Security Administration records to obtain the information, the 1967 Census of Business and Manufactures was able to avoid sending questionnaires to and requesting responses from approximately 1,000,000 small employers from whom data had been collected by a mail canvass in recent prior censuses. This project involved obtaining information on sales or receipts and payrolls from the Internal Revenue Service records, and employment (employment inferred from wage items were not directly reported) and industrial codes from the Social Security Administration records. Even though computer matching was feasible on the basis of EI number, the many types of complexities encountered delayed the Census. It may have cost the government more than it would have cost to collect the information from the field, and also may

35

have resulted in somewhat lower-quality information. In any event, it avoided sending questionnaires to about 1,000,000 small businessmen, and spared them the burden of response. With the background of experience for 1967, there are plans and expectations that the cost can be reduced and timeliness improved for future censuses.

2. The Annual Survey of Manufactures and the monthly business sample surveys of the Bureau of the Census involve record linkage with Internal Revenue Service and Social Security Administration records in order to identify and introduce births into the samples, to improve the efficiency of the samples by taking account of major changes in size, and to help control the continuing completeness of coverage by identifying companies that had ceased activity but retained their legal existence, had been dropped from the Census sample surveys, and had then again engaged in business activity.

3. A current area being developed is the creation and maintenance of a classified mailing list of business concerns and establishments. Much of this activity already is done by the Bureau of the Census in taking the Censuses of Business and Manufactures, for *County Business Patterns,* and in order to achieve the other results from linked records as described above. However, there is a program to develop and maintain a reasonably current classified register showing companies and establishments by industrial codes and employment sizes on a continuing or annual basis. It is hoped that such a register will be of assistance in improving the coordination of statistics for companies and establishments collected by different agencies in addition to facilitating the major programs of each of the agencies in these areas. The massive changes in terms of births and deaths of the legal entities that are covered, the changes of address, and the changes in size have made the problem a bigger and more difficult one than might be initially surmised.

I believe that the above listing, although incomplete, is an impressive indication of what has been done. It is also impressive, perhaps, that present legislation and restrictions on confidentiality of information have not been a great obstacle to accomplishing a wide range of record-linking projects. Most of the projects have been done by Census Bureau staff, with the cooperation of the other agencies. The Census Bureau can accomplish the linking of records in a manner that protects the confidentiality of each of the various record systems in the same manner as the Census records are protected, and consequently they do have or can arrange access to most other records for worthwhile studies.

I think, in addition, that while the list is impressive in what has been accomplished, it is also impressive in that with all of the record-linking studies that have been done, relatively few if any major breakthroughs have occurred that involve the interrelating of different types of items from different record systems, although several of those cited provide or have the potential to provide interesting new information. I believe that the lack of major breakthroughs from record-matching results partly because of the limits on the information available in the records, and partly because of the far greater potentiality and flexibility of censuses and surveys in meeting the need for interrelated data. (There is much to be gained from sample record-matching studies conducted jointly with direct data collection to fill in information gaps, as discussed later.) Several of the record-linking studies interrelate new information, such as the study interrelating socio-economic characteristics in the 1960 Population Census with subsequent deaths. While conceptually this was a significant development, the low match rates in this study are a problem. Its special value was that for this particular kind of information there is no reasonable alternative through direct collection. The use of censuses or surveys to collect information on deaths has proven to be quite unsatisfactory. The studies interrelating Internal Revenue Service corporate tax data to Census of Manufactures and Business data have been valuable in facilitating the interpretation of various measures from the Internal Revenue Service data and the relationships between them and Census information.

What Can Be Accomplished, In Addition, By Comprehensive Record-Linking?

A review of the data content of the comprehensive federal record systems listed above that are candidates for matching, and of what has been done, does not show great potential, in my judgment, for obtaining new kinds of information, especially for cross-sectional type studies. There is greater promise for longitudinal studies, including record-linking over time within a single system of records, as well as across agencies, but here, again, there are serious problems and limitations. It should be kept in mind that data from most of the record sources (including the already assembled longitudinal data in the Social Security Administration and Internal Revenue Service records) are already or can be tabulated for general statistical purposes without record-linking.

Before proceeding with comprehensive record-linking studies it is important to determine what remains to be accomplished by linking the records that is worthwhile, and what additional benefits are to be gained by linking them on a comprehensive basis instead of using a much less costly small-scale sample permitting more careful work.

The decennial Census already has in it most of the types of information that are in the individual tax returns, although nothing like all of the income detail. The Current Population Survey, with its supplements, covers a wide range of additional subjects, and other subjects are included in other sample surveys. Sample surveys have proved to be powerful instruments of great flexibility for varying the content and concept in data collection to achieve the types of information needed. The problems of censuses and surveys are those of memory in retrospective recall, accuracy of response, and cost. (Nevertheless, experience indicates that the cost of a sample survey may be lower than for a reasonably adequately controlled record-linking study on a sample of comparable size — without the problems of record-linking that have been discussed, and with far less difficulty than a comprehensive linking of the records.) Some record-linking studies may go a long way in resolving the measurement of accuracy of response problems, but when one undertakes to develop information from interrelated records, it is not unusual to find that the desired information is not there or is not in the form needed to achieve one's particular purposes or goals. Record-linking studies that can be achieved at relatively low cost in fact often do not have the potential for providing the needed information, especially because of the limited additional information content achieved by linking the records that can be readily linked, or because of the problems in linking and interpreting the results.

I believe that an examination of the records listed above will show promise for some cross-sectional studies, and especially for some longitudinal studies that have not been done and that may be worthwhile. I see no reason for these to be attempted, at least initially, on a comprehensive basis instead of on a sample basis. Moreover, few of these are so great in their potential as to add to a new order of magnitude of richness to what can be accomplished without record-linking. There is a potential for a number of useful studies, but not anything like the depth of analysis that I believe the recommendations for the creation of large-scale matched records have anticipated. The costs of a comprehensive approach, carefully done, may reasonably outweigh the potential benefits many times.

Administrative records especially have or show the potential for developing longitudinal information, and here I think that special attention should be given to the value of what can be accomplished. Samples of the order of 1/1,000, or 1/100 are relatively small as compared with comprehensive record-linking, they can produce a great deal, and may adequately serve the total needs. At least, such sample studies should be accomplished first, and the value of record-matching for additional large-scale use established before one engages in costly large-scale record-matching operations.

A prime need commonly expressed at the present time is for longitudinal information on various groups in the population, *e.g.*, the characteristics of youngsters who make various decisions for their future as they proceed through high school and into college or work, and the circumstances under which these decisions were made. A good deal of activity is being undertaken to develop such information. But it is not adequately available from the records, matched or unmatched, and the project calls for difficult and

39

costly longitudinal studies with original data collection supplemented by selected information from school records, and perhaps other records as well.

To take another illustration, the same kinds of arguments hold for the value of longitudinal information on the life circumstances affecting people on welfare, how these circumstances change through migration and educational experiences and other factors. Even inter-generational changes might be studied. These call for direct study, in both retrospective and repeated longitudinal inquiries, with direct data collection supplemented by information from welfare and other linked records. Numerous other similar studies could be cited.

A type of study that has considerable potential for the agency or group responsible for a particular program is to obtain *both* cross-sectional and longitudinal information and *both* attitudinal and factual information for a sample of their clients. Generally, the needed information goes far beyond what could become available simply by linking existing records. Thus, the Social Security Administration has arranged for extensive supplemental collection of information on the aged population, beneficiaries of the Social Insurance program, non-beneficiaries and potential beneficiaries. The content of these studies has gone well beyond what could have been obtained by a simple linking of Social Security Administration files with Census records, or Current Population Survey records. The richness has been provided by extensive supplementation of the information in the records, obtained by special collection of information for samples of the groups of interest.

Much could be done, and more will be done, by doing more tabulation of some of the information that is starting to become available in the longitudinal files of the Internal Revenue Service. Far more could be done if the machine-readable records contained more of the information in the original reports. Undoubtedly, bringing in additional supplemental information from other sources on social and demographic characteristics of the persons covered in the tax form, and of their households, will have added value. Small sample studies, when these have proved the value of such information and provided guidance in how to proceed, can be enlarged later.

SOME CONCLUDING REMARKS
AND RECOMMENDATIONS

I believe that the material presented fully supports the views I expressed in the brief summary and in the introduction under the heading of "Some preliminary Comments." A few additional comments are appropriate at this point, and these are summarized below as remarks on some topics that I believe deserve additional emphasis.

1. *Access to micro data and maintenance of confidentiality.* One of the major goals discussed in the Kaysen and other reports recommending the creation of a federal data center and the integration of records was the need for improved access to micro data. I believe that this is a legitimate need, but serving this need is independent of whether or not the records are integrated. The principal problem is improved access to micro records for statistical purposes, including records that may be integrated and those that are not.

   I believe that progesss has been made in improving access to micro data through special tabulations, but it has not gone far enough. More is needed and should be done. On the other hand, the confidentiality of records must be observed, and this introduces serious conflict with access to micro records, and especially to integrated micro records.

   The recommendations of the Kaysen Committee and others have assumed that various federal agencies could have direct access to the micro records through terminals, and subject to a computer monitoring program that would identify and refuse to output information that would constitute disclosure. The Appendix is a paper prepared on the problem of confidentiality and disclosure of information, and includes discussion of this and related questions. I shall not repeat the discussion here. My principal conclusions from the arguments presented there are:

   a. The issue of disclosure, unfortunately, is not a clear-cut legal one. It involves judgments and decisions depending on the nature and sensitivity of the data, and on precedents. In the long run presumably the disclosure problems can be resolved, and disclosure controlled through the use of monitor programs. However, I suspect that supplemental human review may be needed for a long time, if not indefinitely, when dealing with some of the more difficult disclosure problems. Ethical as well as legal issues are involved.

b. The issue is made far more difficult by the fact that, because of confidentiality problems, the retrieval and use of information from a set of micro records may preclude the subsequent retrieval and use of other information. This is demonstrated in the appended paper. It means that priorities in the order of retrieval and use must be established and observed. Access within disclosure restrictions cannot be allowed without taking account of priorities and future needs. Otherwise the retrieval of information for some minor or trivial use may preempt the information, and make it impossible to retrieve other information needed for other far more important purposes.

c. As a consequence, I believe that access to confidential micro records cannot be achieved under the arrangements that have been proposed. There are some possible alternatives suggested here for further consideration.

    i. The public use sample approach, which the Bureau of the Census has introduced, has great potential for meeting this need, so long as the information is restricted to relatively small samples in order to meet confidentiality requirements. With this approach the full micro records for the samples are made available to the public in machine-readable form, but with the detailed geographic and certain other information removed. This approach has proved exceedingly useful. It is being extended by the Bureau of the Census for 1970, from a 1/1000 sample to several different 1/100 samples. The public use sample approach also has confidentiality problems, as discussed in the appended paper, and I urge that the Commission recommend future consideration and review of these. It is a useful tool, and legitimate boundaries of its use should be more clearly established.

ii. In addition to the suggestion in (i), and not as an alternative to it, I believe that a data center created along the lines and in the general setting recommended by the Kaysen Committee could make an effective contribution. I refer to placing the Bureau of the Census and the former Office of Statistical Standards under a Director of Statistics in the Executive Office of the President. In addition, a data center would be established to have as its goal a strong service function to statistical users, including those who need access to micro information. I am not sure whether the data center should be a parallel agency to the Bureau of the Census or an important organizational unit within it.

I do not support the recommendation for massive integration of records on a record by record basis in the data center. The center should have the function of taking the lead in evaluating the need for, and establishing, policies for the preservation of records. It could serve in a liaison capacity in achieving access to micro records through special tabulations on a custom basis of confidential records that are active and retained by the agencies. It could be adequately staffed to supplement the agency services. Discussion of the details of such an approach is, again, beyond the scope of the present paper, but I believe something along this line could greatly strengthen the ability to provide statistical services, and needs fuller consideration and development.

iii. There should be additional assessments of the potential for research studies to be accomplished within the confidentiality net, so that research persons, for example, become subject to the same disclosure rules as regular employees of the Bureau of the Census. The results to be published from the research can then be examined for disclosure, but it is not necessary for all of the intermediate stages of data examination and analysis to be so restricted. There used to be greater participation along this line, but it has been tightened in recent years. There are problems to be examined and carefully administered controls would be necessary, but I don't believe the difficulties are insurmountable.

2. *Extension to local record systems.* There is a tremendous wealth of detail in the various local record systems. At the same time there are serious gaps in the records (different gaps in different records), with unmeasured segments of the population not covered in any of the records. The long-range potentials, as these records are increasingly computerized and as common identification systems are introduced, are very great. The integration of local records is not the subject of this paper. Nevertheless, it is related, and I would like to suggest that statistical uses should *not* serve as the spearhead of local record integration. Federal and local statistical agencies should cooperate and provide strong leadership in the application of standard classification systems and definitions, with or without record integration, so that statistical needs can be increasingly served by local record systems advances. I believe that this is important and the best strategy from the point of view of cost-effectiveness, as well as in achieving worthwhile statistical advances.

Along this line, there are new developments in increasingly effective ways of facilitating the summarization of statistics for small areas from the various record systems, and these hold potential for immediate use of both local and federal records. The creation for the 1970 Census, by the Bureau of the Census, with the cooperation of other federal agencies and local communities, of the Address Coding Guides, the geographic base files, and the extension and current maintenance of these have important implications. Further discussion of this potential is beyond the scope of the present paper, too, but I believe it is an area of very great promise for helping meet the needs for relatively up-to-date small-area statistics. The interrelation, on a small-area basis, of various records with each other and with the results of the census will be an important advance in meeting the needs for small-area information, and in interrelating information from the different sources. Many of these gains can be achieved, I believe, by introducing and using the new geographic coding and analytical systems, without having to achieve record by record linkage. When local record integration is achieved for other purposes, there will be additional statistical benefits from the application of the geographic coding and analytical procedures. The continuing development and maintenance of the geographic base files and related tools is at a state where, with encouragement, support and leadership, it can make increasingly worthwhile contributions.

3. *Desirability of an integrated record developmental study for a small sample.* The extensive interest expressed in what can be accomplished with record integration deserves careful analysis. In my judgment, a massive record integration effort should not be launched. Instead, a plan should be prepared for more fully exploring some of the needs and potentials and then making them more explicit by planning a relatively small sample study. This might begin with one or more Current Population Survey samples, which could be linked with the Internal Revenue Service longitudinal records, the Social Security Administration records, and others. The study can be extended by supplemental inquiries through the Current Population Survey interviewers. The inquiries could include additional cross-sectional information, and longitudinal information through retrospective inquiries. It could be further extended, if desired, by additional inquiries in the future, for the identical people, and by matching additional information from the administrative records, thus providing additional value as a longitudinal study. With a

sample of the order of 1/1000 much can be done, and I would anticipate that such a program could be accomplished without Congressional or public opposition. In fact, the recent report by the Gallagher Committee anticipated such a development.

The present study, described earlier, linking Current Population Survey, Social Security Administration and Internal Revenue Service records is an effort from which lessons can be learned.

This proposal is at a stage where it calls for further discussion and exploration. There are many problems, and perhaps also worthwhile payoffs. I believe that exploration of this general approach is one way to initiate additional work on the integration of available records for statistical purposes, along with the continued development and use of studies and projects that integrate records to serve identified needs.

REFERENCES

"Report on the Committee on the Preservation and Use of Economic Data to the Social Science Research Council," Richard Ruggles, Chairman, April 1965. (Reprinted in *The Computer and Invasion of Privacy*.)

Edgar S. Dunn, Jr., "Statistical Evaluation Report No. 6 — Review of Proposal for a National Data Center," Office of Statistical Standards, Bureau of the Budget, November 1965. (Reprinted in *The Computer and Invasion of Privacy*.)

"The Computer and Invasion of Privacy," hearings before a Subcommittee on Government Operations, House of Representatives, 89th Congress, Second Session, July 26-28, 1966.

"Report of the Task Force on the Storage of and Access to Government Statistics," Carl Kaysen, Chairman, Executive Office of the President, Bureau of the Budget, October 1966.

"Privacy and the National Data Bank Concept," 35th Report by the Committee on Government Operations, 90th Congress, 2nd Session, House Report No. 1842, August 2, 1968.

H. B. Newcombe, J. M. Kennedy, S. J. Axford and A. P. James "Automatic Linking of Vital Records," *Science*, 130, 1959, pp. 954-959.

B. J. Tepping, "A Model for Optimum Linkage of Records," *Journal of the American Statistical Association*, Volume 63, No. 324, December 1968, pp. 1321-1332.

I. P. Fellegi and A. B. Sunter, "A Theory for Record Linkage," *Journal of the American Statistical Association*, Volume 64, No. 328, December 1969, pp. 1183-1210.

Bureau of the Census, "List of References on Results and Methodology of Matching Studies," *Response Research Branch Report* (No. 66-4) February 1, 1966 (unpublished).

Maxwell R. Conklin, "Time Series for Individual Plants from the Annual Survey of Manufactures and Related Data," *1964 Proceeding of the Business and Economics Statistics Section, American Statistical Association*, pp. 404-410.

Joseph Steinberg (Social Security Administration), "Interacting Data Systems and the Measurement of Income Size Distributions," prepared for Conference on Income and Wealth, University of Pennsylvania, March 24-25, 1967 (unpublished).

Evelyn M. Kitagawa and Philip M. Hauser, "Education Differentials in Mortality by Cause of Death: U.S. 1960," in *Demography*, Volume 5, No. 5., 1968, pp. 318-353.

Bureau of the Census, *Evaluation and Research Program of the U.S. Censuses of Population and Housing, 1960*: No. 1 Background, Procedures, and Forms (1963); No. 2. Record Check Studies of Population Coverage (1964); No. 5 Accuracy of Data on Population Coverage as Measured by CPS-Census Match (1965); No. 6 The Employer Record Check (1968); No. 8 Record Check Study of Accuracy of Income Reporting (1970).

Morris H. Hansen, "Improved Federal Statistics to Serve Tomorrow's Urban and Regional Problems," Regents' Lecture, UCLA, Institute of Government and Public Affairs, February 1966.

Morris H. Hansen, "Insuring Confidentiality of Individual Records in Data Storage and Retrieval for Statistical Purposes," prepared for the 1971 Fall Joint Computer Conference, American Federation of Information Processing Societies, Law Vegas, Nevada, November 16-18, 1971.

International Symposium and Automation of Population Register Systems, *Proceedings*, Jerusalem, Israel, September 1967.

APPENDIX

Insuring Confidentiality of Individual Records in Data Storage and Retrieval for Statistical Purposes[1]

Much has been written about the question of privacy and the need for the protection of confidentiality of individual records in data storage and retrieval systems. The ability to insure confidentiality is a prime tool in the protection of privacy. The goal of this paper is to summarize from the point of view of a statistician some of the aspects and principles of confidentiality and some of the implications of these principles for computer-based storage and retrieval systems for statistical purposes. The remarks will have special relevance to open retrieval systems, that is, retrieval systems in which customers for information retrieval are the general public, or perhaps specified agencies or groups or individuals, and these customers can retrieve any desired statistics from the confidential records in the files subject to a review to insure that the output conforms to prescribed rules designed to avoid disclosure of individual information. These rules may be concerned with the minimum number of cases on which an individual statistics or frequency count is based or with other aspects, as is discussed later. The access to the data may be restricted to certain authorized types of data through control passwords or keys.

Meaning of Confidentiality

What is meant by confidentiality needs clarification. An obvious meaning is that the individual records, with the names or other identifying information included, will not be made available to other than authorized persons. But beyond this the definition of

---

1 To be presented at 1971 Fall Joint Computer Conference, November 16-18, Las Vegas, Nevada.

what is adequate protection of confidentiality needs further clarification.

The Census Bureau has a well-established and well-earned record for preservation of confidentiality of its records. Much of this paper will draw on the Census Bureau experience as an illustration. With the great concern of the Congress and others over the potential for invasion of privacy in statistical information systems, and especially the proposed and much-discussed federal statistical data center, it is useful to examine how the Census Bureau has come to be widely accepted as a model in the confidentiality protection given to its records. It will be seen that the experience points to serious and as yet unresolved problems, and that the problems are especially difficult for a storage and retrieval system such as a federal data center with access to statistical summaries by persons not authorized to see the individual confidential records.

The Census law (Title 13, U.S.C., Sec. 9-a-2) provides that there shall not be ". . . . any publication [or information otherwise made available] whereby the data furnished by any particular establishment or individual under this title can be identified."

Various interpretations can be made of this language. One is that *no inference* can be made about the results reported by any individual. This is not a tolerable interpretation. At the other extreme, the law cannot reasonably be interpreted to mean that there is no violation of confidentiality provided the name or address (or other specific identification such as Social Security number) is not associated with the information and made available.

A reasonable as distinguished from a rigorous or literal interpretation of the language of the law is required if any statistics are to be published.[2] For example, the publication of an aggregate of retail sales for hardware stores in a county reveals that no individual hardware store had sales of a greater amount that this aggregate, and this much is revealed about each individual hardware store. Similarly, sometimes the existence (or nonexistence) of an item in each report can be inferred from the publication of statistical aggregates. Thus, the fact that in an age distribution for a

---

2 Here and elsewhere in this paper the term "publication" refers to any means of making information available to persons who do not have authorized access to the confidential records and who are not subject to penalties for disclosure.

specified area from a population census no person is reported as over 75 years of age reveals for each individual person that his age was reported as under 75 years.[3] In publishing statistics for large areas such considerations may be of little consequence. But in publishing statistics for smaller and smaller areas the problem increases, and the primary role of the decennial census is to produce small area statistics. Especially statistics are needed and produced from the decennial Censuses of Population and Housing for counties, cities, towns, census tracts, and even city blocks within cities or other communities. The storage and retrieval of geographically detailed statistical information may also be a primary goal of other information systems based on a set of administrative records or integrated from administrative systems and perhaps also from statistical surveys.

Years of experience and precedent in publishing statistics by the Bureau of the Census without serious problems suggest the acceptability of the rules and principles that have been followed to avoid unreasonable disclosure of data for individuals in statistical aggregates. However, the computer adds new capabilities as its capacities and applications increase, and these may call for reexamination and some new rules and principles. It is desirable to have recognized, in applying past principles and in developing any new ones, and as has been illustrated in the above discussion, that if *any* statistics are to be published nondisclosure cannot be absolute. Rules for nondisclosure are necessarily based on an interpretation of what is reasonable, and supported by precedents and past experience.

Some Principles and Questions for Guiding Nondisclosure In Protecting Confidentiality

Some relevant principles or questions concerning rules for protecting confidentiality of individual records will be presented. Clear and unequivocal answers may not exist. Nevertheless, reasonable decisions have been made and must be made, in order to publish census and other statistical results.

---

3   Additional illustrations are presented in 1.

WHAT CONSTITUTES PROTECTION AGAINST EXACT OR APPROXIMATE DISCLOSURE?

Protection against *exact* or *approximate* disclosure of specific items of information in a record must be provided. However, "approximate" disclosure must be interpreted or defined. Issues concerning the approximate disclosure of magnitudes, as distinguished from frequency counts, involve some special considerations.

Illustration: In some studies the Census Bureau has interpreted the disclosure of a magnitude, X, as not to be an approximate disclosure when the range of interpretation is of the order of (.75 to 1.5) X. Frequencies in a distribution may automatically meet this condition if intervals are broad enough for the upper limit of the interval to be at least double the lower limit, as in the following illustration:

Number of Employees

Less than 5
5—9
10—24
25—49
50—99
100—199, etc.

Under this rule even an individual case may be reported in such an interval without making an approximate disclosure. Of course the individual is not identified, but frequencies as low as 0, 1, 2 or 3 are shown in such intervals, as in employment size classes for retail stores, by type, within a county, for example, and a person with commonly available local knowledge may be able to identify a particular store identified by a frequency of 1, and its reported employment within the range of the class interval.

EFFECT OF SENSITIVITY OF THE INFORMATION

Should disclosure rules take some account of the sensitivity of the information, and be more restricted with highly sensitive information than with less sensitive information? Some information loses sensitivity with time; some may not, or the sensitivity may increase with time. Some information is essentially in the public

51

domain. These factors should, and in fact, do have some impact on the confidentiality treatment, but still without completely specified formal rules.[4] For example, is there any point in regarding the size of a family or a household (which often is known to everyone in the neighborhood) as equally confidential as the income of the head of the household? Similarly, should the industry code derived from the types of production reported by a manufacturing company be protected as confidential, when often the company spends much money to let the public know of the types of products it makes or the services in which it is engaged? Should the number of employees reported for a plant be protected as equally confidential as the reported sales?

Such questions may have more difficult implications than is readily apparent. Thus, in some instances the number of persons in a household may indicate illegal occupancy to a landlord or to housing code authorities. Again, the industry in which a company is classified may affect the rate of taxation for unemployment compensation. If a company is classified in a high-risk industry instead of a lower-risk one, and if the industry code derived from a confidential statistical report of a company is made public, will it influence the company's tax rate?

DISCLOSURES WITH SUPPLEMENTAL KNOWLEDGE OR COLLUSION

It is necessary to provide protection against disclosures that can be achieved by collusion, or by supplemental knowledge in addition to one's knowledge of his own affairs? A common rule in avoiding disclosure is that there must be at least three nontrivial cases aggregated in a cell (based on aggregates of magnitudes) so that, for example, a business respondent will not know his competitors' response. Presumably it is not feasible, and the Census Bureau accepts the principle that it is not feasible, to protect against disclosure by collusion. Otherwise, again, nothing could be published. However, the issue of possible disclosure through taking advantage of supplemental knowledge needs further attention,

---

4 Allan F. Westin has expressed a need for developing a classification system for personal information to identify types that need various degrees of control. See, for example, *Privacy and Freedom* (Atheneum, 1967).

especially in view of the computer capabilities. There is an important difference between analysis to achieve disclosures, with and without the computer. Consider, as an illustration, a cross-tabulation made in great detail.

Assume 10,000 persons in a file for an area, and information for each person on 50 characteristics (something like the results of the questions in a 1970 Population and Housing Census sample questionnaire). Suppose that the record includes some characteristics with two alternative responses, as for sex. Others may have three, five, ten, or twenty alternative classifications (as with ten intervals for an age tabulation). A question such as occupation may be recorded and tabulated in 100 or many more classes.

If we assume 10 of the questions have 2 alternatives,
10 of the questions have 3 alternatives,
10 of the questions have 5 alternatives,
10 of the questions have 10 alternatives,
10 of the questions have 20 alternatives,

and if we conceive of a cross-tabulation in the fullest possible detail of these 50 questions the number of possible cells becomes $2^{10} \times 3^{10} \times 5^{10} \times 20^{10} = 10^{38}$ cells, which is an astronomical number. It is likely that in such a detailed cross-tabulation each person would be unique, with each cell showing a frequency of zero of 1.

A cross-tabulation of only five of these questions (one from each of the indicated numbers of alternatives) would yield a tabulation with about 6,000 cells, so that a population of 10,000 would have an average of 1.7 per cell in such a tabulation. Of course, many cells may be impossible or blank, and some cells might have several cases. Nevertheless, tabulations in such detail may make it feasible for a person or organization (such as a welfare or taxing agency or a credit bureau) with certain of the same information on some of the people to identify many of them in the tabulation and ascertain other information for them. With a computer the comparison and identification become far more feasible. Consequently, consideration must be given to the amount of detail in which tabulations will be made available in order to preserve confidentiality. Or should and can any possible violations of confidentiality be ignored that can be achieved only through the use of extensive supplemental information? In the computer age this seems unreasonable.

Some interesting discussion and examples of principles and procedures for using collateral information to extract information for individual records from a statistical data bank with retrieval allowed only for statistical aggregates, and by obtaining legitimate responses to queries, is given in an article by Hoffman and Miller.

The presence of errors, or differences in time reference or in the treatment of individual items of information in two sets of records, is common. Such errors or differences would make more difficult the problem of using collateral information to extract individual information from statistics derived from a set of confidential records used for statistical purposes. However, with sufficiently extensive and detailed independent information available to use in identification, and even in the presence of such errors or differences, the probability of correctly identifying a person and picking up the desired confidential information increases as the number of cells in a cross-tabulation is increased, or with appropriately designed queries of increasing detail.

INDIRECT DISCLOSURES

Indirect as well as direct disclosures must be considered, and these can be a major source of difficulty. Thus, suppose a small county has six hardware stores, and that a city within the county has four of them. If retail sales are published for the county, and also for the city (we assume each would individually meet disclosure requirements) an indirect disclosure occurs. Each of the two stores in the balance of the county could directly determine his competitor's sales by taking the difference between the county statistics and the city statistics. Thus, if disclosure is to be avoided the data for the city can be made available, and not the county, or for the county and not the city. Indirect disclosures should be avoided, at least in any sensitive type of information.

54

PRIORITIES NEEDED IN STATISTICS SUBJECT TO IN-DIRECT DISCLOSURE RESTRAINTS

The consequences of indirect disclosures are that priorities are necessary in determining which statistics will be made available and which will not, in order to avoid making available some relatively unimportant information and thereby subsequently denying statistics that have highly important uses. The providing of information forecloses making information available for an alternative, as illustrated above. As another and more serious illustration, it is often true that in the Manufactures or Business Census information can be shown for a state total, or for a metropolitan area total, but not for both, and many similar situations arise. Exactly the same kinds of problems can arise in the publications of Population and Housing Census data, especially for small areas where the frequencies get small. In these Censuses, however, some of the data may be less sensitive, and disclosure analysis may not need to be pressed as rigorously. For sensitive data, however, the question becomes: how should one determine the priorities? Obviously, it is public interest and utility that should be determining, but this problem poses many questions beyond the scope of this discussion. Of particular importance, however, is the consequence that the priority problem means that the first comer, who may have a limited use or need in terms of public interest, may foreclose the possibility of later retrieval of other more important information. The question of priorities adds great complexity to the design of any such retrieval system for information that is subject to confidentiality restraints.

RANDOM MODIFICATION OF DATA TO AVOID APPROXIMATE DISCLOSURE

There has been some consideration of random modification of data within the range of, for example, a factor of .5 to 1.5, with the choice of factor within the range made at random, as a means of avoiding approximate disclosure. With this approach an actual report of 850 employees in an establishment might be modified to become 595 = 850 (.7) where the .7 was chosen at random from

55

the interval .5 to 1.5. The average effect of such modifications on simple aggregates or averages would be relatively small (over a large experience) and numbers so modified in reports can be subjected to less rigorous disclosure rules or even no disclosure analysis. In the case of attributes the approach must be modified to change some fraction of ones to zeros and of zeros to ones, where changes are made at random in ways that do not unduly violate internal consistency of the data for the individual record.

The impact may be more serious with cross-tabulations where the independent variables — those used in sorting into various classes or cells — have been so modified. In this latter case a bias is introduced that may or may not be serious in its magnitude. Such a bias is not necessarily reduced simply by increasing the number of cases within a class.

The random modification of data to avoid approximate disclosure has been considered extensively for various applications in the Bureau of the Census over the past decade or more, but has actually been applied to a very limited extent, so far as I am aware. It has developed and been discussed independently, and again, with limited applications, as a means of preserving confidentiality in retrieval or publication of information (See reference 4 and 5). This approach deserves more exploration. It may be that an announced program of random modification of a relatively small fraction of the records selected at random can accomplish much in avoiding disclosure for all of the records in the set.

DISCLOSURE WITH STATISTICAL
INFORMATION FROM SAMPLES

If information in some statistics is based on a sample of a population, the chance of disclosure is reduced, and the thinner the sample, the less the chance of disclosure in statistical tabulations of a given amount of detail.

For a small enough sampling fraction, even if disclosure rules are not fully observed, the chance of pay-off may be small enough to make prohibitive (as a practical matter) the cost of taking advantage of the potentials for disclosure.

In recognition of this principle the Census Bureau decided to put in the public domain the statistical data recorded for each household from the 1960 Census for a 1 in 1000 sample of households after deleting certain information from the records that would facilitate identification. Of course the name and address were deleted. In addition, geographic identification was deleted below the level of broad city-size class within geographic divisions of the country (there are nine geographic divisions, each consisting of several states). In addition, some extreme cases were modified for sensitive types of information so that, for example, the upper boundary of income reported may have been reduced. Beyond this, the full household information was included in a magnetic tape file on a set of punched cards for the 1/1000 sample, including the housing information and the full listing of individual household members, with the information reported for each individual member. The purpose was to make it feasible for various users to make their own summaries or cross-tabulations or correlations to meet a wide range of needs. It was a great success, with a large number of users of the tape putting it to many uses that could not be served directly by the Census tabulations.

From the point of view of confidentiality, anyone who has a supplemental source of more limited information but that duplicates a number of items of information in the Census file for individuals or families or households for some part of the population could use that information to identify many of the individual cases in this sample that were also in his file. Of course he could expect to find less than 1 in 1000 of the cases in his file, but for those found he would then have identified the additional information in the 1/1000 file.

Suppose, for example, that a credit bureau had records for a "chunk" of the population in a metropolitan area, including, perhaps, information on age for the head of the family, the number of persons in the family (not necessarily the same as in the household), occupation of the head of the household, whether the home was owned or rented, and the value of the home or the amount of the rent paid. With such information, and even with errors and with differences in time references in both sets, he might run his tape against the Census 1/1000 sample tape, perhaps for a large area or areas, and identify with a fairly good chance of success (but with much less than certainty) the cases in the 1/1000 file that were also in his records. He would thereby acquire the additional Census information for the identified cases (including misinformation for cases that were misidentified). But it would cost him a considerable amount both in efforts and dollars, and at the very best he could expect to find a pay-off of less than 1/1000 in the sense of obtaining Census information for the cases in his file. The possibility of misuse arises only in the case of someone with a file of supplemental information that is sufficiently relevant for some subgroup of the population. Even then the pay-off presumably would be very small because of the presence of errors and time reference differences in each source, and the great effort in relation to the number of successful matches (and of course he would not know which of his linked records were the unsuccessful matches). The pay-off might be small not only because of the very small fraction of "finds," but also because the information in the Census records, in general, is not all that sensitive.

Presumably because of such factors no evidence has come to light of any such misuse. At the same time the 1/1000 sample has served many highly useful purposes, so much so that the Census Bureau is proposing to extend the program along the same lines for 1970, and to increase the size of sample from 1/1000 to 1/100.

DISCLOSURE OF DISCLOSURE RULES

There is some thought that rules for disclosure should not be disclosed, and that the availability of the rules will increase the ability of one who wishes to arrive at desired disclosures through analysis of the information that is made available. On this principle, apparently, the Bureau of the Census has not published its various disclosure rules in full, although some of the rules are more or less obvious, and have been made available.

SOME IMPLICATIONS FOR AN OPEN RETRIEVAL SYSTEM

There is need to bring the issues of confidentiality as related to storage and retrieval of information into fuller discussion. The implications of some of the points and principles that have been made above may not be obvious, and study and exploration are needed.

There is no basis for simply assuming that an all-powerful software system can be designed that will take care of the problems of preserving confidentiality in a national statistical data center if one were to be created. Obviously, such a software system cannot be designed until the principles and specific rules of what constitute disclosure and nondisclosure are agreed upon. Unless the principle of *reasonable disclosure,* instead of no disclosure, is adopted, it appears that little or no information could be made available. If the principle of reasonable disclosure is adopted, it will be necessary to define what constitutes reasonable disclosure.

It also must be determined how far the disclosure system will protect against the potentials for disclosure that are made possible by the use of extensive supplemental information acquired through other sources. The availability of such supplemental information can make it feasible to extract increasing amounts of confidential information by making increasingly detailed tabulations or queries, as illustrated earlier, as well as from records such as the 1/1000 sample. Unless the system makes no attempt to protect the disclosure of additional information from sources that have extensive and detailed supplemental information, the disclosure rules may have to be so designed that few of the kinds of anticipated uses from, say, a national statistical data center could be served.

A particularly difficult problem is that of indirect disclosure, through comparisons or analyses of successive tabulations or results of queries. With disclosure analysis that takes account of indirect disclosures many requests might have to be drastically curtailed after a few initial uses. If there were no auditing for indirect disclosure anyone could specify changes in the classifications or specifications for a sequence of tabulations in such a way as to reveal, after analysis, the desired characteristics of many or all of the individual records. Some computer programs have been prepared for dealing with indirect disclosure analysis, and are in use in the Bureau of the Census, but the complexities in a system of open access (subject to restraints on disclosures) seem enormously challenging. A system of recording which has retrieved information, what kinds and how much, for post-audit on a judgmental basis may offer sufficient protection, especially if a rule of reason is used.

But suppose the problem of indirect disclosure is solved (and in theory, at least, it appears that it can be solved), the problem of priorities still remains. Must all high-priority statistics be listed in advance? Is this feasible? If not, minor or trivial uses of the data may override the subsequent possibility of acquiring information the need for which was not originally foreseen. One unimportant use may foreclose any possibility of providing information on an urgent and unforeseen current problem.

The issue of priorities is not a new one, as we have seen. It exists in a system in which there is no general access to the stored records. It appears that the problem may be greater in a system that allows access without going into a judgment filter of evaluating public interest and need, or potentials for foreclosing future uses, as is now done in the Bureau of the Census activities. This problem may be a sufficiently serious one to foreclose effective development of anything like a federal statistical data center or data bank that retains confidential records in storage, and permits access by the public or specified groups to statistical tabulations that are audited for disclosure by computer software. The priority problem remains even if other problems prove manageable and can be brought under control.

There is need for fuller discussion of some of these issues by scientific and professional groups. It is not sufficient for these discussions to be conducted separately and in isolation. There is need for interchange using some organized approaches arranged to discuss the issues and problems.

REFERENCES

1. P. Hirsch, "The World's Biggest Data Bank," *Datamation,* May 1970, pp. 66-73.

2. A. F. Westin, *Privacy and Freedom,* Atheneum, New York, 1967.

3. L. J. Hoffman and W. F. Miller, "Getting a Personal Dossier from a Statistical Data Bank," *Datamation,* May 1970, pp. 74-75.

4. R. F. Boruch, "Educational Research and the Confidentiality of Data," *ACE Research Reports,* Vol. 4, No. 4 1969.

5. R. F. Boruch, "Maintaining Confidentiality of Data in Educational Research: A Systemic Analysis," *American Psychologist,* Vol. 26, No. 5 May 1971, pp. 413-430.

6. I. P. Fellegi and A. B. Sunter, "A Theory for Record Linkage," *Journal of the American Statistical Association,* Vol. 64, No. 328, 1968, pp. 1183-1210.

7. I. P. Felliegi, "On the Question of Statistical Confidentiality," (unpublished) Revision of a paper given at the 1970 annual meetings of the American Statistical Association.

8. "The Computer and Invasion of Privacy," *Hearings before a Subcommittee of the Committee on Government Operations,* House of Representatives, 89th Congress, 2nd Session, July 26-28, 1966.

9. *Report of the task force on the storage of and access to government statistics,* C. Kaysen, Chairman, Executive Office of the President, Bureau of the Budget, October 1966.

10. "Privacy and the National Data Bank Concept," *35th Report by the Committee on Government Operations,* 90th Congress, 2nd Session, House Report No. 1842, August 2, 1968.

11. E. V. Comber, "Management of Confidential Information," *AFIPS Conference Proceedings,* Vol. 35, 1969 Fall Joint Computer Conference.

12. M. H. Hansen, "Some Aspects of Confidentiality in Information Systems," *Papers from the Eighth Annual Conference of the Urban Regional Information Systems Association,* Louisville, Kentucky, September 1970.

CHAPTER 2

THE APPLICATION OF STATISTICAL TECHNIQUES

Part A

Statistics and Data Analysis in the Food and Drug Administration

By
Cuthbert Daniel
Edward R. Tufte
Joseph A. Kadane

TABLE OF CONTENTS

SUMMARY OF REPORT

The Bureau of Drugs has regulatory responsibility for all medicinal drugs and devices developed, produced, and consumed; it develops standards and conducts research on the efficacy, reliability, and safety of drugs; it reviews New Drug Applications, operates an adverse reaction reporting system, and performs many other drug-related functions. The vast scope of these responsibilities is indicated by the following figures:

--In 1970 doctors wrote about two billion prescriptions, including some 225 million for "mind-affecting drugs" — stimulants, sedatives, tranquilizers, and the like. By 1975, there will be three to five billion prescriptions written each year.

--About 1.5 million hospital admissions each year are due to illnesses caused by drugs.

--In recent years, the FDA has had to review over 4,000 drugs for efficacy.

The Bureau of Drugs received a budget in FY 1971 of $17 million — a very small budget for the job to be done. About one penny per prescription written will be spent this year by the

Bureau of Drugs to evaluate the safety and efficacy of old and new drugs, to inspect the manufacturer of drugs, to certify some types of drugs, to assess adverse reactions caused by all drugs, and to perform its other tasks. It is in the context of such a small budget and limited scientific competence that the Bureau's statistical work is done.

With respect to the statistical work of the Bureau of Drugs, we have found:

1. The last one and a half years have seen a considerable improvement. There is still a long way to go.
2. To do its job adequately at present, the Bureau needs about ten Ph.D. level statisticians and data analysts of various types. It now has two to four of those needed.
3. About ten statisticians with less training are needed. Half of these are now at work.
4. The computer operations in support of statistical work are negligible. In the short run, three scientific programmers would make better use of the currently under-used facility.
5. Statisticians should fully participate as peers in the review of New Drug Applications.
6. The FDA and the drug industry should work to assure that material included in New Drug Applications is relevant to the drug under consideration.
7. The New Drug Applications (with the exception of legitimate trade secrets contained in them) and the FDA's evaluation of those applications should be made public and open to all interested parties.
8. Drug surveillance and adverse reactions reporting are very weak within the Bureau and currently produce little useful output. The Bureau needs external help. The Bureau should participate in the letting of large-scale contracts for the monitoring of drug reactions. In planning such proposals, not enough attention has been given to the analysis of the data.

SECTION O - **THE WORK OF THIS REPORT**

We have gathered information for this report from interviews, including meetings with many officials in the Food and Drug

Administration (FDA), statisticians employed in several drug houses, officers of the Pharmaceutical Manufacturers Association, several drug researchers and statisticians with academic affiliations, and others. We were met with uniform courtesy by these busy men and women. In addition, we have consulted many printed sources, including the *FDA Papers,* some internal FDA materials, the extensive Congressional hearings dealing with drugs and the FDA, and some of the many books, papers, and newspaper articles published on the subject.

This report first describes the responsibilities of the Bureau of Drugs and the role of statistical analysis in assuring that drugs meet the legal requirements of safety and efficacy. We then turn to our specific conclusions and recommendations in six areas related to the statistical work of the Bureau of Drugs.

SECTION I — THE RESPONSIBILITIES OF THE BUREAU OF DRUGS IN THE FOOD AND DRUG ADMINISTRATION

The Bureau of Drugs has the basic regulatory responsibilities for medicinal drugs and devices developed, produced, and consumed in the United States. According to the February 1, 1970 reorganization statement for the Food and Drug Administration, the Bureau of Drugs

> develops standards and medical policy and conducts research on efficacy, reliability, and safety of drugs and devices for man; reviews and evaluates New Drug Applications and claims for investigational drugs; conducts clinical studies on safety and efficacy of drugs and devices; operates an adverse drug reaction reporting system; oversees surveillance and compliance programs on drugs and devices; provides scientific and technical support in drug biology and drug chemistry; assumes responsibility for regulations, model codes, and other standards covering drug industry practices and fosters development of good manufacturing practices; oversees the antibiotic and insulin certification program.[1]

---

1 *FDA Papers,* May 1970.

The vast scope of these responsibilities is indicated by the following figures for drug usage under FDA responsibility:

--In 1970 consumer expenditures for prescription and non-prescription drugs and devices were about $19 billion.[2]

--In 1970 doctors wrote about two billion prescriptions. Some 225 million of these prescriptions were for "mind-affecting drugs" — stimulants, sedatives, tranquilizers, and the like.[3]

It is estimated that by 1975 doctors will write three billion prescriptions.[4]

--Dr. Charles C. Edwards, the current FDA commissioner, wrote: "According to the 'Drug Utilization Review and Control Report', made by Dr. Donald C. Brodie of the Health Services and Mental Health Administration and issued last April (1970), it has been estimated that the incidence of complication in drug therapy is roughly 10 percent, and that approximately 5 percent of the patients admitted for medical treatment in general hospitals are admitted because of serious drug reactions. It is also estimated that approximately 1.5 million hospital admissions a year are due to illnesses caused by drugs."[5]

--In FY 1969, the FDA (among its many tasks with respect to drugs): reviewed over 2,500 original and supplemental applications for new drugs for human use, certified over 24,000 batches of antibiotics, insulin, and colors, initiated 220 establishment inspections under the Intensified Drug Inspection Program, and expanded testing for bioavailability of drugs and research on mycotoxins, cyclamates, and oral contraceptives.[6]

--In recent years the FDA has started to implement the

2 Charles C. Edwards, "Rational Drug Therapeutics," FDA Papers, February 1971, p.4.

3 "Growing Use of Minding-Affecting Drugs Stirs Concern," New York Times, March 14, 1971, p. 36.

4 Charles C. Edwards, Interview, U.S. News & World Report, April 19, 1971, p. 52.

5 Charles C. Edwards, "Rational Drug Therapeutics", FDA Papers, February 1971, p. 4.

6 FDA background material.

1962 Kefauver-Harris Amendments to the Food, Drug, and Cosmetic Act. These amendments require that drugs be shown to be efficacious, as well as safe. The 1962 law applied to new drugs coming on the market as well as to drugs that came on the market between 1938 and 1962. The law has thus required the FDA to make some judgment about the efficacy of thousands of drugs. The basic job was given to 30 review panels of physicians and dentists selected by the National Academy of Sciences-National Research Council Drug Efficacy Study Policy Advisory Committee. These panels produced 2,824 reports for 4,349 drug products. For the last two years the FDA has reviewed these reports involving more than 10,000 drug claims (plus the estimated five times as many similar products not studied) in an effort to reach a decision as to which drugs did not meet the efficacy requirements. This difficult job has been carried on along with the usual work of the FDA.

The range of work is shown in the specific responsibilities given to the Offices within the Bureau of Drugs:

Of New Drugs: Evaluates, for safety and efficacy, New Drug Applications (NDA's) for marketing new drugs; evaluates adequacy of proposed labeling for use and warning against misuse; evaluates manufacturing and laboratory methods, facilities, and controls in factories producing new drugs; reviews notices of claimed investigational exemption for new drugs (IND's) and recommends action to restrict or stop further testing; reviews clinical investigators and scientific investigations of investigational new drugs and New Drug Application areas and coordinates follow-up with the Office of Compliance.

Divisions: Anti-Infective Drugs, Cardiopulmonary and Renal Drugs; Dental and Surgical Adjuncts; Metabolism and Endocrine Drugs; Neuropharmacological Drugs; Oncology and Radiopharmaceuticals, and Scientific Investigations.

Of Marketed Drugs: Evaluates safety and efficacy data and proposed labeling in supplements to New Drug Applications; carries out continuing surveillance and medical evalu-

71

ation of labeling, clinical experience, and reports required of applicants for all drugs and devices for which new drug approval is in effect; reviews inspections and other findings to determine if new drugs are being marketed in accord with commitments in New Drug Applications; makes recommendations on withdrawal of approval of the NDA; takes final action on antibiotic and insulin samples submitted for certification and on requests for exemptions from antibiotic certification; reviews for safety, reliability, and effectiveness the new and marketed therapeutic and clinical devices and recommends action on significant hazards or potential danger from inadequacy of direction for use or warning and cautionary information; obtains and evaluates reports of adverse drug reactions.

Divisions: Certification Services, Clinical and Medical Devices, Drug Experience, Cardiopulmonary-Renal Drug Surveillance, Metabolic-Endocrine Drug Surveillance, Neuropharmacological Drug Surveillance, and Surgical-Dental Drug Surveillance.

Of Compliance (Drugs): Advises the Bureau Director and other officials on the law, regulations, legal-administrative problems, regulatory problems, and administrative policies concerning regulatory responsibilities for drugs and devices; conducts studies to determine medical policy and support regulatory action; develops compliance and surveillance programs covering regulated industries; develops or coordinates development of regulations and other standards covering industry practices and fosters development of good manufacturing practices; conducts programs to encourage voluntary compliance by industry; on request, supports and guides District offices in handling legal actions and provides headquarters case development, coordination, and assistance in contested cases; develops and coordinates studies on degree of compliance by regulated industries with statutes and regulations enforced by FDA; monitors and evaluates professional journal advertising and promotional and related labeling to determine veracity of claims.

Divisions: Case Guidance (Drugs), Compliance Programs (Drugs), Drug Advertising, Industry Services (Drugs), Medical Review, and Policy and Regulations.

Of Pharmaceutical Sciences: Provides scientific support for drug compliance programs; develops scientific support for drug compliance programs; develops scientific standards and conducts research on composition, quality, and safety of drugs; operates system for continuous appraisal and improvement of current and proposed drug standards and specifications; devises new chemical, physical, and biological methods to analyze drugs in pharmaceutical preparations and in tissues and body fluids; investigates mechanisms of the underlying chemical reactions; explores use of novel instruments and equipment; designs and participates in collaborative studies to establish the reliability of new methods and to validate important discoveries relating to drug examinations; operates the National Center for Drug Analysis (St. Louis) and the National Center for Antibiotics and Insulin Analysis (Washington); cooperates with the Committee of Revision of the U.S. Pharmacopeia (USP) and the National Formulary (NF) to compose and assemble monographs for inclusion in official drug compendia.

Divisions: Drug Biology, Drug Chemistry, National Center for Antibiotics and Insulin Analysis, and National Center for Drug Analysis.[7]

In order to perform all these jobs in FY 1971, the Bureau of Drugs received a budget of $17 million. This figure, though painfully small, represents a significant increase over previous appropriations. By almost any standard, it is a very small budget for the job to be done. One way to put it into perspective: for each prescription filled this year in the United States, about one penny will be spent by the Bureau of Drugs to evaluate the safety and efficacy of new and old drugs, to inspect the manufacture of drugs, to certify some drugs, and to assess the adverse reactions of all drugs.

---

7 *FDA Papers,* May 1970.

It is in this context that we turn to the role of statistics and quantitative analysis in the Bureau of Drugs.

SECTION II — **THE ROLE OF STATISTICS AND DATA ANALYSIS IN THE BUREAU OF DRUGS**

In this section we seek to

(1) show how some types of statistical analysis, when combined with good medical judgment, are necessary if the Bureau of Drugs is to meet its responsibilities under the law,

(2) point to the particular places in the Bureau of Drugs where particular quantitative and statistical tools would prove useful, and

(3) evaluate the current statistical and quantitative work in the Bureau of Drugs in comparison to the work it needs.

The basic job of the Bureau of Drugs is to assess evidence concerning drugs. Such evidence consists of chemical and pharmacological data, the results of experiments on test animals, and human experience with drugs. The assessment of such evidence requires a diversity of skills although the decisions on the clinical significance of the effects of a drug on humans must rest with clinically trained officials. A large part of the evidence on which the decision-making official relies is quantitative, in the form of counts, measurements, or subjective records from a number of cases — measurements which are often taken by a number of observers in different clinics. Single examples rarely suffice, except when they indicate that more cases should be accumulated. At the other extreme a full enumeration of a population is rarely needed or indeed possible.

The officials making decisions about drugs must usually deal with quantitative evidence gained from experimental designs collecting data which are samples of a larger population. Statistics is the art and science of dealing with samples, constructing experimental designs, and analyzing quantitative data — and its techniques can, upon occasion, contribute to the collection of useful information about drugs and the making of sound decisions concerning the safety and efficacy of drugs.

Experienced statisticians and data analysts can contribute to the solution of such problems as:

--How are data taken in different clinics and in different clinical trials to be combined or contrasted? This difficult problem occurs in a great many New Drug Applications as well as when the drug is on the market.

--What is the most economical way to monitor the effects of total drug consumption in the nation?

--What types of experimental designs will reliably and economically obtain information about the safety and efficacy of a drug?

--What constitutes a fair set of tests for the claimed therapeutic equivalence of two or more drugs manufactured by different companies?

--Does the average life span of this set of 20 mice — which have been treated with drug A at a low dose-level throughout their lives — differ importantly from the life span of this other set, which have had no drug A?

--Does a bias in the selection of patients for treatment or control groups invalidate the results of a particular study?

--Does the method of data analysis bias the results? Would another method show a different conclusion?

--How large a sample is required to detect a side-effect that occurs with a frequency of less than one in a thousand?

--Can drug A be judged better than drug B, the present drug of choice, for treating a particular infectious disease?

--Does the finding of 17 defective bottles of a manufactured product justify withdrawal from market, or a more intense search?

--Do early human trials on a few volunteers give a sufficiently clear picture of safety and efficacy to justify larger trials to look for human variation, for the dependence of response on dosage, and for relatively rare side effects?

--Or consider a more detailed question: 20 test organisms are often used in standard toxicological trials for estimating the "no effect dose." Suppose a dose or doses schedule for some

75

fixed period is found to affect adversely *none* of the 20 test organisms. What can be said about the true proportion of the whole population that may respond adversely? In this particular example, all that can be said with tolerable security (i.e., with a 95 percent confidence of being right) is that less than 14 percent of the population will be affected. It is assumed that there is *no* error of measurement or judgment in making the study and in concluding that no animal was adversely affected. If there is such error, then the limiting proportion is greater than 14 percent. This example is given space here because it is a near-scandalous fact that nearly all otherwise qualified toxicologists have difficulty believing this relation, even though its logic was clearly understood by Blaise Pascal in 1640.

All these questions require mature clinical judgment as well as statistical backing. Sometimes, of course, the case is so clear that professional statistical aid is not needed. But in complex problems (lacking cookbook solutions), and in close decisions, the statistician will play a key role, easing the clinician's problem by warning him that the data and its analysis do not warrant a claim, or by telling him that there is little doubt that a real gain is present. At times there will be a conflict between statistical and medical judgment. Medical doctors may be convinced by personal observation of a single case. Often they will be right in their judgment and perhaps only a single replication is needed for proof. But generally the way to find out if they are right is to look quantitatively at more cases, in a controlled design, adjusting for patient, diagnostic, and clinic variation. The collaboration between doctors and statisticians will not always be a happy one — but it is a necessary collaboration to guarantee objectivity in the work of the Bureau of Drugs.

It is now time to relate specific statistical and quantitative techniques to specific sections in the Bureau of Drugs. We first present a list of statistical aids in generation, collection, evaluation, and interpretation of data. We then give a table showing the relationship between these statistical tools and the work of the Bureau.

The following statistical tools may be useful in the assessment of the safety and efficacy of drugs:

a. Learning about the properties of large populations by full enumeration. Censuses. For example, the full record of qualified clinicians.
b. Sampling large populations to make projections (inferences) about the whole. For example, how is the percent defective bottles of a drug distributed, both among batches for one producer and among producers?
c. Estimating population properties, and differences between properties of several populations. For example, differences in effects of drugs, dose-dependence by bioassay.
d. Controlling quality (of data, of products, of system operation) by sampling continuous processes. Making decisions using variable data about shifts in the underlying system. For example, quality control charts for purity or strength of insulin batches from several producers.
e. Data analysis and fitting equations to data. Concise summary of complex quantitative information. For example, representing a process in which ten independently operating conditions affect each property of the product.
f. Designing experiments and comparative tests. Reducing bias and increasing precision in multifactor experiments.
g. Managing large files of information with computer. Accrual, storage, editing, retrieval, tabulation. For example, name and chemical composition for all prescription drugs.
h. Developing model-equations to fit processes that require probabilistic description.

Chart 1 shows how these statistical methods are related to the function of the Bureau of Drugs. An asterisk (*) indicates that some statistical work in the particular area is now being carried out. An X indicates that significantly more statistical aid is required to meet the present needs of the Bureau. We find a considerable shortage in almost all areas, although the last year has seen considerable improvement with respect to statistical help. We suspect that two or three years ago there would have been few asterisks — indicating that some statistical work is done in a particular area – in our table. Thus we believe that the statistical work in the Bureau of Drugs is moving in the right direction, but the responsibilities of the Bureau of Drugs to patients, to physicians, and to the pharmaceutical industry can only be fully met when decisions are based on data of guaranteed quality, and are analyzed by competent clinicians and statisticians.

Given that statistical tools have helped and will continue to help the Bureau of Drugs, we now turn to findings and recommendations with respect to statistical operations in five aspects of the work of the Bureau of Drugs.

BUREAU OF DRUG FUNCTIONS

Statistical Areas	New Drug Applications	Compliance	Pharmaceutical Testing	Post-Marketing Surveys	Clinical Research and Spec. Studies
Census, Surveys	*	*	X	*	
Sampling		* X	X	X	
Estimation Bioassay	* X	* X	X	* X	* X
Quality Control		X	X		
Data Analysis, Fitting Equations	* X		* X	* X	* X
Design of Experiments	* X		X		* X
Data Processing	* X	* X	* X	* X	
Statistical Modeling				X	

CHART 1

SECTION III – THE STATISTICAL WORK OF THE BUREAU OF DRUGS: FINDINGS, CONCLUSIONS, AND RECOMMENDATIONS

1. New Drug Applications
2. Drug Surveillance and Evaluation
3. Computer Operations

4. External Statistical Support for the Bureau of Drugs
5. The Bureau of Drugs: A Place for Statisticians

1. New Drug Applications

Some 70-80 New Drug Applications (NDA's) are submitted each year to the Bureau of Drugs. The Bureau evaluates the evidence supporting the safety and efficacy of the drug in order to decide if the drug can be placed on the market. The table shows the number of new NDA's and resubmissions received in 1969 and 1970 by the Bureau, as well as the number of Investigational New Drugs (IND's).

FY	New NDA's	Resubmissions	IND's
1969	71	149	835
1970	75	119	1122

The volume of material in each NDA is large, from a few hundred to many thousands of pages. Each records, among other things, the details of one or more clinical trials, sometimes as many as 20. At present it appears that the Bureau does not have sufficient professional staff to do justice to all this work. Some trials are studied carefully, some necessarily only scanned. This is unfair to the applicants, to the medical and pharmacological FDA officials who must make decisions on the NDA's acceptability, and to the general public who are affected by those decisions.

Statisticians in the Bureau of Drugs have started to participate in the evaluation of the NDA. *Their participation should be extended so that statistical judgment is applied at the beginning of the NDA evaluation process.* Statistical thinking has played a major and useful role in the recent FDA guidelines on drug testing (one general set and 29 sets covering specific types of drugs). These guidelines, negotiated between the FDA and the industry, help set ground rules for useful experimental designs. The introduction to the general guidelines states:

Statistical expertise is required in planning, design, execution and analysis of clinical investigations and clinical pharmacology in order to ensure the validity of estimates of parameters for safety and efficacy obtained from these

79

studies. It is always desirable in planning and conducting such studies to have the active participation of biostatistician(s).

This is followed by a listing of the usual principles of good clinical trial design, most of which are of statistical origin.

The classification of clinical trials into Phases I, II, and III (respectively toxicological trials on small numbers of subjects, perhaps 3-14; efficacy and safety trials on larger closely monitored groups, say 20-200; larger trials for details on dose-dependency, tolerance, side effects, requiring usually from 100 to 1000 subjects) corresponds also to increasing statistical requirements, both in their planning and in their analysis.

Put in rough time order of their appearance, statistical methods would be expected to be decisive in:

1. Specifying target populations and corresponding sampling schemes. (Diseased or healthy population? A placebo or present drug of choice for control? etc.)
2. Setting size of trial (allowances for dropouts).
3. Randomization in allocating treatments to subjects (overall, blocked or otherwise restricted).
4. Monitoring quality control on data accrual and editing.
5. Interim cross-tabulating and analysis.
6. Final data analysis (specified in as much detail as possible beforehand). Numerical analysis of multiply-classified data, never exactly matched on all important factors.

The continued development and acceptance of the guidelines on drug testing may help break an unhealthy pattern of conflict and confusion between the FDA and those applying for a New Drug Application. The vicious circle (described in our interviews with employees of the FDA and the drug houses as well as officials in the Pharmaceutical Manufacturers Association) traps the NDA applicant and the FDA in a huge volume of research reports, clinical data, bibliographies, and other materials all going to make up NDA's consisting, in at least one case, of 180 volumes of material, each three inches thick.

Although our interviewees disagree somewhat on where the responsibility for the problem rests, they all describe the following pattern: An NDA is submitted and the FDA has 180 days to review it. Since the FDA lacks the scientific resources to evaluate the large number of NDA's in the time allowed, it sometimes holds the NDA for a few months and then informs the manufacturer that the NDA is incomplete. New material must be submitted and then the 180-day clock is started again. The applicants for an NDA, aware of the many ways in which an NDA can be "incomplete," often submit NDA's containing every sort of material possibly relevant to the new drug as well as a good deal of material of no relevance. Such material is frequently submitted because genuine evidence for safety and efficacy is simply lacking. In fact, a major share (perhaps more than half) of NDA's are rejected out of hand for obvious shortcomings. We suspect that some NDA's are submitted merely on the hope that they might get by.

One FDA official described a similar problem with the material submitted for the assessment of the efficacy of a drug: "In one instance, in the objections filed to our implementation of the NAS-NRC recommendations, there was submitted a list of more than 100 so-called scientific studies and reports purporting to show something regarding a particular drug. It took considerable time for our legal and scientific staffs to establish that this evidence was mostly irrelevant and obviously inadequate.

"Such a submission does a disservice to the Food and Drug Administration (even if we prevail), to you who are upholding professional standards, and to the public for whom we should all be spending our time more productively, and finally to the drug industry."[8] Employees of the drug houses (both in our interviews and as reported in a paper by Louis Lasagna) also indicate mixed experiences with the FDA review of NDA's. Lasagna wrote: "One hears conflicting stories about FDA's handling of NDA's. Some drug house employees state that they have been treated in exemplary fashion by FDA monitors; others complain of stupidity, arrogance, unreasonable demands, and delays lasting for years."[9]

---

8   John Jennings, M.D., Assistant to the Commissioner for Medical Affairs, quoted in the FDA Papers, September 1970.

9   Louis Lasagna, "1938-1968; The FDA, the Drug Industry, the Medical Profession, and the Public," in John E. Blake, ed., Safeguarding the Public; Historical Aspects of Drug Control (Baltimore: The Johns Hopkins Press, 1970), p. 175.

The generally proposed solutions to this widely recognized problem are to raise the level of scientific competence of the FDA (so that the review of the NDA can be completed in the 180-day time period without having to negotiate for further time), and to make changes in the procedures for handling NDA's. Such solutions are badly needed. We are concerned in this report with the problem of voluminous and irrelevant NDA's because, as statisticians continue to take a more active role in the review of NDA's, they too will find their skills wasted in wading through the masses of marginal material.

As a modest step toward reducing these difficulties, we recommend that the cooperation displayed in developing guidelines for research designs for new drugs be continued by the statisticians of the drug houses and those of the FDA. A special problem, deserving the contemplation of both sets of professional statisticians, is the assessment of multiclinic data. New drugs are often tested on small groups of patients in many different places by many different investigators. The quality of the data generated ranges from fraudulent to superior. Even without bad data, combining the voluminous results of many different small, dissimilar clinical trials is difficult and time consuming. These problems with compatability of data need help from all sources in the FDA and the industry.

The law requires the FDA to protect "trade secrets" in the NDA's from becoming public knowledge. At present the FDA interprets this law to mean that the entire NDA is to be protected. We believe that this interpretation should be re-evaluated in order to allow greater scientific and public oversight of the NDA process. We recommend that the FDA publish the reasons for its decisions on the NDA, along with the relevant studies of the drug submitted in support of the NDA. The publication of the analysis of the NDA and the studies decisive to the analysis would have important advantages over the current system. First, the FDA would be going on record in publishing reasons for its actions. In itself, this could lead to better decisions and strengthen the non-political character of those decisions. Second, it would create a publicly accessible body of common tradition on what constitutes acceptable evidence for the safety and efficacy of a drug. Third, by making clearer what is specifically required with respect to clinical and statistical evidence, the publication procedure might reduce the submission of overly long NDA's.

We have not looked into the specific mechanics of publication. Once the FDA has written down the reasons for its decision, the obvious steps toward publication include: selecting the appropriate material for publication, checking it for legitimate trade secrets, and distributing the material to a subscription list. Subscribers would include drug companies, medical schools, statisticians, drug authorities in other countries, as well as those in other government agencies, such as National Institutes of Health (NIH). Individual physicians might be interested in the material on drugs of special concern for them. We hope that the publication of this material would widen the scientific audience interested in the evidence offered in support of decisions concerning the safety and efficacy of new drugs, as well as improve the quality of the decisions and the evidence submitted in the NDA. We believe that this proposal could prove to be of major importance and it should be given a fair trial.

2. Drug Surveillance and Evaluation

The purposes of monitoring the experiences with drugs on the market are to detect adverse reactions and to improve the efficacy of drug therapy. Assessing the costs and benefits of particular drugs is an important and difficult enterprise requiring medical, statistical, and computer expertise. In this brief report, we will indicate the scope of the problem of drug surveillance and evaluation. We will then consider FDA's response to the problem, including its plan for developing a national drug monitoring program as well as its current adverse reaction program.

An effective drug reaction monitoring system would provide information for a cost-benefit analysis of drug usage. Such information would include:

"(i) the definition of reasonably precise probabilities for the efficacy and toxicity of alternative treatments available for a given condition; and (ii) computer-based correlation of patients' characteristics and drug response so that the doctor will be able to tailor drug treatment to the needs of the individual patient with a predictability of response that is not available today."[10]

A decade ago, the first oral contraceptives were made available and shown to be highly effective and widely acceptable. Side effects were noted from the start, but oral contraceptives have become increasingly accepted nonetheless. Many of these side effects are transient and disappear after a time, and many occur in some users and not in others. Other possible side effects are potentially very serious and occur seldom enough that an individual physician cannot hope to make judgments about them on the basis of his own experience. It is this latter class of side effects with which I shall be concerned.

There are two aspects of public policy with respect to such effects which I believe require clear identification.

There is, first, the right of an informed individual to elect to take a reasonable risk in order to achieve some goal which he believes desirable. I make several trips a year from Chicago to Washington. Purely for convenience I travel by air and not by rail. I am one of the few who examined the available information on risk in the two modes of travel and I judge that I am accepting a non-negligible risk in choosing the convenience of air travel, but I do it quite deliberately. On the other hand, I no longer smoke cigarettes, although I was once a regular smoker. The benefits were in that case outweighed for me by a number of serious disadvantages. I am a strong believer in the freedom of the informed individual to decide for himself how to balance benefits and risks which primarily concern him, and I include here the right of the patient, consulting with her physician, to elect to accept some risk in return for the benefits of oral contraceptives. To me, the role of government in this area is clear — it is to be sure both physicians and patients are as well-informed about the state of knowledge on the benefits and

---

10 Louis Lasagna, "The Pharmaceutical Revolution: Its Impact on Science and Society," *Science*, 66, 5 December 1969, p. 1228.

risks of oral contraceptives as it is reasonably possible to make them.

A second aspect of the public policy is of comparable importance. It is to protect the public from clearly unreasonable risks, both by seeing that the risks are adequately studied and understood and, in some cases, by eliminating them from the environment. In some respects the level of concern by government should be much greater than that of even a prudent individual. For example, an increase in the level of ionizing radiation over the United States due, perhaps, to building nuclear power stations, would increase the risk that I might get leukemia. If the increase were small, I might reasonably ignore it, as an individual. The government, however, must weigh the combined risk to all of us against the benefits which additional nuclear power plants might provide.

In either case it must be emphasized that reasonable judgments are only likely to arise out of weighing of risks and benefits. It is common to hear that "even one avoidable death is too many," or that the "only acceptable level of pesticide residue on food products must be zero." Neither as governments nor as individuals do we in fact behave this way, and the refusal to weigh risks against benefits often results in the blind acceptance of risks which analysis would show to be unreasonably high. I believe, for example, that the almost disastrous errors made in the program of safety-testing for the Salk vaccine in the mid-1950's resulted from an unwillingness to accept the notion that there might be a measurable risk and to seek to evaluate its magnitude. A typical example of a known risk which we accept in return for benefit is the requirement of smallpox vaccination for school children. A small but definite number of children die as a result of being vaccinated. We accept such costs as necessary to achieve a greater benefit. [11]

---

11 Statement of Paul Meier, Ph.D., Professor of Statistics, Department of Statistics, University of Chicago, in Competitive Problems in the Drugs Industry, Hearings Before the Subcommittee on Monopoly of the Senate Select Committee on Small Business, Part 16 (February-March, 1970) 6548-6549.

85

CURRENT DRUG MONITORING

As noted earlier, there are a good many adverse reactions to therapeutic drugs. Perhaps 1.5 million hospital admissions yearly are due to illnesses caused by drugs. For certain illnesses drugs obviously have tremendous benefits. In general, however, cost-benefit data for particular drugs are remarkably thin. "Decisions regarding drug treatment must frequently be made without adequate knowledge of the clinical effects of the drugs at issue. The extent of this problem was recently emphasized in a report by the Divison of Medical Sciences of the National Academy of Science-National Research Council (NAS-NRC) following an intensive review of over 3,000 drug formulations marketed between 1938 and 1962. The review panels of this *Drug Efficacy Study* rated about 7 percent of the preparations as 'ineffective,' and with a large proportion (a majority) of the remainder, the information supplied by manufacturers was considered insufficient to fully assess efficacy. (20 percent of all drug claims were rated as 'effective'; 39 percent of all drugs were rated as 'effective.') Individual members of the various panels were also invited to submit their thoughts on the insights gained from their participation in this study, and, according to the report, 'letter after letter expresses concern and surprise about the generally poor quality of the evidence of efficacy of the drugs reviewed."[12]

Consider one of the most widely studied drugs, halothane. In their formal recommendations, the authors of *The National Halothane Study* comment on the shortage of information:

We recommend the establishment of a cooperating group of institutions to serve as a panel-laboratory for the acquisition of trustworthy information on new drugs (not merely anesthetics) as they come into use.

In the history of medicine, it is doubtful whether any drug was ever more extensively studied both before and after its introduction than halothane. Yet, after halothane had been given to patients perhaps ten million times, it was impossible to give firm, reliable answers to many basic questions

---

12 Hershel Jick, *et.al.*, "Comprehensive Drug Surveillance," *Journal of the American Medical Association*, 213 (August 31, 1970), p. 1455.

about its effects. Two such questions were: "How does the death rate after operations under halothane anesthesia compare with death rates when other anesthetics are used?" "Does halothane induce significantly more hepatic dysfunction than other widely used anesthetics?" The National Halothane Study attempted to answer these questions by using existing records. Although 856,500 operations were brought under scrutiny, the answers given are predictably and regrettably short of those desired. For example, the important questions of nonfatal hepatic injury was not taken up by the study. The limitations of knowledge on halothane are certainly not peculiar to it. Limitations at least equally compelling apply to nearly any drug introduced in the past. Had halothane been administered a few scores of thousands of times in the context of any experimental informational-gathering system, similar in kind to a cooperative randomized clinical trial, reliable information might have been acquired for over-all death rates, and possibly for nonfatal hepatic injury as well.[13]

A similar situation holds for the oral contraceptives, potent drugs used by over eight million women. The FDA Advisory Committee on Obstetrics and Gynecology in August, 1969 recommended:

"The Food and Drug Administration assures adequate surveillance of approved contraceptive drugs.

The inadequacy of surveillance of contraceptive drug use in the United States and other countries is apparent. Voluntary reporting of adverse reactions tends to be capricious and may be misleading....

"Strengthen the surveillance system of the Food and Drug Administration.

This recommendation from the previous report has not been satisfactorily implemented. A system should be devised so that when adverse reaction reports are received, they are

---

13 J. P. Bunker, W. H. Forrest, F. Mosteller, and L. D. Vandan, *The National Halothane Study* (Washington, D.C., U.S. GPO, 1969) pp. 417-418 Part VI, "Formal Recommendations" by J. P. Bunker.

made readily and immediately accessible."[14]

Neither recommendation has been carried out.

Even for widely consumed drugs, post-marketing studies of low-incidence effects are conducted at a slow pace. The "Sartwell Report": a retrospective study of thromboembolism and oral contraceptives begins indicating the time scale involved: "The suspicion that oral contraceptives might predispose women toward vascular occlusive phenomena arose about 1961, largely from the publication of case reports. An *ad hoc* committee in 1963 advised that 'comprehensive and critical' studies to look into the possibility be conducted. Nevertheless, little was done in this direction, despite the great increase in the use of these potent drugs. By the time the Advisory Committee on Obstetrics and Gynecology of the Food and Drug Administration began to prepare its first report on the oral contraceptives in 1965, it was evident that an epidemiologic study was even more urgently needed than in 1963. The present study was begun in November 1965, in direct response to this need."[15] And this study itself was published almost four years later in August 1969. It formed a large share of the evidence that led the Advisory Committee on Obstetrics and Gynecology to conclude that there was an etiologic relation between thromboembolic disorders and the use of oral contraceptives.

CURRENT PRACTICE IN DRUG MONITORING IN THE FDA

(1) The FDA has neither the scientific talent nor the resources to conduct serious long-term studies of drug reactions in human population. It is unlikely that the FDA will, in the next few years, be able to attract the medical, statistical, and computing talent for such studies.

(2) We have reviewed two proposals circulating within the FDA concerning long-run studies of drug and chemical reactions.

---

14 Second Report on the Oral Contraceptives (Washington, D.C. U.S. GPO, August 1, 1969), p. 8.

15 P. E. Startwell, A. T. Masi, F. G. Arthes, G.G. Greene, and H. E. Smith, "Thromboembolism and Oral Contraceptives: An Epidemiological Case-Control Study," in Advisory Committee on Obstetrics and Gynecology, Food and Drug Administration, *Second Report on the Oral Contraceptives* (Washington, U.S. GPO, August 1, 1969), p. 21.

One proposal soliciting contracts for a pilot study of a National Drug Monitoring Program is well thought out except for the actual analysis of the data. Past experience indicates that such data analysis problems are usually difficult. Thus while we feel that the FDA should award contracts for long-run studies of drug reactions, further work is needed in the preparation of the proposals in order to assure adequate analysis of the data. The second proposal, concerning the long-run safety evaluation of environmental chemicals, needs further work with respect to design and analysis of the planned experiments.

(3) The adverse reaction drug monitoring system operating within the FDA obtains about 25,000 reports per year of adverse reactions from drug houses, hospitals, and others. The law requires the manufacturer of a drug to report periodically to FDA on any information it has of a possible "adverse reaction." Federal and private hospitals under contracts also submit accounts of such reactions to FDA. Additionally private physicians occasionally write to FDA about specific cases. These statements are examined by physicians employed by FDA. Presently the private hospital contracts are being phased out and the adverse reaction reports are being put on a computer.

Unfortunately these cannot be used for reaching secure conclusions. Causation cannot usually be inferred from fragmentary reports of the kind received by FDA. There is no sampling plan, and hence no sense in which the results are representative. Little systematic statistical analysis can be done since there is no way to standardize the adverse drug experiences with respect to patient characteristics or favorable reactions to the drug.

In the past, a selection of 40 or 50 adverse reaction reports, chosen by the staff on an intuitive basis, was published monthly by FDA. This system had the twin faults of quite possibly overlooking important adverse reactions, and of discouraging the use of effective drugs that were not responsible for the reaction reported. As a result this practice has been abandoned, and no published output is forthcoming from the adverse drug reaction program of FDA.

The FDA could require, as part of the approval of NDA, a designed prospective study to monitor the drug's impact. This has already been done in the case of L-Dopa, a particularly effective drug which was given early conditional approval. Such studies permit randomization and thus easy interpretability of results. Furthermore, this method curtails the tendency to collect large amounts of unneeded information. We feel that this approach warrants more emphasis than it has received in the past.

In conclusion, we find that in dealing with problems of adverse drug reactions, the FDA has collected, and proposed to collect, large amounts of information without adequate thought about the use to which the information would be put. Greater involvement of statisticians in decisions about what to do concerning adverse drug reactions could have the desirable effect of deemphasizing large computer systems with "all the information" available, and emphasizing instead economical collection and interpretation of data to answer the important questions.

CONCLUSIONS AND RECOMMENDATIONS

Systematic drug surveillance and evaluation would provide valuable information about the safety and effectiveness of the drugs prescribed in the two billion prescriptions written per year. Information is now available for only a few drugs. The FDA, however, does not have the capability to gather further information — although it is the agency that must judge the safety and effectiveness of drugs. We recommend that the FDA, in collaboration with other government agencies related to health, seek the funds for contracting for large-scale systematic surveillance and evaluation of major therapeutic drugs — including some over-the-counter drugs. Such cost-benefit information concerning drugs will be difficult to obtain and will require the combined efforts of clinicians, epidemiologists, systems analysts, and statisticians. The Bureau of Drugs also needs to make greater use of its statisticians in planning such drug surveillance projects, particularly with respect to data analysis.

3. Computer Operations

There is very little statistical programming and computerized data analysis in the Bureau of Drugs. The under-utilized computer available is used mainly for administrative purposes and assorted record-keeping. Only one scientific programmer is available in the Bureau of Drugs. There is a single terminal to a large machine in Washington along with inconvenient and slow access to the FDA machine. It is often said that statisticians cannot be expected to work effectively or happily without large scale computer facilities, and this statement is often true. But two qualifications should be made. It is not necessary that every statistician or statistical group have sole control of such a center. Much statistical work, some of it of major status, can be done with little or no large scale computer service.

We have observed inefficient hand calculations by Bureau statisticians of long experience but evidently poor training. We suppose that a considerable fraction of the demand for computer services comes from the frustration and delay caused by such time-wasting work by hand and desk calculators. The lack of programming support has also led to some inefficient efforts at statistical programming by Ph.D. level staff.

The Bureau of Drugs needs much greater support with respect to scientific programming: data-processing facilities of an order of magnitude greater and better than those now existing are predictably needed by the Bureau in the long run.

In view of the costs and poor record of large new computer operations, higher priorities in the Bureau, and the present incomplete plans of the Bureau, we make the following short-run recommendations:

(a) the addition of three scientific programmers in direct support of the statistical work of the Bureau;

(b) a serious effort to make effective use of the currently under-used facilities now available;

(c) efforts to improve routine computational practices now done by hand or machine. We suggest three programmers only as a serious start. It may well be that as the Bureau becomes better able to handle its work, a much larger programming effort will be required.

4. External Statistical Support for the Bureau of Drugs

The social importance of the work of the Bureau is self-evident.

91

Therefore we must consider what external aid can be marshalled in its support. Our suggestions fall into immediate and long-term categories.

The most obvious immediate aid could come from a group of interested senior statisticians (biometricians and biostatisticians) who would give more visibility to the Bureau's needs for able staff statisticians. Careful recommendation of individuals to whom the Bureau does not have ready access (first-rate graduate students and new Ph.D.'s, experienced statisticians not now known to be considering job changes, etc.) could gather fresh talent. We feel that the current procedures for recruiting new statistical talent into the Bureau need additional support and improvement. Another reason for care in making new appointments is the irreversibility of such appointments. While the civil service rules quite rightly protect appointees from capricious termination, they may work to retain the relatively incompetent worker in the office where his or her presence is extremely costly. We believe this has already happened a good many times in the Bureau. We do not feel it is necessary here to give a listing of all the attributes of an organization that will attract and retain a large group of professional statisticians. It must be clear to the present administrators that prospects for advancement, for professional contacts, and for the time needed to think about major problems, must be guaranteed to able staff members.

Two major long-term problems that need more time than the Bureau now has available are outlined below. They are both of immediate interest, but even tentative solutions seem some distance in the future.

1. *Cost-benefit analysis in drug development and distribution.*

Little quantitative thinking appears to have been done on weighing the gains against the losses in developing and distributing a new drug. In the development stages a complex but obscure interplay of ethical, legal, and financial considerations undoubtedly takes place behind the study of the drug's safety and efficacy. After distribution, only minor effort, grossly disproportionate to the seriousness of problem, is now made to collect safety (and adverse reaction) information even though

92

such information is required by law. The result is that the consuming public constitutes the membership of a poorly conducted clinical trial. Surely here is an opportunity for a major contribution by statisticians and clinicians of FDA; but equally surely an external group could be expected to make a useful contribution.

2. *Studies of long-term and rare side effects.*

A valuable start in the area of extensive small animal trials has been made in the memorandum of November 9, 1970, submitted to the Commission of FDA. This proposal recommends a large facility (the "Pine Bluff facility") to house large numbers of test organism under controlled conditions, with, of course, a large staff. Part of its work would be to evaluate the life-long effects of "environmental chemicals" which includes drugs.

No consideration seems to have been given in that memorandum to the study of the simultaneous exposure of individual animals to more than one material. Since all humans are exposed to more than one environmental chemical, these studies will gain in validity if multiple exposures can be arranged. It is not supposed here that this extension will be easy, but only that it should be worked on by several groups, externally as well as within the Bureau of Drugs. While several proposals for nationwide monitoring of adverse drug reactions and rare side effects are now being circulated, it does not appear to us that sufficient statistical effort has been put into these plans. An external Bureau of Drugs biometric advisory committee should, not, of course, control such plans, but it might provide insights that would not otherwise be forthcoming.

Recent symposia on the teratogenicity, carcinogenicity, and mutagenicity of many environmental chemicals including drugs, indicate that these fields are well advanced and are now able to detect many such effects in small animals and in micro-organisms. This implied an increased effort of several orders of magnitude when translated into full scale studies of all suspected new drugs and chemicals. Again, sustained and sympathetic study by statistical groups outside the Bureau but in close touch with its work, seems necessary.

5. The Bureau of Drugs: A Place for Statisticians

The Bureau of Drugs needs roughly ten statisticians of Ph.D. level or equivalent training. Of the ten needed, two to four are now at work. The number ten is not given casually and is not inflated against future compromise. It is, rather, a minimum that will soon be exceeded if the Bureau is to advance rapidly toward meeting its legal responsibilities. The primary responsibility of the Bureau is to reach sound conclusions on NDA's promptly. About 70 new NDA's are submitted each year. We concurr with Dr. Charles Anello's judgment that these require, on average, one month's attention from a senior statistician. Thus roughly six statistician years are needed for this work alone. We do not have good estimates of the time required for making summary reports on each of the thousand-odd IND's received every year, for review of protocols submitted for new drug studies, and for reviewing the supplements and additions that are frequently made to each NDA. Nor is it possible to produce an exact analysis of the time required for statistical contributions to the large drug-monitoring programs in view. Almost all requests for statistical aid in compliance problems are now simply postponed. It seems modest indeed to judge that four person-years of the time of senior statisticians will be required to do these jobs.

The ranges of specialization, experience, and competence are as wide for statisticians as for members of any other profession. Several of the new recruits should be biometricians or possibly epidemiologists; several should have had more than a year of experience in applied statistics. Most graduating Ph.D. level statisticians are not immediately qualified to do the work of the Bureau of Drugs: the Bureau needs men and women experienced in the analysis of clinical and biometric data. Thus, in recruiting new statisticians, a premium should be placed on relevant experience. The new statisticians are needed for direct work in NDA's, for improving the many sampling programs of the Bureau, for the statistical research in many areas not now at satisfactory levels (example: advanced analysis of complex data from drugs supplied by different manufacturers), for aid in designing the large computer system the Bureau of Drugs will ultimately need, for mature advice to the Commissioner and his Assistants, for developing and supervising the complex systems that will be required for monitoring a national adverse drug reaction system, and finally for studying the largely unsolved problems connected with detecting the effects of long-term, multiple-drug dose-schedules.

About ten statisticians of lesser education and with less technical statistical knowledge are also required for the difficult and important sort of auditing plus the detecting that many IND's and NDA's call for. There are dozens of other pieces of useful work that such statisticians can (and do) perform in the Bureau, but these do not require the training of the group described in the paragraphs above. A majority of this group are already on the job.

Listing of these problems requiring mature biostatistical contributions should not be taken to imply that no start has been made. There have in fact been large improvements in the last year. The Bureau is fortunate in its present biometric head (Dr. Charles Anello). Lengthy discussions with Dr. Anello have not revealed any major differences of opinion as to objectives or means of accomplishing them. Indeed this section of our report may be read as reflecting our thoughts on how best to aid him.

THE APPLICATION OF STATISTICAL TECHNIQUES

Part B

A Survey
of the Use
# of Sample Evidence
in the
Federal Communications
Commission

By

A. C. Rosander

TABLE OF CONTENTS

INTRODUCTION

The Federal Communications Commission (FCC) functions in two broad areas: regulation of common carriers, and regulation of radio and television broadcasting. The regulation of common carriers in telephone, telegraph, and radio involves four major aspects: tariffs, rates, quality of service, and entry into the field. The regulation of radio and television broadcasting involves original licensing, renewal of licenses, and entry into the field. In granting licenses the factor of major importance is service to the community. Related aspects subject to regulation or study include transfer of ownership, use of prime time, new methods such as CATV (community antenna television), new uses such as data transmission, multiple ownership, and major operating changes such as increase in power.

A wide variety of sample studies are being used by the industry in reporting to the Commission. The Commission does not have any continuous sample study comparable to the passenger ticket sample of the Civil Aeronautics Board or the waybill sample authorized by the Interstate Commerce Commission, nor does it specify in sufficient detail guidelines to be used on conducting studies and surveys.

The first part of this chapter is a summary of several sample surveys in the communications area with an appraisal of each. These are the study by the A. D. Little Co. of Telegram Speed Requirements, a study introduced into the FCC Docket No. 18128, of the impact of different AT&T rate schedules on private line customers, and two TV audience surveys.

The second part comments on two cases in which the FCC set forth guidelines to be followed by reporting companies in their application of statistical techniques. In Docket No. 18774 the Commission deals with the problems of selecting a representative sample of persons in a community to consult about community problems. In Docket No. 18703 the FCC sets down some general guidelines to be followed by common carrier hearing proceedings by parties who intend to offer statistical studies in evidence.

Part 3 contains the writer's observations on ways to improve use of statistical techniques at the FCC, general problems and difficulties encountered at the FCC, and a list of recommendations.

EXAMPLES OF SAMPLE SURVEYS

A. D. Little Study of Telegram Speed Requirements

The sample survey of telegram speed requirements was laid out as follows:

TYPE OF CUSTOMER	SAMPLE SIZE	TOTAL FRAME
Large and medium corporations	1064	56,616 (lists)
Small businesses	102	areas and
Private households	509	telephone
		directories

The purpose of the study was to survey users and potential users of telegram service to determine speed of service requirements and develop service standards.

The strata used in the sample plan included two sizes of companies, small businesses and private households, seven groups with regard to industrial classification, and four groups relating to geographical area. Additional stratification was introduced with regard to the business function or purpose of the telegram such as shipping, purchasing, sales, etc.

The data were collected by a telephone questionnaire although follow-up was made by interview on business non-respondents. A total of 27 interviews were obtained out of a group of 33 refusals selected for recall after replacements. Businesses which refused to participate (a total of 60) were replaced by other businesses that did participate.

The frames for selecting medium and large corporations were private lists totalling 29,531 corporations with net assets of over $1,000,000 and 27,085 corporations with net assets between $50,000 and $1,000,000.

The frames for the household sample consisted of selecting 50 areas of the U.S. in a first stage sample, and then 10 households from each area using telephone directories. The sample of small businesses was selected at the same time as the household sample, using businesses listed in the white pages of the telephone directory.

From the telephone interview, information such as the following was obtained:

1. About how many domestic telegrams do you send daily, weekly or monthly?
2. What do you estimate to be the average times from sender to receiver on a regular telegram?
3. Do you regard telegram service as generally satisfactory or unsatisfactory?
4. What is your average volume of outgoing telegrams?
5. What is the longest delay you are aware of over the last three months?
6. What percent of the telegrams you send do you regard as urgent?
7. What time interval would you be satisfied with for delivery of your urgent messages?

(There were many more questions like these.)

Frequency distributions were constructed showing frequency of companies and telegrams by *desired speed* for urgent, non-urgent telegrams, by geographical areas and for the U.S. as a whole. Medians, means, and standard deviations were computed for these distributions. A frequency distribution is shown for total

103

volume, for company estimates of telegrams considered urgent. A distribution is given of company estimates of average delivery time experiences but only about 20 percent of the companies answered. No attempt apparently was made to study *actual speed* for telegram service from origin to destination. Actually companies were sampled, not telegrams. No measure was obtained for actual service rendered.

The measures of service used included distributions of desired speed, the mean and median and standard deviation, some cumulative distributions, and a loss function of the form $y = kt^a$ where t is delay time.

Three conditions affecting a sample design are listed: size of subclass such as a day or a month, variability of the data required, *and* level of precision desired in the estimates.

APPRAISAL OF STUDY

A summary of the appraisal of the foregoing study follows. The report states that considerations of time and expense made any personal interview study impractical. In this appraisal these conditions are not considered for a simple reason: they are used far too often to justify an inadequate or weak technical study.

1. It is stated that the data received by telephone were reliable. No audit sample check was made to support this.
2. The telephone method is not necessarily superior to questionnaires or interviews, especially when one considers the larger amount of facts and judgments required.
3. Who was interviewed? Who was the source of information? This was never described.
4. There was no measure of actual telegram service, no sampling of telegrams.
5. How could one person or two persons answer for a large corporation?
6. The frame of large and medium corporations was much too small, which not only raises questions of sampling but also the question of proper weighting. For larger corporations with net assets of $1,000,000 or more, the private list contained 29,531 names but the Internal Revenue Service

count for this same class for the same year (end of 1967) is 113,568.

7. The questions asked were many and varied requiring intimate knowledge of telegram practices in the company. There is nothing said about the competence of the person answering.

8. Many leading questions were used and the person probed for an answer in order apparently to reduce non-responses. There may have been some "forced response" just to satisfy the inquirer. (Obviously one can use loaded questions in a telephone interview as well as in a personal interview or on a questionnaire. In addition, "pressure" can be used in a telephone interview.)

9. The selection of the household sample appears to be awkward and inefficient.

10. The selection of a corporation sample using known information about classes of telegrams was quite in order.

11. The use of substitutions for non-respondents was contrary to acceptable quality sampling practice.

12. The use of the mean, median, and standard deviation for the highly skewed distribution has limited usefulness. The cumulative distributions are much superior.

13. No attempt was made to use replication or to calculate any sampling errors.

14. No attempt was made to sample actual telegram service. The sample was used to obtain opinions on desired service.

15. It is quite clear that both the sampling and interview procedures could be greatly improved. Departures from acceptable standards of sampling practice are numerous.

American Telephone and Telegraph Private Case Docket No. 18128.

The purpose of this sample study which was introduced into Docket 18128 was to measure the impact of four different rate schedules on private line customers. A sample of 101 customers was selected and an analysis made of each customer by the account manager regularly assigned to that account. The judgments were to be estimates of Telpak channel miles to be expected under each rate schedule at the end of 1971. The account manager, it is alleged, is familiar with future communication plans of customers.

The universe and sample, excluding customers with less than 500 channel miles, are:

Customer Strata	Universe Number	Miles (million)	Sample Number	Percent of Miles*
Airlines	62	5.7	10	56%
Truckers	329	1.1	10	9
Railroads	35	.8	5	70
All other	1,350	16.9	75	72
Government	1	17.4	1	100
Sub Total	1,777	41.9	101	79%
Excluded	17,923	1.0		
Total	19,700	42.9		

*Base is stratum universe miles.

In each stratum accounts were ordered by size before selection. Instead of a size or volume of business stratification, selection was made with probability proportional to size (pps).

The account manager filled out forms based on his appraisal of what this account would do under each proposed rate schedule.

It was estimated that the total channel miles in use on December 31, 1971, would be 43,284,000 with a relative standard error of 4.8 percent.

No attempt was made to measure the variation which arises because judgments of account managers were being used as the raw data.

APPRAISAL OF STUDY

Apparently the sample by strata was assigned rather arbitrarily. Its effectiveness is not made clear. Nor is there any evidence to show it was really needed. The truckers, for example, average less than the 500 miles, which was the dividing line between inclusion and exclusion.

In a study of this kind some attempt should be made to determine variation due to the judgment of account managers since this was the source of the raw data. Their relative variation could easily be as large or larger than the relative sampling error of 4.8 percent.

There is no point in stressing sampling problems and sampling errors as is so often done when non-sampling errors are just as large or larger. Nothing was found in the record on this extremely important point.

Television Audience Surveys

Two private sample surveys currently give estimates of households watching TV programs by station in a specified city or market area by 15 minute periods. One of these is conducted by the A. C. Nielsen Company, the other by the American Research Bureau. These surveys are very important because they are used extensively by both industry and by the Commission. While their shortcomings are known and are described by both companies, the data are used widely primarily because they are the only data available.

An enumeration of how the data are collected from sample households will reveal their shortcomings.

1. The frame is telephone listings.
2. Sample consists of cooperating households.
3. Each market area is sampled at least twice a year. A new sample is drawn for each study.
4. Sample households usually keep diaries for four weeks although some may keep them for two weeks.
5. The binomial model is assumed to apply to percentages.

Diary records show for every 15 minute period, the station, program and person or persons *watching* a program for 5 minutes or more. The final results are therefore subject to whatever response errors exist in the diaries.

In addition there are the errors due to non-response – those households drawn into the sample who refuse to take part in the survey. There is also the error due to the use of telephone directories as frames for sampling. Standard errors are calculated for estimated percentages and aggregate houscholds listening, but these are derived on the questionnaires, assumptions that the model used matches the environment of the sample, and that knowing the magnitude of these "standard errors" is sufficient without knowing the magnitude of the other sources of error.

It is not clear what method of estimation is used to obtain proportions on the one hand and aggregate audiences on the other.

Since the American Research Bureau apparently uses similar sampling and reporting procedures as Nielsen, they will not be discussed.

AUDIT OF AUDIENCE ESTIMATES

This problem of rating programs and estimating the size of the viewing or listening audience is so important that the industry appointed a committee to make a study of radio listening and the audit of TV ratings. The group was called the Broadcasting Rating Council and NAB Research Committee.[1]

The basic objective was to find one or more methods of accurately measuring the full and complete radio audience by times of day and station. The problems to be researched included unit of time, individuals or households, audience in and out of home, defining a listener, testing various diary methods, automobile radio listening, quality controls necessary for testing the best diary measure, readiness to be interviewed (non-response).

In connection with TV ratings it was reported that a study was under way of the effect of sample households who refuse to cooperate. Another project contemplated called for an independent university group seeking to establish more accurate and reliable methods of measuring audiences.

The National Rating Council reports[2] as follows:

1. Outside accounting firms have been hired to audit procedures of the rating bureaus to determine if they do what they claim they do. This is a detailed procedural audit carried out in field offices and in households where diaries are filled out. The audit does not attempt to appraise any of the sampling or other techniques employed.
2. The validity of the diary method is being studied but some difficult legal and other problems have been encountered.

---

1   Material in this part is from a statement of D. H. McGannon, Chairman of the Committee, before a special subcommittee of the House of Representatives, Washington, September 26, 1964.

2   In a telephone conversation with Kenneth Baker, January 8, 1971.

3. Effect of non-cooperators is being studied. The refusal rate may be as high as 40 percent.

4. No attempt has been made to establish more accurate and reliable methods of measuring audiences, although it has been under consideration, and a question was raised about estimates for one station.

EXAMPLES OF FCC EFFORTS TO IMPROVE STATISTICAL TECHNIQUES

Community Surveys for Broadcast Licensing

In Docket No. 18774 adopted December 19, 1969, the Commission describes, in a 38—question and answer format, a primer for broadcast applicants to follow in ascertaining community problems. These community problems or needs meet the full range of community activities and economic, social, political, and cultural interests. Specific areas listed included government, education, religion, agricultural, business, labor, the professions, racial and ethnic groups, and eleemosynary organizations.

According to this Docket, applicants in ascertaining community problems should consult two groups of people: (1) leaders of a representative range of groups in the community to be served, (2) a representative range of members of the general public who may not be officials of community organizations.

The Docket contains survey specification guidelines at several points:

1. "The applicant should indicate by cross-sectional survey, statistically reliable sampling, or other valid method that the range of group leaders and individuals consulted is truly representative of the community."

2. The applicant may use any valid method he choses to obtain representative leaders and members of the general public.

3. A professional-type survey is inadequate because it is stated, "a professional service by itself does not effectuate a dialogue between responsible parties in the applicant and community leaders and members of the general public."

4. "A sufficient number (of members of the general public

109

should be consulted) to constitute a representative range of groups and leaders and members of the general public to give a valid basis for determining the problems of the community. The number of consultations will vary of course with the size of the city in question and the number of distinct groups or organizations."

5. Apparently the omission of one group from the survey is serious. The survey "is defective if omission of that group would leave the applicant without 'a representative range of groups and leaders . . .' Omission of consultation with a significant group . . .would leave the process of group selection subject to question."

6. "It is not the purpose of the consultations to elicit program selections. The purpose is to ascertain what the person consulted believes to be the problems of the community . . .Thus, a leader in the education field could be a useful source for information as to educational matters; a labor leader, on labor matters . . .The applicant, the broadcaster is considered to have expertise in programming, and he has the responsibility for determining what broadcast matter he believes should be presented to provide information on the community problems he has ascertained and evaluated.

7. A questionnaire may be used, but it should serve as a guide for consultations.

COMMENTS ON DOCKET NO. 18774

One major problem in ascertaining community problems by applicants is the selection of a sample of persons to be consulted. Docket No. 18774 is concerned primarily with this problem. (The other major problem which is not dealt with in this docket is the interpretation of what the surveyed persons says are community problems or needs.)

The docket referred to "representative range of groups," representative leaders and members, which the survey is to reflect. (Any reference to the collection of the required information by a "survey" or "study" seems to be carefully avoided. The expression used is "ascertainment of community problems."

In reality this is a survey of the opinions of leaders and others

110

in a specified area. In large areas this survey *has to be* a sample survey, either a judgment sample or more preferably a probability sample. In any event, stratification by significant community groups is required. In very small communities the leaders would almost surely be included 100 percent, and the general public most effectively sampled on a random basis. In a large area both leaders and public would have to be sampled.

When a proper probability sample is designed and implemented, the concept of "representative," whether applied to groups, leaders, or non-leaders, is automatically preserved. This, of course, is well known in probability sampling theory and practice.

This Docket refers repeatedly to "consultation," not to interviews, and to the need for "dialogue" between applicant and the public in connection with these surveys. It does, however, approve the use of questionnaires but only as a guide for consultations.

The Docket says the size of the sample should be sufficient to constitute a "representative range of groups and leaders and members of the general public . . ." It also states that the number will vary according to the size of the city and the number of community groups. As indicated above, if the sample is properly designed the criterion of "representative" is automatically satisfied and becomes unnecessary and superfluous.

The sample is used to discover community problems and needs as well as to determine their significance presumably in terms of frequency mentioned or discussed, or in terms of urgency. It is not difficult to design a sample to yield this information. Apparently how much weight is given to a leader's views as against the general public's views is left to the applicant.

A very important point that is not discussed is how as a result of this consultation, dialogue or open-ended interview, the applicant or his representative interprets what the speaker considered to be the community needs. If respondent gives ten problems, do you ask for priorities? What about leaders who give conflicting or dramatically opposed needs? Suppose the majority of the general public do not agree with one (or more) leaders? Clearly, this question opens up a wide range of difficult problems which apparently are now resolved by the applicant. A question arises as to whether the Commission should provide general guidelines in this area, as well as guidelines obviously aimed at getting a fair and unbiased sample of leaders and the general public in the area in question.

Introduction of Statistical Data, Appendix A, Docket No. 18703

On October 7, 1970, the Federal Communications Commission in Appendix A of Docket No. 18703 laid down some general guidelines for parties to follow who intend to offer statistical studies in evidence in common carrier hearing proceedings. (See Appendix, Section 1.363 (a) of Appendix A, Docket No. 18703.)

These guidelines serve the same general purpose as those used by the Interstate Commerce Commission, and apparently arose from a similar set of circumstances — namely the unsatisfactory nature of many of the original verified statements, studies, exhibits, and testimony, thereby requiring lengthy hearings and cross-examinations to develop for the record the types and amounts of sample survey evidence required by the hearing examiner and his staff for appraisal and decision making.

The statement relative to the introduction of statistical data goes beyond the ICC guidelines which are limited to probability sample surveys, and includes in addition, evidence submitted from experiments and from econometric models and analyses. It also calls for a description of relevant computer programs and summary descriptions of input data. This more comprehensive coverage of sample evidence and statistical data generally is highly desirable, and no doubt represents the wider variety of statistical and mathematical sophistication now appearing in some FCC proceedings.

OBSERVATIONS

Potential Applications and Improvements

The present survey of the Federal Communications Commission reveals that its basic operations include a wide variety of applications of probability sampling and other statistical and mathematical techniques.

At the same time, it is quite clear that the Commission is not getting the full benefit of the power and versatility of applied mathematical statistics. During the past 30 years tremendous

advances have been made in sample survey techniques, in interviewing and questionnaire methods, in quality control applied to
service operations. The full benefit of this theory and practice will
not be available to the Commission until it develops an in-house
capability in these areas. When this is done, many operations will
be expedited, many aspects of hearing proceedings will be accelerated, but even more important the basis for better decisions in
many problems will be available.

The guidelines for submitting statistical data, as indicated
above, were a real advance in expediting proceedings. They could
be improved, it seems to the writer, if they were laid out in more
detail in four parts:

1. Sample surveys for objective data (measurements).
2. Sample surveys for opinions (these guidelines would supplement those in item 1 above.)
3. Design of experiments.
4. Mathematical models.

Mathematical models raise legal issues while the other techniques do not. The major emphasis should be on how well the
model describes the real world, and the need to make tests and
studies to determine this before the model is submitted in a proceeding. Model building is so difficult and complex, so devoid of
uniqueness, so subject to countless variations that it needs to receive much more detailed treatment in a set of guidelines. Any set
of guidelines, however, should be general, not specific, so that it
does not prove self-defeating by preventing utilization of technical
advances and improvements.

In Docket No. 18774 dealing with community surveys, it is
pointed out that a professional study is not required. Regardless of
what it is called, the ascertainment of community problems clearly
involves two problems:

1. The sampling of people: leaders and non-leaders.
2. Obtaining valid responses from this sample of people.

Making available to applicants the know-how developed in
sampling and interviewing during the past 30 years is certainly
going to improve what apparently 7,000 applicants are doing and
what the Commission requires of them in Docket No. 18774.

Actually these applicants are required to do a job for which they are not trained or in which they are unlikely to have had any experience. Making a valid determination of community needs is not simply a question of talking to some people, as the Commission makes quite clear.

Other problems or areas where substantial improvements could be made include the following:

1. Making adequate estimates from samples of radio and TV audiences.
2. The quality of service rendered in connection with telephone and telegraph service. The Commission should conduct continuous sample surveys of quality of service.
3. The Commission should conduct periodic sample surveys of public opinions about both radio and TV programs.
4. The Commission should not have to rely upon the industry or outsiders for information basic to its regulatory function.
5. The Commission should consider the use of sampling as a method in indicating and measuring compliance with its laws, rules, and regulations.

Problems and Difficulties

There are no professional persons who are experts in sampling, and in sampling opinion. Know-how in this area is apparently not available to the Commission and thinking about sampling seems to follow that of the political pollsters. Words like "cross-section," "quotas," and "representative" come from pollsters and others, not from probability sampling theory or practice.

There is a tendency to settle for judgment sampling or at best very poor probability sampling, apparently due to complaints from industry about time and cost burden. The Commission should reconsider prevailing ideas about time and cost restraints where the interests of millions of American consumers and customers are at stake in decisions, as in telephone rates and telegraph service, and radio and TV programs. The absence of a separate staff of statisticians who are experts in statistical aspects of FCC problems has led to fragmentation of sampling and statistical work.

Audits of rating bureaus' operations should be done under ground rules set by the Commission. Audit by NAB is not enough although no doubt it is helpful since it represents customers of the rating bureau as well as the industry.

A technical appraisal of the sample design and related aspects is needed, as well as a procedural audit.

Large companies like American Telephone and Telegraph, and Western Union, as well as TV networks, have extensive technical sampling, statistical, and mathematical know-how. The Commission needs a matching know-how of its own to appraise studies, analyses, testimony, exhibits, and other materials submitted in proceedings before the Commission.

Broadcast rating and other significant estimates should be appraised by the Commission using its own expertise in sampling and opinion sample surveys. The Commission should not rely on private ratings of industry for basic data needed for regulation.

In making community studies, the Commission asks the applicant to make a study by whatever valid method he chooses; however, very few of the 7,000 possible applicants have sufficient know-how to do this — that is to conduct an acceptable quality sample survey of community needs and problems. There is a need to improve community surveys.

Some work has been done in developing a mathematical model of television broadcasting. This project as well as other significant applications of mathematical models and statistical analyses are being hampered by lack of adequate professional staff.

Recommendations

1. The Commission should make a comprehensive survey of the Commission's operation and activities to determine significant statistical problems and statistical aspects of problems and to form the foundation of a statistical program for the Commission.

2. The Commission should organize an independent staff of professional applied mathematical statisticians and supporting personnel as needed to initiate, develop, and implement this program. The staff should have expertise in sample surveys gener-

115

ally, in sample surveys of opinion, in statistical and mathematical model-building, in design of experiments, and in statistical quality control techniques applicable to service industries and operations. This capability is greatly needed in order to handle the many important sampling and other technical statistical aspects of studies and evidence being presented in preceedings before the Commission, and to provide the Commission with the technical statistical know-how required to carry out its regulatory functions generally.

This staff and its supporting personnel should be at a high level in the agency organization so that the chief statistician can be in close contact with high level officials relative to Commission policy, program, and operation. This way the staff can be most effective in helping management resolve its problems.

If the statisticians are "layered" in, with several layers of organization above them, or isolated from the real problems of the Commission, or only one or two professional statisticians are hired, it is better not to have them at all, for they will be simply frustrated and ineffective. The Commission should develop a real statistical program with an effective staff of professional statisticians, or postpone action until such a program can be started.

3. As a result of experience with the instructions relative to statistical data described in Appendix A of Docket No. 18703, there is a need to develop, during the next five years, more detailed guidelines for four basic types of sample and statistical studies:

   1. Sample surveys for factual information including use of expert judgments as a source of data.
   2. Supplement these with additional guidelines especially applicable to sample surveys of opinions and attitudes.
   3. Design, implementation, and analysis of experiments.
   4. Statistical and mathematical model building.

   Experience with guidelines for sample surveys in the Interstate Commerce Commission would strongly suggest a more detailed listing and description of any guidelines if they are really going to "guide" the user. (Guidelines should remain general and flexible so as not to impede progress in the future.)

4. The Commission should design and implement the sample surveys and other studies required to yield continuous information needed to perform its regulatory function, such as:

1. The quality of long distance telephone service.
2. The quality of telegraph service.
3. Information relating to the nature and cost of telephone service.
4. Information relating to the nature and cost of telegraph service.
5. Sample surveys of TV audiences.
6. Sample surveys of radio audiences.

5. An important part of the statistical program should be the planning and organizing of seminars in probability sampling and related techniques, and their implications for hearing examiners and other professional personnel, and the preparation of a series of manuals on the role of sample surveys in collecting and appraising sample data and sample evidence. In the Commission as well as in the other agencies surveyed, there is a real need to explain to non-statisticians, including high level officials and hearing examiners, what statistics mean, the nature and importance of sample surveys, the nature and role of data derived from these surveys, the problems involved in collecting and appraising acceptable quality sample evidence, and the nature and limitations of the various types of decisions made therefrom. This is a problem of communicating the power, versatility and applicability of statistical techniques to officials and others who are not at all aware of how applied statistics can help them resolve current problems and improve present procedures.

CHAPTER 3

Part A

448-559 O - 71 - 9

Federal Government Involvement in Data Collection for Subnational Areas

By
Morris B. Ullman

TABLE OF CONTENTS

121

Appendixes marked (*) were prepared by the agency involved.

PART I — GENERAL BACKGROUND

Introduction

Federal government data are collected, collated and made available for many types of subnational areas and regions, states, counties, political subdivisions of counties, cities, census tracts and blocks.[1] These basic areas are combined and recombined into a large variety of administrative areas, metropolitan areas, planning areas, poverty areas, and other combinations required for planning, administering, and evaluating federal, federal-state, state and local programs.

The variety of published federal data and areas for which they are shown has been organized by the Bureau of the Census in two directories: a 380-page "Directory of Federal Statistics for States, a Guide to Sources, 1967" and a 164-page "Directory of Federal Statistics for Local Areas, a Guide to Sources, 1966." Because these directories deal primarily with published material, they do

---

1 The 1967 Census of Governments counts 81,299 governments in the United States: the federal government, the 50 states, 3,049 counties, 18,049 municipalities, townships, school districts, and special districts. Many of these units have taxing powers, and all are responsible for some public functions.

not indicate the additional detailed information which exists in unpublished form. Nor does this exhaust the supply of small area data. A third, 678-page publication, also prepared by the Bureau of the Census, the "Directory of Nonfederal Statistics for States and Local Areas," covers the publications of the states and other organizations producing data in this geographic detail.

For statistical presentations of state data by regions, the most widely used model is the four region and nine division grouping of states developed by the Bureau of the Census over the last century. However, agencies such as the Office of Business Economics and the Office of Education use different state groupings when they feel it will present their data in a more meaningful way. Recognizing the advantages of standardization, a Commerce Department committee reviewed the groupings over a three-year period (1952-1955) and submitted a new grouping[2] to the Office of Statistical Standards (now Statistical Policy and Management Information Systems Division, Office of Management and Budget). Using states as building blocks posed such disadvantages that the Committee felt the cost of any changeover would be warranted only if the use of the new areas were made government-wide. No action was taken to achieve this result and the traditional areas are still in use.

In the case of administrative areas used by federal agencies, operational conditions related to their respective programs have been paramount in the designation of areas which use states as building blocks. A large number of such areas are now in use. [3] Proposals to centralize federal activities in "sub-capitols" have been made from time to time, but attempts to assemble federal activities in specified centers have not been successful. In March 1969, President Nixon directed the major grant agencies to concentrate their activities in eight (later amended to ten) centers. In

---

2   The proposed areas as well as general considerations for the organization of such areas were presented in a chapter in *Regional Income, Studies in Income and Wealth*, Vol. 21 in a chapter "The Geographic Area in Regional Economic Research" by Morris B. Ullman and Robert C. Klove. (Princeton University Press, 1957, pp. 87-111.)

3   A summary of such areas used by the federal government was presented to the International Statistical Institute meetings in 1955 by Robert W. Burgess, then Director of the Census.

November 1970, the directive was made government-wide and progress toward this goal is being made. If the use of these ten regional centers becomes sufficiently widespread, there will be a need to use these areas for statistical presentation either in place of, or in addition to, the existing regions.

The most detailed subnational data are those produced in the decennial Censuses of Population and Housing. The results are presented both for political units and for certain "analytic" groupings such as Standard Metropolitan Statistical Areas (defined by the Office of Management and Budget) and urbanized areas. These areas are used widely because of the availability of information for these "building blocks." [4]

In surveying the federal-state-local data collection effort, it is important to note the overwhelming magnitude of the federal role in relation to the others. The research resources and tools developed in federal data-gathering programs often have utility in the operations of the states. The local areas cannot devote their resources to the type of development effort undertaken in the larger scale federal projects. The development of sample survey techniques, computer technology, major classification schemes, and such materials as the extensive map files and geographic resources of the Bureau of the Census, illustrate the products of the federal development effort.

Yet the federal government's leadership role, though undeniable, is lightly asserted and not always recognized. In practice, the leader consults and cooperates with partners rather than directing them. It is a healthy relationship, based on mutual respect. The resources developed for federal programs should continue to be available to those units of government that have use for them, especially when the result will be economy of operations, improvement of data, and easing of the burden on respondents.

This paper is divided into three parts. Part I provides background information intended to develop a picture of the various interests in subnational data. Part II considers come of the prob-

---

4 Detailed descriptions of both basic and developed areas are included in the Census reports and in the 1970 Census Users' Dictionary which is part of the *Census Users' Guide* (Part I, pp. 75-90), U.S. Government Printing Office, 1970.

lems and issues involved and advances a number of suggestions for future developments in this area. Selected programs illustrating a number of important activities in detail have been included in Part III — Appendixes.

Federal Interests

In 1971, more than $30 billion were transferred from the federal government to state and local governments for the implementation of programs in which the federal government had an interest. This amount, four times greater than the comparable federal outlay in 1960, continues to grow. In 1971, it represented 14 percent of total federal spending and 20 percent of state-local revenues. In addition to the above transfers, indirect assistance is provided through national programs operated directly by the federal government, technical assistance provided by federal agencies, state and local participation in federal training programs, and other activities.

Further demonstrating the need for subnational data is the widespread geographic distribution of federal activities. About 90 percent of federal employees work outside the Washington, D.C. metropolitan area. In addition, every federal program has to be justified to the representatives of the 50 states in the Senate and to the 435 members of the House of Representatives, each of whom is concerned with the impact on his local constituency.

Thus, the logistics of federal program operations alone require considerable local data. Studying the impact and evaluating the results of federal programs often requires taking into consideration a sub-area of the Nation. An example is the analysis of economic impact of a new national park on the surrounding area.

Federal programs are often closely related to similar programs in states and local areas. If we keep this in mind, three types of operation emerge:

A. The program is run entirely by the federal government as in the case of the veterans hospitals, internal revenue collections and social security.

B. The program is administered through the states with financing wholly or partly by the federal government, with requirements specified to achieve the federal purpose — for example, the U.S. Employment Service Offices.

C. The program is administered by the state or the local government, with the federal interest expressed through marginal projects, technical assistance, or in other ways.

Statistical operations are closely linked to administration, and we find all three of these modes of operation also present in the statistical programs. The censuses, which are the principal general source of local data comparable across the nation, are of Type A and are completely federally administered and controlled. Federal-state cooperative programs are of Type B and are the source of data on agriculture, labor, and vital statistics, as well as for data on other areas. As an example of Type C, the Federal Highway Administration subsidizes efforts by local transportation planning agencies to improve their information sources so that there can be better reporting of program information. Similarly, the Model Cities program has had a contractor develop City Demonstration Agency Information System (CDIS) to provide a model for cities for the development of their own data resources.

Many federal allocations to the states are based on population and income. To provide needed information, annual state estimates of population are prepared by the Bureau of the Census and quarterly and annual estimates of state income are prepared by the Office of Business Economics. The Population Division of the Bureau of the Census is now involved in a federal-state cooperative program for the preparation and publication of county population estimates. The Regional Income Division of the Office of Business Economics uses data from unemployment insurance and social security to prepare basic economic data for counties. These data are then combined into a system of 172 economic areas and other groupings for analysis of water resources, power utilization, pollution control and other problems.

The collection of current data through federal-state cooperative programs is particularly worthy of further study and development. [5]

---

5 Programs of this category are described in Working Paper No. 1, "Federal-State-Local Cooperative Arrangements in Statistics," Office of Statistical Standards, Bureau of the Budget, 1966. Recent information for some of the programs covered is presented in the Appendixes G to K, which are intended to supplement rather than replace the descriptions in the publication cited.

By using existing state organizations to collect information to federal specifications, comparable data are obtained, duplication is avoided, and economies are effected for both the federal government and the cooperating jurisdiction. The principal programs now using a technique of this type include a joint agriculture statistics program administered by the Statistical Reporting Service of the Department of Agriculture through the state agriculture statisticians; the employment, hours and earnings, job vacancies, and labor turnover programs administered by the Bureau of Labor Statistics through the state Employment Security Offices; and the vital statistics program administered by the National Center for Health Statistics through the state Registrars of Vital Statistics. The cooperative programs, which are not limited to these three agencies, each have developed different patterns of operation and financing as circumstances dictated.

In some instances (*e.g.*, the Census building permit program), the arrangement has been for the federal agency to collect documents from local administrations and furnish copies to the state, which previously had not developed a program of its own in this area.

Further developments now being explored in vital statistics and education would have the state, under a cost-sharing arrangement, collect, edit, code and carry through the operation up to the tabulation stage, furnishing to Washington, under specific instructions and with provision for quality control, machine-ready cards or tape. A procedure of this type has been used for some time in gathering labor statistics.

Health and crime statistics, which occupy a great deal of attention today, are also undergoing similar developments. New legislation provides for technical assistance to the states in setting up state centers for health statistics. In the Law Enforcement Assistance Administration of the U.S. Department of Justice a statistics center has been established to coordinate and collect information on the various aspects of crime. In addition to nationally conducted projects, grants are given to the states to assist them in developing better data on criminal justice in their jurisdictions.

Data gathered to federal specifications on a national scale, in contrast to independent local collections, have the advantages of uniformity and scale. One set of specific concepts is used to produce data comparable from one area to another. The magnitude of the undertakings and the cumulative expenditures involved make it possible to develop skilled staff and resources. This results in more attention to detail, to concepts, definitions and classifications, and to logistic requirements. It facilitates exchange of experiences and encourages research leading to improved methods of data collection. The benefits of scale already achieved include the development of the standard industrial classifications, the application of sampling theory, and the development of data processing computer techniques.

State and Local Interests

State and local areas, faced with problems similar to those of the federal government and usually with more direct administrative responsibilities, have also assembled a large amount of data, but, except for federal-state cooperative programs, have generally not provided for comparability with other areas – and sometimes have been unable to get comparability even within the areas of their jurisdiction. The need for such comparability has been recognized by the National Governors Conference. In 1966 and 1967 it sponsored a National Conference on Comparative Statistics. The principal recommendation resulting from this conference was for each state to organize a central group to coordinate statistics within the state and to act as a channel for overall coordination with other states. Sixteen states now have such a central office with varying degrees of coordinating responsibility.

In the case of the states, and even more the cities, the recent tendency has been to promote the development of data resources to make available information needed for local decisions. Many of these efforts have been described at the annual meetings of the American Statistical Association at sessions arranged by the Committee on Small Area Statistics, a standing group which can trace its history back for 40 years. [6]

---

6   The papers presented at these meetings are published by the Census Bureau in their GE-40 series. A recent summary "Information Systems in State and Local Governments" by Edward F. Hearle of Booz-Allan Hamilton, Inc., was prepared for the Annual Review of Information Science and Technology, Vol. 5, Encyclopedia Brittanica, Inc., 1970.

A search of the available literature, as Edward F. Hearle notes, can be rather disappointing. Most of the written material "describes systems concepts that the literature's author feels might be, or should be, developed. Relatively little solid operating achievement is reported." However, the paucity of achievement literature should not be interpreted as an absence of activity. Most of the information systems are limited in scope — local land records, police records, etc., and the technicians involved are probably so immersed in the details of operation that, as yet, they have not taken time to describe their experiences. The existence of widespread activity is attested by the fact that the recently formed (1965) Urban and Regional Information Systems Association (URISA) has about 1,000 members from all levels of government, all types of interests and all sections of the country.

The federal Office of Management and Budget has also recognized the need for more coordination of federal-state needs and has issued circulars providing guidelines to federal agencies for cooperating with state and local governments to coordinate and improve information systems (Circular A-90).

Because of this widespread interest, and the fact that these local information systems make use of the summary material from the major censuses as well as from other federally-involved sources, federal agencies have increasingly paid attention to their delivery systems. In many instances, the local information systems can obtain data on cards or tapes from the federal agencies, and, conversely, federal agencies can obtain information from these data systems. For example, the Federal Highway Administration is encouraging the use of administrative funds to improve the data assembling activities of 400 local highway planning agencies.

The possibility of obtaining improved information from local areas has also led to two other noteworthy programs. Under the sponsorship of a group of nine federal agencies, Housing and Urban Development has contracted for the preparation of six operational and computer-based prototype municipal information systems. The aim is to develop fully documented programs which may have application to other municipalities. The effort has been designated USAC by the Urban Information Systems Interagency Committee.

Also, with the cooperation of other federal agencies and state and local governments, the Bureau of the Census conducted projects in New Haven and in the Los Angeles area to develop systems to interrelate more closely the results of the censuses and local records. Two major developments of this program are computer coding of addresses by geographic unit (down to the block-side) and contributions to computer mapping. A series of 12 publications and three computer program packages have already resulted from the New Haven Census Use project.

The Census Bureau with the participation of the Office of Management and Budget and other agencies conducted a series of intergovernmental seminars on federal statistics for state and local government use. Through the Spring of 1971, 332 participants from 224 organizations spent a week in Washington becoming acquainted with federal data programs. All but two of the states, and 74 largest cities and 103 planning organizations and university research centers were represented at these seminars.

Still another successful project is under the direction of the federal Bureau of Standards. The Bureau, in promulgating federal information processing standards, has established liaison with 50 state coordinators through the National Association for State Information Systems. Through this mechanism state coordinators participate in planning and are informed of the development of federal and international standards. Because the program of the Bureau of Standards also includes the development of a catalog of available classifications which can be used in statistical work as well as other information processing activity, it can make a distinct contribution by providing tools for increasing the comparability of statistical data from the local to the international level.

Nongovernment Interests

Federal subnational data have tremendous interest for nongovernmental users. These publicly collected data are indispensable for much social and economic research, for marketing analyses, for developing and justifying the positions of various public interest groups and, in general, for implementing the democratic process by the presentation of generally accepted facts.

133

In considering uses of local area data by individuals concerned with evaluation of consumer activities, one must take into account that most persons interested in such problems have difficulty articulating their data needs and lack the skills for manipulating the data which may be available. The growth of organizations concerned with the problems of the consumer may encourage more sophisticated approaches and help overcome this educational problem in the use of data for personal and public purposes.

Along with the interest in data goes a concern among non-governmental groups to protect respondents from burdensome inquiries and invasions of their privacy. These concerns have an impact on subnational data and often outweigh expressed needs for more data. Business groups especially are apt to request more detailed information while expressing concern over the added reporting burden.

Recognizing the interests and needs of non-governmental groups, many federal agencies involve them in their planning through professional committees, advisory groups, and in other ways. The American Statistical Association, for example, has committees, many of long standing, which advise on programs of the Office of Management and Budget, the Census Bureau, agricultural statistics, small area statistics and social insurance statistics and training. Its members, and the members of other professional societies, also serve on other advisory groups organized by federal agencies.

The Business Advisory Council on Federal Reports was organized by the principal trade associations shortly after the passage of the Federal Reports Act in 1942 primarily to guard against excessive burden on business respondents. The Federal Statistics Users' Conference was organized in 1956 by non-federal organizations to make their needs for improved data known to the Congress and to federal agencies. Both of these organizations are privately financed.

Discussion of invasion of privacy grew intense when a national data bank was proposed. The concern for protection of privacy was expressed by several congressmen, the American Civil Liberties Union, and a number of lawyers and scientists who testified before congressional committees on this problem. [7] This problem also has been explored in technical journals, both legal and statistical, as well as in general publications.

Nevertheless, non-governmental users are simultaneously demanding improvement of the delivery system for government statistics by requesting tapes and special tabulations, and making widespread use of government publications such as the County and City Data Book of the Bureau of the Census, the annual reports on Employment and Earnings for States and Areas of the Bureau of Labor Statistics and the compilation of Internal Revenue data by zip code areas.

PART II — **PROBLEMS AND PROPOSALS**

Introduction

, As we have seen, the federal government is heavily involved in producing subnational data for its own use, for state and local governments and for other groups. The information collected at public expense is made available not only through conventional publications but also on a service basis. Copies of tables, data tapes, and special tabulations are furnished at cost where such action is consistent with public policy and does not interfere with the regular work load of the producing agency. In certain cases data are purchased by service organizations, both public and private, which then deal directly with the consumer.

The continuing interplay between need and resources, and the priority conflicts between the functions of the government as a user of data and as a service organization give rise to policy issues and problems. In order to draw attention to some of these issues, a few general problems are discussed below.

The following principles implicit in both federal-state cooperative data collection and federal production of small area data may be summarized in this fashion:

1. Overlapping federal-state-local requirements for data provide opportunities for coordination, economics, and data

---

7 E.g., *The Computer and Invasion of Privacy, Hearings before a subcommittee of the Committee on Government Operations* House of Representatives, Washington, D.C.: U.S. Government Printing Office, July 26-28, 1966.

improvement.

2. As the producer and/or coordinator of comparable sub-national data collection, the federal government has the responsibility to develop a delivery system which will facilitate the availability of the data to the agencies using the information produced.

3. Federally produced subnational data, as the output of publicly financed enterprises, should be available to all who need such data.

4. As the largest partner in the federal-state relationship, the federal government should recognize, and should be prepared to implement, a leadership role in the production of meaningful and comparable subnational data.

5. The leadership role of the federal government must include better coordination of its own concepts and operations in order to facilitate its coordination with state and local data gathering activities.

6. The implementation of revenue sharing, now under consideration in Congress, will increase the need for comparable subnational data. Federal needs for evaluating and implementing its programs will continue and the needs of the states for comparable information will probably increase.

The application of these principles is discussed under three headings: "Federal-State-Local Cooperation in Data Collection," "Producer-User Communication" and "The Federal Leadership Role." In addition, because of the widespread interest, a section is included on "The Proposal for a Mid-Decade Census." No attempt is made, however, to evaluate this proposal.

Federal-State-Local Cooperation in Data Collection

Coordinating the actions of the 50 states and other independent jurisdictions is obviously a complex task. Local considerations and resources, as well as the inclination to use previously applied procedures, are paramount within each individual unit. The welding of the diverse elements into one information system will require prolonged planning, training and implementation. Systems suitable for large units may be too ambitious for small units. Conversely, that system which the smaller units find adequate may not satisfy the needs of the larger unit.

The advantages of comparability, the need to eliminate duplication, and the economies of joint operations have been factors in the development of federal-state-local cooperative programs. The principle of comparability of concepts for data from the local level up to the international level, so that information can be summarized and transmitted upward, is an attractive goal. The ability to compare their data with that of other states is a need expressed by the National Governors Conference and by other organizations. To ease the burden on respondents, duplicate requests from federal and state sources could be eliminated. Further, the federal government stands to gain in its own operations from the availability of good state and local data.

The sharing of experience and techniques is another advantage of making resources available for mutual benefit. The federal government and large states have acquired experienced staffs and developed research efforts aimed at improving their data collection activities, which smaller states cannot match. On the other hand, the smaller states may provide better test situations for innovations.

The existing federal-state-local cooperative efforts — principally in agriculture, labor, and vital statistics — have long histories. The benefits obtained through shared costs and experience lead one to believe that other programs could benefit from similar arrangements. To develop information on potential action and work out plans for such cooperation requires detailed study. It may be advisable, therefore, to consider possibilities such as the following:

1. A cooperative task force of federal and state personnel to examine further areas where cooperation in data collection would be mutually beneficial. Because any activities which may result from these efforts will require executive approval, high level sponsorship is important.
2. Further encouragement to the states to develop agencies which will coordinate internal statistical activity and serve as a channel to the federal government and the other states. These agencies also could serve to implement activities sug-

137

gested elsewhere in this section.

3. An annual conference on comparative statistics sponsored and staffed by a federal agency in a manner similar to the annual Conference on Labor Statistics.
4. Recognition that enhancing federal-state-local cooperation is a significant function of the federal agency responsible for coordination of statistical activities.

Cooperative programs raise the problem of financing. In considering the application of these programs, the following financial pattern has been suggested:

a. The federal government should pay for data collection activities where the overwhelming priority is to assemble nationally-needed data and the best channel is through state offices.
b. The state or local government should finance the collection of data necessary for their operations. Where federal needs can be served by incremental activities, the federal government should pay the marginal cost.

The difficulty in applying this pattern is the definition of the phrase "necessary for their operation." No standard criteria are suggested. The appropriate financing will have to be determined on a case-by-case basis.

Another problem arises from the conflict of federal and state legislation. In entering into agreements with the states, federal agencies lacking specific authority require the states to compete with other bidders for contractual undertakings. Even when sole source arrangements can be made, the federal requirement for payment before work is started conflicts with state requirements for payment after work is completed.

Over the years various devices have been developed to overcome these difficulties. In some instances, direct dealing with states has been exempted from the usual contracting requirements by specific legislation.

It may be advisable to review existing legislative impediments to dealing directly with the states, and to develop general legislation which facilitates contracting and financial arrangements aimed at enhancing federal-state cooperation.

Producer-User Communication

It is assumed that a governmental unit which produces statistical data will do so in the specific form needed for immediate use, and will also deliver the product in a form convenient to as wide a group of users as possible. The distribution function involves added effort and cost. Moreover, in the case of fund allocation, distribution often suffers because it is at the end of the process when resources and time are uusually close to exhaustion. In the case of current repetitive operations, the conduct of the next survey usually takes priority over elaboration and distribution of the prior survey. The development of analytical, historical, and trend information seldom is given attention unless required for specific purposes.

Priority is given to the needs of the agency conducting the survey and, in the case of program produced data, needs beyond those of the specific program may be only casually considered. For multi-purpose surveys, however, the needs of many users are made known through direct communication with the agency, through advisory committees, through professional literature, and in similar ways. The Bureau of the Census, in planning the 1970 Census, conducted a series of user conferences across the country. Personnel from Agriculture and Labor and other agencies with federal-state programs meet regularly with their state counterparts.

When results become available, the usual sequence is a prompt release (usually preliminary) of the most important data, a regular report, and the more detailed final publication and special studies. With the advent of the computer, other delivery systems have been developed, such as making tapes available.

In spite of the general pattern, however, a frequently heard comment is that potential users are unaware of material, especially unpublished material. As a result, agencies are issuing catalogues of their publications, as well as lists of unpublished material available for the cost of making copies. The ability to charge for copies of such material is limited, however, to agencies having specific legislative authority. Other agencies must provide service out of their regular appropriated funds.

Federal Leadership

In view of their similar problems and requirements, it would appear helpful to coordinate the data gathering of the 50 states and, at least, to provide a way for the technicians engaged in this activity to exchange experiences. Such an exchange now occurs in organizations of state officials and in professional societies, but in this setting their discussions are submerged in broader program requirements and concentration on data gathering problems is difficult.

As the largest partner, the federal government should play a leading role. Gropings toward this role are evident in specific federal-state programs; the Departments of Labor and Agriculture have assumed leadership in their areas. The need for further action is evident in the attempts of the Departments of Housing and Urban Development, Treasury, and Health, Education and Welfare to encourage and develop prototypes for local information systems, usually with inadequate resources and with minimal involvement of the federal agency.

The coordination effort should also take into account the distinction between the information needed for day-to-day operations, foremost in the mind of program managers, and the broader, more analytic type of data needed for planning and research. The broader concerns of the federal government are important in evaluating the use of resources for those long-range purposes.

Evidence of the need for and value of federal leadership is apparent in specific programs. Federal initiatives such as the Census-conducted International Seminars on Federal Statistics for State and Local Government Use are welcomed, and the recommendation by the National Governors' Conference for broader coordination indicates interest in further progress.

In order to share technical and substantive information among those engaged in data collection, the federal government should specifically assume a leadership role and, in addition to the suggestions mentioned above, consider the following:

1. The federal government should promote more research into statistical methods with state and local applications, make more use of local records with federal survey data (after the

pattern of the Census Use Studies in New Haven and Los Angeles), make more coordinated estimates such as those developed by Census and OBE, and support more work on the development of classification schemes.

2. Technical assistance from the federal government and the larger states should be made available to smaller states attempting to improve their statistical services.

3. The federal government should have a basic training program for state and local statistical personnel covering both data gathering and use. The federal government could be responsible for overhead and training costs, while the state and local governments paid the salaries and expenses of their personnel during training.

4. Responsibility for promoting the federal leadership role and coordinating federal efforts designed to help states and local areas should be recognized as a significant function of a specific federal agency, backed by adequate staff and funding.

5. The federal leadership role should be expressed in particular programs through continuing technical consultation and guidance. Federal personnel should be available to act as consultants in state agencies where problems can be solved in the context of daily work.

PART III — APPENDIXES

The following appendixes have been assembled to provide background and further detail for topics and projects referred to earlier in this report. Many of these summaries have been prepared by the agencies involved; these are marked with an asterisk in the Table of Contents. The other statements have been taken from published material or abstracted from other documents issued by the sponsoring organization.

Appendix A — Governmental Units

Table A-1. Governmental Units in the United States

Type of government	1967	1962	1957*
Total	81,299	91,237	102,392
U.S. Government	1	1	1
State governments	50	50	50
Local governments	81,248	91,186	102,341
Counties	3,049	3,043	3,050
Municipalities	18,048	18,000	17,215
Townships	17,105	17,142	17,198
School districts	21,782	34,678	50,454
Special districts	21,264	18,323	14,424

*Adjusted to include units in Alaska and Hawaii, which were reported separately prior to adoption of statehood in 1959.

Source: Vol. 1, *1967 Census of Governments*, Governmental Organizations.

Table A-2. Local Governments
by Type, by States: 1967

Areas	Local Gov. Total	Local Governments other than School Districts				School Dist.
		Counties	Munici-palities	Town ships	Special Dist.	
Alabama	796	67	359	—	251	119
Alaska	61	9	51	—	—	1
Arizona	394	14	62	—	76	242
Arkansas	1,252	75	423	—	352	402
California	3,864	57	400	—	2,168	1,239
Colorado	1,252	62	251	—	748	191
Connecticut	413	—	34	149	221	9
Delaware	170	3	52	—	65	50
Dist. of Col.	2	—	1	—	1	—
Florida	827	67	383	—	310	67
Georgia	1,203	159	512	—	338	194
Hawaii	19	3	1	—	15	—
Idaho	871	44	194	—	513	120
Illinois	6,453	102	1,256	1,432	2,313	1,350
Indiana	2,669	92	550	1,009	619	399
Iowa	1,802	99	945	—	280	470
Kansas	3,668	105	623	1,543	1,037	360
Kentucky	952	120	359	—	273	200
Louisiana	733	62	270	—	334	67
Maine	698	16	21	469	127	65
Maryland	361	23	151	—	187	—
Massachusetts	654	12	39	312	247	44
Michigan	2,903	83	522	1,253	110	935
Minnesota	4,184	87	850	1,817	148	1,282
Mississippi	783	82	268	—	272	161
Missouri	2,917	114	856	343	734	870
Montana	1,103	56	125	—	209	713
Nebraska	4,391	93	538	486	952	2,322
Nevada	146	17	17	—	95	17
New Hampshire	515	10	13	222	80	181
New Jersey	1,421	21	335	232	311	522
New Mexico	307	32	88	—	97	90
New York	3,485	57	616	931	965	916
North Carolina	752	100	437	—	215	—
North Dakota	2,757	53	357	1,378	431	588
Ohio	3,283	88	933	1,324	228	710
Oklahoma	1,733	77	522	—	214	960
Oregon	1,456	36	222	—	800	398
Pennsylvania	4,998	66	1,005	1,554	1,624	740
Rhode Island	109	—	8	31	67	3
South Carolina	561	46	259	—	148	108
South Dakota	3,510	64	306	1,050	106	1,984
Tennessee	791	94	297	—	366	14
Texas	3,446	254	883	—	1,001	1,300
Utah	445	29	213	—	163	40
Vermont	656	14	65	238	72	367
Virginia	373	96	229	—	48	—
Washington	1,652	39	267	63	937	346
West Virginia	455	55	225	—	120	55
Wisconsin	2,490	72	568	1,259	62	519
Wyoming	472	23	87	—	185	177

Local governments only; excludes Federal government and the 50 state government. Source: Vol. 1, 1967 Census of Governments, *Governmental Organizations.*

Appendix B — **Federal Aid to State and Local Governments**

To place federal-state statistical relationships in perspective, Table B-1 from the Special Analyses volume of the Budget of the United States Government outlines the programs involving transfers of funds for federal purposes. These grants do not include many of the programs mentioned in other parts of this paper, since many of the statistical activities are paid for from the funds appropriated to the federal agency. The presence of a grant program, however, is bound to have an effect on the nature of the cooperation to be expected.

Table B-2 from the same source is also included to show the trend in this type of outlay, both in absolute terms and relatively.

Table B-1. Federal-Aid Outlays In Relation To Total Federal Outlays And To State-Local Revenue

| Fiscal year | Federal aid | | | |
| | | As a percent of— | | |
	Amount (millions)	Total Federal outlays	Domestic Federal outlays [1]	State-local revenue [2]
1959	$6,669	7.2	15.9	13.5
1960	7,040	7.6	16.4	12.7
1961	7,112	7.3	15.4	12.0
1962	7,893	7.4	15.8	12.3
1963	8,634	7.8	16.5	12.5
1964	10,141	8.6	17.9	13.4
1965	10,904	9.2	18.4	13.4
1966	12,960	9.7	19.2	14.2
1967	15,240	9.6	19.5	15.3
1968	18,599	10.4	20.9	16.9
1969	20,255	11.0	21.3	17.4
1970	23,955	12.2	21.9	18.2
1971 estimate	30,297	14.2	23.4	20.2
1972 estimate	38,288	16.7	26.5	22.4

[1] Excluding outlays for defense, space, and international programs.
[2] Excludes State-local revenue from publicly operated utilities and liquor stores.

Source: *Special Analysis*, Budget of the United States, p. 239.

144

Table B-2. Federal Aid To State And Local Governments
(Expenditures in Millions of Dollars)

Agency and program	Func-tional code	1970 actual	1971 estimate	1972 estimate
National defense:				
Executive Office of the President: Office of Emergency Preparedness—Federal contributions to State and local planning	059	*	*	--------
Department of Defense—Military:				
Civil defense shelters and financial assistance	051	27.0	26.2	28.6
Construction of Army National Guard centers	051	10.1	8.0	10.0
Atomic Energy Commission	058	9.3	7.6	4.3
Total, national defense	---	46.4	41.8	42.9
International affairs and finance:				
Department of State:				
East-West Cultural and Technical Interchange Center	153	4.8	5.5	5.8
International Center, Washington, D.C.	151	--------	.2	.2
Total, international affairs and finance	---	4.8	5.7	6.0
Agriculture and rural development:				
Department of Agriculture:				
Commodity Credit Corporation and Consumer and Marketing Service: Removal of surplus agricultural commodities and value of commodities donated	351	433.7	448.5	463.1
Rural water and waste disposal facilities	352	25.4	38.2	61.0
Mutual and self-help housing	352	--------	1.5	2.0
Rural housing for domestic farm labor	352	6.2	4.0	2.0
Resource conservation and development	354	8.4	12.4	14.0
Consumer protective programs	355	19.2	24.4	24.4
Cooperative agricultural extension service	355	106.4	137.5	161.4
Water Bank Act Program	354	--------	--------	10.1
Other	355	1.4	1.4	.6
Total, agriculture and rural development	---	600.8	667.9	738.6
Natural resources:				
Department of Agriculture:				
Watershed protection and flood prevention	401	93.4	100.7	98.8
Grants for forest protection, utilization, and basic scientific research	402	19.9	20.7	20.7
National forest and grassland funds: payments to States and counties (shared revenue)	402	78.7	73.2	82.8
Assistance to States for tree planting	402	.9	.8	.8
Department of Defense—Civil: Corps of Engineers:				
Flood control	401	19.4	5.9	1.0
Payments to States, Flood Control Act of 1954 (shared revenue)	401	2.8	2.7	2.8
Department of the Interior:				
Payments to States and counties (shared revenue)	402	86.2	85.7	92.3
Bureau of Reclamation	401	1.5	.9	.8
Mine drainage and solid waste disposal	403	*	.1	.2
Fish and wildlife restoration and management	405	43.2	58.0	62.7
Outdoor recreational areas (Land and Water Conservation Fund)	405	45.7	60.0	110.0
Preservation of historic properties	405	*	*	*

See footnotes at end of table.

Table B-2. Federal Aid To State And Local Governments
(Expenditures in Millions of Dollars) - Continued

Agency and program	Func-tional code	1970 actual	1971 estimate	1972 estimate
Natural resources—Continued				
Federal Power Commission: Payments to States (shared revenue)	401	*	*	*
Tennessee Valley Authority: Payments in lieu of taxes (shared revenue)	401	16.1	20.0	26.8
Water Resources Council	401	2.4	3.5	3.0
Environmental Protection Agency	401	194.2	444.8	1,029.6
Total, natural resources	---	**606.4**	**877.2**	**1,532.4**
Commerce and transportation:				
Funds appropriated to the President:				
Public works acceleration	507	.8	3.0	----------
Appalachian development	507	184.4	264.2	282.4
Department of Commerce:				
State marine schools	502	.4	.5	.5
Regional development	507	.9	2.8	8.9
Promotion of tourism	506	----------	----------	.4
National Bureau of Standards	506	.2	.4	.2
National Oceanic and Atmospheric Administration	506	----------	.9	..1
Economic development assistance	507	156.5	152.2	158.3
Department of the Interior: Resources management	507	2.1	4.6	5.8
Department of Transportation:				
Forest and public lands highways	503	32.9	28.4	31.6
Highway beautification	503	1.0	.5	1.3
Highway safety	503	----------	----------	13.0
Federal-aid highways (trust fund)	503	4,299.5	4,590.5	4,579.8
Urban mass transportation facilities	503	104.5	179.2	290.3
Federal aid for airports and airways [2]	501	83.2	134.0	147.0
Other	502	1.3	4.6	5.2
Total, commerce and transportation	---	**4,865.3**	**5,365.8**	**5,525.8**
Community development and housing:				
Funds appropriated to the President:				
Office of Economic Opportunity: Community Action programs	551	647.8	656.4	679.2
Department of Housing and Urban Development:				
Model city grants	551	75.7	358.1	442.3
Urban renewal	552	1,053.7	1,035.0	1,300.0
Open space land and urban beautification	552	43.4	72.0	100.0
New community assistance	552	----------	.6	2.0
Grants for basic water and sewer facilities	553	109.0	140.5	170.0
Grants for neighborhood facilities	553	23.4	33.0	38.0
Urban planning grants	554	41.2	50.0	48.0
Community development training programs	554	2.4	4.0	3.0
Low-rent public housing programs	555	435.9	655.5	758.9
National Homeownership Foundation	555	----------	----------	.3
Community development	553	----------	----------	150.0
Total, community development and housing	---	**2,432.5**	**3,005.1**	**3,691.7**

See footnotes at end of table.

Table B-2. Federal Aid To State And Local Governments
(Expenditures in Millions of Dollars) - Continued

Agency and program	Func-tional code	1970 actual	1971 estimate	1972 estimate
Education and manpower:				
Funds appropriated to the President: Office of Economic Opportunity [3]	601	899.9	796.9	256.0
Department of Health, Education, and Welfare:				
Elementary and secondary education	601	1,469.5	1,703.7	1,789.5
Office of Child Development	601			138.4
Assistance to schools in federally affected areas	601	622.0	464.0	437.9
Education of the handicapped	601	31.1	33.0	34.4
Civil rights education	601	3.1	12.2	8.7
Higher education activities	602	342.0	313.3	175.4
(Portion to private institutions)	602	(101.3)	(96.6)	(46.0)
Vocational education	603	285.2	404.9	445.9
Libraries and community services	608	104.9	65.9	42.1
Special institutions for the blind and deaf	608	1.4	1.5	1.6
Education professions development	601	86.1	109.4	113.9
Work incentive activities	604	81.4	138.3	223.4
Emergency school assistance	601		94.9	290.0
Department of Labor:				
Manpower development and training activities	604	420.9	991.0	1,443.5
Grants to States for administration of employment security programs (trust fund)	604	327.7	374.5	395.0
Department of Interior: Bureau of Indian Affairs:				
Education and welfare services	601	16.3	19.6	26.7
National Foundation on the Arts and the Humanities	608	.3	5.9	5.5
Corporation for Public Broadcasting	608	15.0	23.0	35.0
Equal Employment Opportunities Commission	609	.9	1.4	2.8
Other	----	3.7	.4	.4
Total, education and manpower	----	4,711.4	5,553.8	5,866.1
Health:				
Department of Health, Education, and Welfare:				
Hospital construction	651	272.0	240.8	214.3
(Portion to private, nonprofit institutions)	651	(149.6)	(133.2)	(123.3)
Health manpower	651	45.4	68.1	71.8
Comprehensive health planning and services	651	122.0	180.9	178.8
Regional medical programs	653	74.3	80.5	71.8
Construction of health educational and mental health facilities	651	185.8	181.7	178.8
Mental health services and development	653	145.9	147.3	175.8
Health services	651	9.2	6.0	3.0
Environmental health	653	10.0	16.7	12.1
Indian health services and facilities	652	1.0	2.2	.3
Patient care and health services	652	1.6	1.3	1.2
Communicable and chronic diseases	653	1.9	3.4	
Maternal and child health	652	235.8	204.2	250.6
Medical assistance	652	2,726.8	3,250.1	3,383.6
Total, health	---	3,831.4	4,383.3	4,542.2

See footnotes at end of table.

Table B-2. Federal Aid To State And Local Governments
(Expenditures in Millions of Dollars) - Continued

Agency and program	Func-tional code	1970 actual	1971 estimate	1972 estimate
Income security:				
Funds appropriated to the President: Disaster relief___	703	61.0	54.0	42.0
Public assistance:				
Income maintenance payments_____	702	4,716.2	6,439.8	7,531.6
Social services for welfare recipients_____	703	441.4	544.5	554.0
Juvenile delinquency_____	703	3.6	6.6	11.9
Vocational rehabilitation_____	703	296.5	368.9	411.0
Administration on Aging_____	703	16.1	13.9	14.3
Food stamp_____	702	558.7	1,507.3	1,943.3
Child nutrition program and special milk_____	702	379.4	618.4	570.1
Community services_____	703	_____	_____	162.0
Total, income security_____	---	**6,472.7**	**9,556.3**	**11,240.2**
Veterans benefits and services:				
Veterans Administration:				
Aid to State homes_____	804	14.0	16.8	17.7
Grants for construction of State nursing homes_____	804	3.4	5.0	7.5
Administrative expenses_____	804	.5	.9	.7
Total, veterans benefits and services_____	---	**17.9**	**22.7**	**25.9**
General government:				
Department of the Interior:				
Grants to territories_____	909	48.7	62.6	84.3
Internal revenue collections, Virgin Islands (shared revenue)_____	909	14.1	16.1	17.3
Department of Justice: Law enforcement assistance___	908	41.2	337.3	528.7
Treasury Department: Tax collections for Puerto Rico (shared revenue)_____	909	85.2	87.0	90.0
National Capital region:				
Federal payment to District of Columbia_____	909	114.6	143.0	158.0
Washington Metropolitan Transit Agency_____	---	15.8	100.0	112.2
Other_____	---	42.9	55.9	65.9
Total, general government_____	---	**362.5**	**801.9**	**1,056.4**
Allowance for general revenue sharing [4]_____	---	_____	_____	**4,019.0**
Total, grants and shared revenues_____	---	**23,954.7**	**30,296.7**	**38,288.2**

* Less than $100 thousand.
[1] Grants-in-aid unless otherwise specified. Excludes loans which are shown separately in table P–10.
[2] Federal funds in 1970; trust funds in 1971 and 1972.
[3] Manpower programs transferred to Labor Department.
[4] For fiscal 1972; differs from first full-year basis.

Note.—This table is based on the existing system of grant programs; the adoption of revenue sharing could change the functional distribution of the 1972 figures.

Appendix C — Headquarters and Grouping of States for Federal Programs

[Per Statement from the White House, May 21, 1969]

Region I (Boston) — Connecticut, Maine, Massachusetts, New Hampshire, Rhode Island, and Vermont;

Region II (New York City) — New York, New Jersey, Puerto Rico, and the Virgin Islands;

Region III (Philadelphia) — Delaware, District of Columbia, Maryland, Pennsylvania, Virginia, and West Virginia;

Region IV (Atlanta) — Alabama, Florida, Georgia, Kentucky, Mississippi, North Carolina, South Carolina, and Tennessee;

Region V (Chicago) — Illinois, Indiana, Minnesota, Michigan, Ohio, and Wisconsin;

Region VI (Dallas — Fort Worth) — Arkansas, Louisiana, New Mexico, Oklahoma, and Texas;

Region VII (Kansas City) — Iowa, Kansas, Missouri, and Nebraska;

Region VIII (Denver) — Colorado, Montana, North Dakota, South Dakota, Utah, and Wyoming;

Region IX (San Francisco) — Arizona, California, Hawaii, and Nevada;

Region X (Seattle) — Alaska, Idaho, Oregon and Washington.

Appendix D — Population Estimates and Projections Program for States and Local Areas, Bureau of the Census

In its current estimates program for states and small areas the Bureau of the Census annually prepares estimates of the population of states together with estimates of broad age group detail for states. Estimates of the voting age population of states are published biennially. State estimates by race may become part of the regular estimates program in the 1970's.

Estimates are now prepared annually for the 100 largest metropolitan areas and their 290 component counties. During the past decade estimates were also prepared at times for all counties and for all metropolitan counties. Estimates of the population of congressional districts have been generated on an *ad hoc* basis in the past. For the 1970 decade, we will be preparing estimates for congressional districts on a regular basis. Intercensal estimates for states and estimates of the components of population change by race of states, metropolitan areas, and counties are in preparation for the 1960 decade.

In conjunction with this current estimates program, the Bureau has been working for several years with representatives of state agencies in the evolution of a program for the preparation of county estimates largely standardized for data input and methodology. Some 47 states are participants in this federal-state cooperative program. We are currently involved in the test phase of the program, in which various estimating procedures and combinations of procedures are validated against the 1970 census results. As a result of the test we expect to select those methods which best estimate the population of counties for use in a regular county estimates program conducted by the state offices during the coming decade. These estimates will then be published by the Bureau of the Census as an "official" county estimates series.

The Cooperative Program involves no transfer of federal funds. Each state pays its own costs. The Bureau of the Census provides technical assistance and training needed for the furtherance of the program, including periodic meetings with the state agencies at their facilities or elsewhere to review progress and problems in the program.

Concurrently the Bureau will be involved in its own test of methods against the 1970 census, which will result in improved estimates for states and small areas. Procedures for estimating city population totals and population distribution of cities and metropolitan areas by race may be instituted for the coming decade as a result of the tests.

Population projections for states were last prepared by the Bureau in 1967. Interim projections updating this work to reflect the 1970 census results will be released sometime during mid-1971. This will be followed by a full-scale revision of national and state projections in 1972. Projections for metropolitan areas will also be developed during the coming decade.

As part of its clearinghouse function, the Bureau has just published the results of its latest survey of state, metropolitan, and city agencies preparing population estimates. This survey, conducted periodically, has been broadened to include more and more areas. Agencies are also contacted at intervals to determine the current status of their population projections program.

Appendix E — Local-Area Economic Data of the Regional Economics Division, Office of Business Economics

PERSONAL INCOME ESTIMATES

The Regional Economics Division has completed measuring personal income in local areas for seven selected years from 1929 to 1968. Total income has been measured by type of income and by major industrial source. These figures yield a detailed picture of the economic structure of each area. Through them, economic progress or deterioration can be traced and the factors directly responsible identified. In addition, the historical data provide a background for projecting the economic future of the area, and the information for the recent period yields an economic framework which should prove useful in impact analysis.

Page 36 in the May 1970 issue of the *Survey of Current Business* shows the detail in which the personal income estimates are available. Comparable tables can be furnished for any standard metropolitan statistical area (SMSA) and for each county or for any combination of 2,507 non-SMSA counties in the Nation. A cost estimate will be furnished on request.

Although a large amount of information can be provided for most individual counties in the Nation, the income estimates are most reliable, most meaningful, and can be given in greatest industrial detail when the area under study comprises a group of counties that together made up a meaningful economic unit and which is comparatively self-contained with regard to its labor force. This is consistent with an area in which commuting from home to work across area boundaries is at a minimum. We have developed a special data retrieval capability by which we can assemble the personal income figures for any specified combi-

151

nation of counties and/or SMSA's in the Nation.

A major emphasis in local-area income measurement beginning with the 1968 estimates will be the development of much greater industrial detail.

MIGRATION AND DEMOGRAPHIC DATA

A second major source of information has been developed that sheds light on the economic and demographic characteristics of the labor force which underlie the earnings component of income in each county, SMSA, or group of counties. Particular emphasis is placed upon the role that migration plays in affecting the geographic distribution of income.

We obtain annually from the Social Security Administration a tabulation of a 1 percent sample of reports on the social-security-covered labor force. The initial tabulation covers the year 1957; data for 1966 were received in the summer of 1969. We expect to continue to receive these data annually with a three year lag. From this file, one may examine selected characteristics of the social-security-covered work force of an area at a given point in time or as it evolves over time. Tabulations can be prepared to measure not only the quantity and quality of the labor moving into and out of a region (a county or combination of counties) but also of the resident work force as well. For any time period in the span covered, we can measure immigration, outmigration, and the non-migrant social-security-covered labor force of a county or group of counties, cross-classified according to age, race, sex, origin (for immigrants), destination (for outmigrants), industry of employment and level of earnings. Since the basic data are derived from a 1 percent sample, the size of the universe must be kept in mind when designing a tabulation.

Before the tabulations are made available to use by the Social Security Administration, social security numbers and names are removed. Accordingly, individual identification is impossible.

REGIONAL CLASSIFICATION

We have now completed a project in which the Nation's 3,100 plus counties have been classified into 173 economic areas. Each

152

area is designed to represent a complete and integrated economic unit in which interindustry relationships tend to show comparative stability. Initially, 167 such economic areas were delineated. This delineation was distributed widely and as a result of criticisms and suggestions has now been revised. Additional areas were delineated and numerous modifications made in the original groupings. Copies of a map showing the revised classification, together with a statement of concept and methodology, are available on request.

OTHER ACTIVITIES

The Division is engaged in a number of activities, most of which are experimental. Specifically, we are attempting to construct geographic measures of gross product originating by industry, personal consumption expenditures (by state and perhaps by SMSA), a measure of governmental receipts and expenditures, and a method for evaluating the economic impact of a public or private investment made in a local area. The results of these efforts will be published and/or announced in the *Survey of Current Business* as they materialize.

Finally, the Division is engaged in a major effort in which income, employment and population are being projected on a geographic basis for a 10–or–20 year period. Income and employment will be shown in some industrial detail. Presently, the projections are being made for the 173 economic areas noted above. After these have been completed, we shall consider disaggregating the projections to SMSA's or other geographic areas. The availability of these projections will be announced in the *Survey*.

Appendix F — **Selected 1970 Census Geographic Products and Tools**

Address Coding Guide (ACG). — The Address Coding Guide is an inventory of street names, codes identifying the segments into which streets are divided, and the range of address numbers in each street segment. Geographic areas covered are the central city and adjacent city postal-delivery areas within the larger SMSA's.

The ACG can be used to relate addresses and socioeconomic data associated with those addresses to a block face (one side of a city block) and from this to an entire block, census tract, ward, or other desired area formed by aggregating block faces. The ACG also permits the computer matching of mail addresses to assign geographic location codes.

The Address Coding Guide is available on computer tape or as a printed listing on 11 X 14 inch paper.

ADMATCH: An Address Matching System. – The AD-MATCH system is a package of user-oriented computer programs and documentation designed to assist in the assignment of geographic codes to computerized data records containing street addresses. The system is to be used in coordination with the following computer-readable reference sources: Address Coding Guides, Geographic Base Files, or census tract street indexes which many cities have created.

Geographic codes for areas such as census tracts, school districts, and traffic zones can be readily assigned to data records in files of building permits, school census records, etc.

The ADMATCH programs are written in IBM System/360 Assembler Language for operation with the 16K Disk or Tape Operating Systems (DOS or TOS). The minimum core storage requirement is 32K bytes; a line printer and three magnetic tape units are required.

Master Enumeration District List (MEDList). – The MEDList was designed to furnish area and place names, alphabetically, corresponding to numeric identification codes which are used on the summary tapes from the 1970 Census of Population and Housing.

To permit identification of areas for which data have been compiled, the MEDList should be used in conjunction with census maps. MEDList will assist summary tape users in preparing computer programs for processing summary tapes, and will be useful for redistricting and reapportionment purposes since it will include small-area population counts.

The MEDList will be available on magnetic tape, microfilm, and paper copy; it is expected to be released on a state-by-state basis between November 1970 and February 1971.

Note. – Further information on 1970 census geographic products except maps, can be obtained from the Central Users' Service,

Population Division, Bureau of the Census, Washington, D.C. 20233.

1970 Census Maps. — Preliminary versions of the maps described below are currently available; final versions are expected to be available by spring of 1971. There is a $5 minimum purchase order for these map series. Prices are subject to change without notice. Further information on these and other 1970 census maps can be obtained from the Geography Division, Bureau of the Census, Washington, D.C. 20233.

Map Series, Description, and Cost	SCALE	NUMBER OF MAP SHEETS
METROPOLITAN MAPS - For urbanized areas of all existing SMSA's which have been defined prior to the 1970 census, contain all recognized census boundaries down to block level. *$1 per map sheet.*	1″=2,000′.	Ranges from 2 to 137 (Most sets contain 4 to 11 map sheets).
PLACE MAPS - For incorporated and unincorporated places, contain tract and enumeration district boundaries. *$1.50 or more per map sheet (cost dependent on size).*	Varies according to size of place; ranges from 1″=400′ to 1″=1,500′.	Generally, 1 map sheet per place.
COUNTY MAPS - For each county, contain boundaries for minor civil divisions, incorporated places, tracts, and enumeration districts not shown on the two types of maps described above. *$1 per map sheet.*	1″=2mi.	Ranges from 1 to 64 per county (1 map sheet per county except for very large counties).

Appendix G — Cooperative Federal-State Arrangements for Agriculture Statistics Programs

CURRENT ORGANIZATION

Today, the USDA's Statistical Reporting Service has cooperative agreements covering the collection of statistical data on crops and livestock in 47 states — with 41 state Departments of Agriculture and with six state agricultural colleges, universities, or experiment stations. Additional cooperative agreements covering dairy manufacturing statistics are in effect with 29 state Departments of

Agriculture and one state agricultural college. The federal statistician in charge in the states operates a joint office usually made up of both federal and state personnel and is generally recognized by the state agency as being responsible for all agricultural statistics programs in the state. Crop and livestock reports for the few states in which there are no cooperative arrangements are supported solely by federal funds of the Statistical Reporting Service.

For the current fiscal year the federal appropriation for the Statistical Reporting Service is about $17.8 million, while the 47 cooperating states are spending about $3.1 million for cooperative and state statistical programs. The additional state funds made possible the collection and publication of such supplementary data as (1) crop acreages, production and livestock numbers for within-state areas such as crop reporting districts or counties; (2) special commodity surveys, and (3) other special studies on such subjects as farm labor, prices, and marketing problems. Another major use of these funds is for preparing and printing state statistical bulletins. The amount of funds provided by individual states varies widely. State farm censuses are conducted in 10 states, financed in various ways by state funds. In most states the SRS state statistician is responsible for the content of this questionnaire and compilation of data. The three sources of funds for state programs are: (a) regular state appropriations; (b) state funds appropriated to match federal funds under provisions of the Research and Marketing Act of 1946; and (c) industry funds provided for gathering specific data relating to an industry. The matching fund program of the Research and Marketing Act has been especially helpful toward developing needed state statistical programs — for example, fruit tree inventories, potato surveys, grain quality and variety surveys, quarterly pig reports, and objective yield counts for fruits and nuts. Regardless of the source of funds the reports are made equally available to everyone.

RECENT DEVELOPMENTS

Until recent years, crop and livestock estimates were largely dependent on non-probability surveys conducted by mail and use of regression techniques for adjustments to census benchmarks every five years. Beginning in the late 1950's, with use of techniques developed through cooperative research at the statistical laboratories, a program was launched for (1) large scale annual enumerations of area sample segments throughout the 48 conterminous states, supplemented by lists of large livestock operators and large employers of farm labor, and (2) monthly objective measurements in sample fields for making yield forecasts and estimates of principal crops.

Currently, there are two general purpose probability sample surveys conducted by *personal enumeration* each year. The first, conducted about June 1, covers agricultural operations on about 17,000 area segments and on an additional 6,000 farms from the large farm list. [1] This survey is designed to obtain data on planted acreages, farm numbers, livestock numbers, farm labor, and various items of economic information. The second, conducted on about December 1, places emphasis on fall-seeded grains and livestock. This survey is conducted as a sub-sample of the June survey. Only one in six of the June segments are included in the December survey; however, a larger list of livestock operators is covered.

The program outlined above has not eliminated the use of the mailed voluntary crop reports. It does, however, make available indications based on probability samples and provides the basis for putting mailed inquiries on a probability basis. For the major crop and livestock items, U.S. figures for acreages and inventory numbers are first established, and then regional figures. Finally state estimates are determined on the basis of indications from the state enumerative and mail sample data. Differences between the sum of the state estimates and the national estimates for a given item are reconciled by appropriate adjustment in the individual state estimates within the range of the standard error. Thus, the state estimates have been placed on a firmer statistical base.

In summary, integration of the federal statistical program with related state agricultural statistical services has a number of advantages. A joint federal-state endeavor under one supervisory head avoids duplication of effort, saves money, reduces reporting burden on farmers and other reporters, and provides both federal and

---

1 The area sample includes operations of about 20,000 "resident" farm operators whose headquarters are located within the segments, and about 40,000 "non-resident" agricultural tracts.

state governments with uniformly consistent data covering a broader range than either could provide independently.

Appendix H — Federal-State Relations in the Collection of Educational Statistics

The educational system in the United States is largely administered or supervised through the states. It follows that any program of data collection on the schools of the United States must involve close coordination between the federal government and the state Departments of Education. Until the establishment of the National Center for Educational Statistics (NCES) in 1965, a considerable amount of the data collected consisted of state summaries furnished by the states, with relatively little data on the individual schools.

Although no single federal-state data collection system has been developed for educational statistics, there has been considerable progress toward more cooperation in recent years. NCES data collection activities are developed in cooperation with the Committee on Educational Data Systems (CEDS), one of two standing committees of the Council of Chief State School Officers. This cooperative development is aimed at maximum utilization of state data systems to minimize respondent burden and to improve the quality of data. The Planning Committee for this group has been meeting four times a year to promote the continuing cooperation between the state Departments of Education and OE in data collection, to discuss the status of ongoing projects, and to develop plans for further cooperation. All plans for public school surveys are reviewed, and, at their request, a nine month notice is given before the actual data collection is undertaken by NCES. This provides time for the states to incorporate the data requirement in their state data systems.

In addition to the basic surveys collected by the National Center for Educational Statistics, other offices of OE collect program information. A major attempt at coordination of such reports has been the establishment of a Joint Federal-State Task Force on Educational Evaluation, by agreement between the Office of Education and the Council of the Chief State School Officers. Two

158

surveys now underway under this program are the Consolidated Program Information Report, which combines reports for 11 programs and an *elementary school survey* to collect information for evaluation of the various programs conducted under the Elementary and Secondary Education and the Vocational Education Acts.

As a basic tool for the improvement of administration as well as for the development of better statistical data, the Educational Standards Branch of NCES has, over the last 20 years, developed a series of terminology handbooks aimed at standardizing the use of standard terms in education. Existing handbooks cover financial, property, staff, and pupil accounting primarily for elementary and secondary education. Just issued is Standard Terminology for Curriculum and Instruction and, in process are handbooks on The State Education Agency, on Community Characteristics, and on Adult/Continuing Education. All these handbooks are developed with extensive participation by state and local personnel as well as other interested authorities and are subject to extensive discussion. A commitment to the handbooks develops in this process, and as a result there tends to be rapid implementation of handbooks as uniform practice when they are formally issued.

The federal-state relationship of the NCES in the area of higher education is of two main types. The most direct relationship involves the acquisition of data for the Higher Education General Information Surveys (HEGIS). Thirty states and the District of Columbia participate directly in the HEGIS data collection. This participation ranges from total responsibility in the state for the distribution and acquisition of HEGIS data with some editing and review and forwarding to the NCES, to simple arrangements in which the institutions mail copies of HEGIS responses to both NCES and the state higher education agency for the latter's review, editing and utilization. In addition, all fifty states acquire and edit, through their respective State Higher Education Facilities Commissions, the data for the facilities portion of HEGIS on a cost-sharing basis.

The less direct relationship derives from the states' participation in planning and developing (with NCES) the survey forms. The states, directly, and through their associations, participate in the planning of HEGIS for each year, and provide input for future

159

survey activity. In addition, the states directly, and through their associations, participate in the NCES and NCES-related developments of uniform and consistent (ultimately universally-accepted) data categories, definitions, and records systems and file structures. A system of handbooks and manuals to implement these terminology and record systems similar to that in elementary and secondary education, is now in process of development.

Grants to states for the strengthening of state Departments of Education (ESEA, Title I) have incorporated the previous provision of the National Defense Education Act for the improvement of statistics. Under the current arrangement, much more is being spent on statistical activities in state offices than under the earlier program. In addition, a number of special projects for the development of improved educational information systems through interstate cooperation have been financed under the special projects provisions of this legislation.

Under new legislation first funded in 1970, grants are being given to State Offices of Education for Comprehensive Planning and Evaluation which will probably accentuate the need for and the use of educational statistics.

Appendix I — Federal Government Involvement in Health Statistics Collection for Subnational Areas

INTRODUCTION

Planning for the health industry is far more concentrated in state and local agencies than is the case for economic and agricultural planning, for example. The situation in the field of health is comparable to that in the field of education.

Thus, while there is great need for national estimates and time series, there is an even greater, and largely unsatisfied, need for data relating to states and local jurisdictions. The lack of comprehensive data in sufficiently fine-grained geographical detail is one of the most serious shortcomings of the health statistics system in the United States. A major effort to remedy this situation, known as the Cooperative Federal-State-Local Health Statistics System, is now in the research and development phase. It was authorized in a section of the Regional Medical Programs and Comprehensive

Health Planning and Services Act of 1970. This plan will be briefly described below, but, first, it is necessary to sketch the situation with regard to subnational data at the present time.

GEOGRAPHIC DETAIL NOW AVAILABLE

Health statistics are viewed as encompassing statistics on the health of people, on the health services they receive, on the resources of facilities and manpower available to provide the services, and certain demographic statistics customarily associated with health statistics, in particular statistics on mortality, natality, stillbirths, marriages and divorces. (Mortality statistics, including fetal mortality, serve both as measures of the health of people and also as essential to the measurement of population growth. Statistics on the environment as it relates to health, though often included as a part of a program of health statistics, are excluded here.)

The only measures of health that are or can be made available in fine-grained (below county and metropolitan area) geographic detail on a comparable basis throughout the country are mortality statistics and statistics on the incidence of mortal diseases. Even these are often not processed in the fine-grained detail because of the cost of abstracting street addresses from the basic records in a form that can be automatically translated into finer geographic subdivisions. These data are regularly available for county and city totals in either published or unpublished form. (The counts for some of the notifiable diseases are known to be very incomplete and are chiefly used to spot outbreaks of epidemics.)

Other measures of health, such as disability, incidence and prevalence of non-reportable diseases, distributions of clinically significant variables, such as blood pressure, and so forth, are available on a continuing nationwide basis only through the National Health Survey, a series of population sample surveys. Thus estimates are produced only for regions, and, in some cases, for geographic divisions and certain large SMSA's. State figures cannot be shown.

The situation with regard to health services is worse. Certain summary data on utilization of hospital services are available regu-

161

larly for each hospital. But data from individual records of service in hospitals are only available from sample surveys capable of producing very little geographic detail. For services to ambulatory patients there are not even national samples of records of patient care (though a continuing national survey is in the design stages). Hence statistics on the services received from physicians and dentists outside of hospitals are limited to those obtained from the *household interviewing part of the National Health Survey,* which provides only the geographic detail indicated above.

Data on in-patient care facilities and on certain categories of health manpower are gathered and maintained reasonably up to date on a complete coverage basis. Consequently, the degree of geographic detail available is potentially unlimited, though Zip Code areas tend to be the smallest building block for small-area analysis. Statistics on in-patient facilities and manpower for counties and metropolitan areas have been published.

Geographic detail for such demographic measures as births, marriages and divorces can be described in exactly the same way as for mortality statistics above, except that for marriages and divorces certain states are still missing from the system.

All of the health data that have been mentioned in the foregoing are produced by the federal government, with the exception of some of the manpower data. The latter are purchased from professional societies which maintain satisfactory inventories of all qualified persons, such as doctors of medicine and dentists. Furthermore, in the case of the vital statistics it should be made clear that the registration is the responsibility of the states, the federal data being processed from copies of the original records purchased by the federal government, while the states duplicate this activity to a great extent to produce their own vital statistics, but in a manner not entirely consistent from state to state.

It should also be added that the value of the small area vital statistics is greatly dependent upon the availability of population denominators for the same small areas. This is true of birth and fertility rates as well as death rates. However, some indices appropriately use the births as the denominator and can be prepared for any small areas desired (providing the cost of taking off the street addresses can be met). Examples of such indices are: the infant mortality rate, the prematurity rate, and the illegitimacy rate.

PLANS FOR THE COOPERATIVE SYSTEM

To eliminate duplication of federal, state, and local data collection and processing activities, to bring about greater uniformity and completeness of coverage, and to make data available in much greater geographic detail than at present, a Cooperative Federal-State-Local Health Statistics System is now being planned.

States will be encouraged to develop strong organizations, spoken of as State Centers for Health Statistics, with the staff and facilities to take on the major part of the data collection and data processing for the system. The federal government will reimburse the states for data provided in machine readable form that meets the federal specifications, and also for a part of the costs of operating the data collection and data processing mechanisms.

The research and development for the Cooperative System is authorized in P.L. 91-515. This research and development phase will proceed on a project-by-project basis, each project being selected to increase knowledge about how the total system ought to be designed — and to help in the development of the capabilities of a State Center for Health Statistics.

The research and demonstration projects of evolving State Centers will focus on particular *modules* within the total health statistics configuration. These program modules will be in such separate areas as vital statistics, health manpower and facilities inventories, hospital discharge surveys, ambulatory care surveys. Individual states would select particular modules to develop under their own contracts, according to their special interests, needs and capabilities. As the projects progressed, states would profit from the experiences of others, and the content and character of the total system would evolve.

Before moving into the full implementation phase of the Cooperative System, new legislative authority will be needed to support the regular reimbursement of the states. As each *module* within a state is developed, reimbursement for that type of data from that state will be added.

In some instances local jurisdictions might bear the same rela-

163

tion to the State Center as the State Center bears to the National Center, and in other instances states will pool their resources to support a Regional Center to take on functions more economically and efficiently performed at that level.

Appendix J — National Criminal Justice Information and Statistics Service

GENERAL

In recent years, appeals for comprehensive statistics about crime, criminals, and the criminal justice system have been expressed by federal agencies, by witnesses testifying in congressional hearings, and by the President's Crime Commission, which added to the demand for statistics a new technological dimension — the need to develop criminal justice information systems and to apply systems analysis techniques to the crime problem. To respond to these needs, the National Criminal Justice Information and Statistics Service has been established. The Service is organized into two centers — a statistics center and a systems analysis and computer center. These centers will study data and informational needs, establish standards and guidelines for state and local programs, initiate national data collection and information systems, and develop uniform systems of classification and definition for use by the criminal justice community.

The activities of the Service can be roughly divided into four distinct areas; (1) Assistance and Training, (2) Improvement of Existing Statistical and Informational Systems, (3) The Development and Operation of a System of Offender Based Transaction Statistics, (4) General Data Collection Systems.

ASSISTANCE AND TRAINING

Criminal Justice in the United States is the responsibility of states and local areas. In order for these jurisdictions to operate effective systems, they must have at their command current and complete statistics and information concerning the system. In order to develop the expertise at the state and local level, the Service plans to develop and operate workshops and training ses-

164

sions to encourage and maintain a high degree of knowledge of statistical methods, information systems and related matters. These workshops, to be held regionally, will have participants from both the states and from local governments. We would expect to hold approximately four conference series per year to cover new developments in both statistics and information systems. Each conference series will consist of several separate meetings to encourage the participation of working-level people responsible for criminal justice information systems and statistics. These workshops will represent the contribution of outstanding professionals acting as contractors and consultants, as well as LEAA staff.

This assistance and training program also will support the development of local statistical projects if the projects can be generalized so that they can be used as prototypes for other agencies. Also development projects such as the preparation of standardized glossaries, are included in this program.

IMPROVING EXISTING SYSTEMS

A related program involves the Service's efforts to directly improve existing statistical and information systems. Though the emphasis of this program is the improvement of state or local systems, it also includes strengthening existing federal statistical series. Most of the funds expended in the program will be in the form of discretionary grants.

TRANSACTION STATISTICS

Statistics relating to the operation of the various parts of the criminal justice system have always been of extremely low quality. Further, different approaches have made it impossible to relate the summary data from one agency with that of another. To correct this situation, most experts have suggested moving to offender based transaction statistics. This approach would require that offenders be followed through the entire criminal justice system with data being recorded at each stage. Thus, we would be provided with data in such areas as arrest procedures, pre-trial activities, court backlogs, plea bargaining, the activities and effects of the corrections systems, and other institutional aspects of the criminal justice system. This will result in the establishment and publication of a national transaction statistical series.

These data will substitute for the currently available summary offender statistics in all parts of the criminal justice system and provide a more definitive view of the effectiveness of each component in the system.

Of equal importance, the technique will also provide a data base for the longitudinal analysis of offenders. This kind of "in depth" analysis will permit criminologists and other behavioral scientists to study the etiology of criminality and crime.

STATISTICAL DATA COLLECTION SYSTEMS

The National Criminal Justice Statistical Research Center is developing a number of new projects and assuming responsibility for a number of projects formerly operated by other agencies. Development work has already begun on a series of three surveys of victims of crime. This series will examine individual victims, commercial victims and institutional victims. The victim surveys will, for the first time, provide such information as: the number of crimes being commmitted, the characteristics of victims, geographic distribution of crime, the effect of the environment on crime and as a by-product, information concerning the effect of crime on the behavior of the general population. The Center hopes to be able to provide such data for geographic regions, large states, and major standard metropolitan statistical areas. In addition to their general usefulness, these data can be used to calibrate data on crimes known to the police which are generally available for smaller areas. This series will also provide a more reliable estimate of the cost of crime than is now available.

The Center is also developing or assuming the responsibility for a number of separate projects which will be combined into a series called National Correctional Statistics. This series will combine National Prisoner Statistics, Uniform Parole Reports, probation statistics and a new series to provide information about jails and their inmates. By the latter part of the decade, the "transaction statistics" program will be integrated into the Correctional Statistics series to increase efficiency and decrease costs.

166

The Center will also continue to collect statistics on the institutions in the field of criminal justice. For example, the annual survey of employment and expenditures will be continued in order to provide the benchmark data necessary for the development of grant requirements.

Appendix K — Selected Federal-State Labor Statistics Programs

THE BLS MONTHLY EMPLOYMENT, HOURS, AND EARNINGS PROGRAM

The Bureau of Labor Statistics and the Manpower Administration (both in U.S. Department of Labor) have cooperative agreements with agencies in each of the 50 states and the District of Columbia, under which a monthly data collection program is conducted.

Reports from approximately 160,000 establishments, representing all nonagricultural industries both public and private, are collected by the state agencies each month. These reports, edited by state personnel, provide data on employment, manhours, and payrolls. Time series are prepared by each state for the state as a whole and for major local areas using the data provided by the reports in conjunction with universe data primarily based upon quarterly reports filed with the state unemployment insurance agency. The monthly data obtained from the reports are forwarded to BLS-Washington for use in preparing national time series on employment, average weekly hours, average hourly earnings, and average weekly earnings.

BLS provides the state agencies with manuals .and supplementary instructions covering all phases of the work including sample selection, editing, and preparation of estimates. BLS also provides the data collection documents. Technical assistance is provided to the state agencies by personal visits of BLS statisticians assigned to each of the Bureau's eight regional offices. These technicians also review the output of each state agency to ensure maintenance of established quality standards.

For the fiscal year ending June 30, 1971, the total cost of the program is approximately 5.0 million dollars, of which 3.5 million represents costs within the states.

The cooperative arrangements are with employment security agencies in 44 states and the District of Columbia, and with labor departments in 6 states.

BLS regards the existing cooperative arrangements as excellent. In fact, the federal-state partnership has functioned so well that new statistical programs are being developed in the same manner.

Additional information regarding the technical aspects of the program may be obtained from the BLS *Handbook of Methods for Surveys and Studies* (Bulletin No. 1458), Chapter 2.

BLS JOB VACANCY-LABOR TURNOVER STATISTICS PROGRAM

The United States Department of Labor's Bureau of Labor Statistics and Manpower Administration have cooperative agreements with agencies in 48 states and the District of Columbia under which the statistical program is operated.

Reports from approximately 50,000 establishments in the manufacturing industries and 20,000 establishments in the nonmanufacturing industries are collected by the state agencies each month. Reports are edited by the state agencies and provide basic data on job vacancies and labor turnover for use in the preparation of estimates. Manufacturing reports are used by the state agencies in the preparation of state and area job vacancy and labor turnover estimates for the Nation as a whole. Nonmanufacturing reports are currently used by the cooperating state agencies to prepare estimates of the number and rate of job vacancies in all nonagricultural industries in 28 selected areas. These areas also collect data on job vacancies by occupation either quarterly or annually.

The BLS provides the state agencies with manuals and, as needed, supplemental instructions covering all phases of the work including sample selection from a universe consisting primarily of quarterly reports filed with the state unemployment insurance agency, editing, and preparation of estimates. The BLS also provide the data collection documents. Technical assistance is provided to the cooperating state agencies by personal visits of BLS statisticians assigned to each of the Bureau's eight regional offices. Regional office personnel also review the output of each state agency to ensure the maintenance of established quality standards.

For the fiscal year ending June 30, 1971, the total cost of the program is approximately 2.5 million dollars, of which 1.9 million represents costs within the states.

BLS regards the existing cooperative arrangements to be eminently satisfactory. It produces a wide range of comparable data with a minimum of duplication through the use of a common collection vehicle and by assuring that all cooperating state agencies adhere to similar procedures and standards.

Additional information regarding the technical aspects of the program are contained in the technical notes in *Employment and Earnings* and the *BLS Handbook of Methods for Surveys and Studies* (Bulletin No. 1458), Chapter 3.

OCCUPATIONAL SAFETY AND HEALTH STATISTICS

As part of the Secretary of Labor's responsibilities under the Occupational Safety and Health Act of 1970, the Bureau of Labor Statistics is initiating a comprehensive safety and health statistics program.

Plans are not yet final, but it is expected that the statistical program will be based on a national sample of 250,000 reports collected semi-annually. A new standard of measurement and reporting is being developed to take into account the much broader definition of work injuries and illnesses included in the legislation. This involves the design of new survey documents and data processing systems. The statistical universe is the entire private economy and other provisions of the act require that the federal government keep similar records of injury experience.

The program will be administered on a federal-state cooperative basis using grants to the states rather than contractual arrangements. This grants program provides greater flexibility for the states. Special grants for state planning and experimentation will provide for federal government funding of 90 percent of the state costs. When the states are able to assume their role of partnership with the Department of Labor, 50 percent of their program cost will be covered by grants. The greater flexibility of the grants approach enables the states, in the statistical area, to supplement the national sample to provide sufficient state detail for their own purposes of compliance and inspection and to conduct research into the causes and costs of work injuries and illnesses.

Technical assistance and training activities as well as the processing of state data will be conducted by the participating states with guidance provided by the BLS Regional Offices.

For FY 1971 the total cost of this program will be approximately $1.5 million, of which $1 million represents grants to states. In the coming fiscal year approximately $4.8 million will be spent as the program becomes fully operational.

Appendix L — The North American Conferences on Labor Statistics

For 20 years, the BLS, in cooperation with the International Association of Governmental Labor Officials, has held a series of conferences on labor statistics. The North American conferences on labor statistics (formerly the Interstate Conference on Labor Statistics) are held annually under the joint sponsorship of the state or provincial labor department hosting the meeting. Participants include administrators and statisticians of federal, state, and provincial labor departments and other agencies, and universities. Essentially, the meeting serves as a medium of exchange and communication of developments in statistical methodology and economic research, involving users as well as producers of statistics. The programs include: (1) subjects of particular interest to labor departments, such as data needed in the administration of labor standards programs; and, (2) economic data such as manpower, prices, budgets, and wages needed by industry, labor, and the public generally in policy decision-making.

The Canadian provinces and federal departments are playing an increasing role in the planning and conduct of the sessions. At the Toronto, Ontario meeting in 1967, which produced the largest attendance ever, it was decided to change the name from Interstate to North American Conference on Labor Statistics. Other sessions in recent years were held at San Francisco, California (1963); Miami Beach, Florida (1964); Storrs, Connecticut (1965); Chicago, Illinois (1966); and Richmond, Virginia (1968); Kiamesha Lake, New York (1969); Houston, Texas (1970); and San Juan, Puerto Rico (1971). There is considerable demand for proceedings of these meetings.

Appendix M – National Conference on Comparative Statistics

The first National Conference on Comparative Statistics was held in Washington, D.C. in February 1966. It gave national recognition to the increasing requirement for comparative statistics and for statistical coordination and standardization, and emphasized the intergovernmental character of many statistical problems.

The Conference, subtitled "Information Needs for Decision Making by State and Local Government," was initiated and sponsored by the National Governors Conference in cooperation with the Council of State Governments. Co-sponsors were the Advisory Commission on Intergovernmental Relations, the U.S. Bureau of the Budget, the U.S. Conference of Mayors, the National Association of Counties, the National League of Cities, and the Municipal Finance Officers Association.

Because of the complexity of this national problem of statistical coordination in government, a special steering committee was established, not only to plan the national meeting, but also to provide recommendations designed to enhance a continuing program of action.

The steering committee urged that each state government establish a statistical coordination and standardization unit to serve as a central clearinghouse for statistical data within the state, to encourage state agencies in improving their statistics, and to assist in developing the recommended standards of statistical classification. It was also recommended that larger cities and counties consider the establishment of statistical coordination units.

Another major recommendation growing out of the steering committee's deliberations expressed the need for a continuing national forum for the development of improved statistical data in functional areas. It was recognized further that a formally constituted National Conference on Comparative Statistics would require staff support and it was therefore recommended that a plan for a permanent secretariat be pursued.

A second conference was held in 1967, but permanent staffing

171

was not established. At present, although central coordination units have been established in individual states and activities are continuing in functional areas, no plans have been made for further national conferences.

Appendix N — **Federal-Aid Highway Planning and Research Program** (Conducted in Cooperation with State Highway Departments)

Beginning with the Hayden-Cartwright Act of 1934, Congress provided that 1.5 percent of the amount of federal-aid funds apportioned for any year to any state might be used for highway planning and research purposes, defined in the current law as "for engineering and economic surveys and investigations, for the planning of future highway programs and the financing thereof, for studies of the economy, safety, and convenience of highway usage and the desirable regulation and equitable taxation thereof, and for research necessary in connection with the planning, design, construction, and maintenance of highways and highway systems, and the regulation and taxation of their use." By 1950 all of the states had begun to participate in comprehensive highway planning surveys and all are continuing to do so.

In this cooperative undertaking, the states set up work programs, make the field surveys, including the collection of statistics needed for program development and evaluation, and summarize and analyze the results. The programs and reports are subject to approval by the FHWA, which assists the states by developing procedures, rendering technical assistance and consolidating data for use in the study of national problems. The states have applied the results of the studies to state problems and the FHWA has applied them to national and regional problems, and to problems common to all or many of the states.

The initial work programs provided for the systematic gathering of certain basic data which had never before been available. The entire network of rural public roads was inventoried, recording data on pavement width and type, information in some detail on all structures, and noting all culture along the highway. Programs were initiated for counting and classifying vehicles and for weighing and measuring trucks to provide data on number, type, size, and weight of the vehicles using the highways. Studies to assess data on service lives of highways, and the total investment in the state highway systems were undertaken. Data were collected on highway income and expenditures. This is but a partial listing of the studies which were undertaken. Some of the information collected is included in the manual *Highway Statistics*.

With the passage of time, there was more extensive and higher level appreciation and utilization of the basic data which had been gathered; data collection was put on a continuing basis, techniques were (and are being) continually improved, and activities were extended to new fields. Research in many aspects of the highway and its appurtenances assumed an increasingly important role in the program. Urban transportation studies evolved from the early, rather crude origin and destination surveys and route studies to today's complex, computerized models.

Beginning with the funds authorized for fiscal year 1964, legislation provides that the 1.5 percent funds shall be available only for planning and research purposes. It also provides for an additional 0.5 percent of the funds provided for federal-aid primary, federal-aid secondary, and federal-aid urban programs apportioned for each fiscal year to be available for planning and research, but without the "use or lose" restriction. Comprehensive, continuing transportation planning in urban areas of 50,000 or more population has also been assured by the 1962 Act through a provision that federal-aid highway funds cannot participate in construction in such areas after July 1, 1965, unless the Secretary of Transportation finds that the projects are based on such planning carried on cooperatively by states and local communities. Federal-aid highway planning funds are contributing heavily to this planning process.

Appendix O — Urban Information Systems Interagency Committee (USAC)

Six cities are currently involved in a major research and development program aimed at improving the ability of cities generally to manage information effectively. These projects are part of an Integrated Municipal Information System (IMIS) program funded by the Department of Housing and Urban Development (HUD) and several other federal agencies. The agencies form the Urban Information Systems Interagency Committee (USAC) chaired by HUD. Other agencies that participate are: the Office of Management and Budget, the Office of Economic Opportunity, and the departments of Transportation; Health, Education, and Welfare; Labor; Commerce; Justice; and Army (Office of Civil Defense).

The IMIS Program is an experiment to learn whether prototype urban information systems can be successfully developed and operated, and then transferred to local jurisdictions elsewhere with a minimum of alteration. Under the IMIS Program, information systems covering all city functions are being developed in Charlotte and Wichita Falls. Each of four other cities is developing subsystems as follows: Dayton, public finance; Long Beach, public safety; Reading, physical and economic development; and St. Paul, human resources development.

Municipalities were selected as the level of government most appropriate for these experimental projects since it is here that most data required for urban program planning and operations are generated.

The systems to be developed by the six municipalities must be operationally based and built upon existing developmental efforts in a national manner as part of a long-term program. Particular attention will be given to data acquisition and data base management, geocoding, protection of confidentiality, and documentation of work. It is estimated that it will take two years to develop and test each of the prototype subsystems, and take three years for each of the integrated systems.

Appendix P — Census Use Study

The Census Use Study, a small-area data research study sponsored by the Bureau of the Census, was established in New Haven, Connecticut, in September 1966 and concluded in July 1969. It was established to explore the current uses of and future needs for small-area data and data handling and display techniques in local,

174

state and federal agencies.

The study had the following objectives:

The development of a system that would allow efficient interrelating of Census Bureau data with other local and state data to meet specific needs.

To investigate the benefits of cooperative data collection between the Census Bureau and other local, state and federal agencies.

To investigate the level of detail and the form in which census data should be made available to local users.

To develop computer programs for use by local communities to allow rapid conversion of census data into information useful for local analysis.

To analyze the results of the study for potential procedures to be incorporated in local community programs to take advantage of census and other information.

To publicize the results so that other areas around the country may benefit from the efforts of the study.

A special census of New Haven, conducted in April 1967 by the Bureau of the Census to test proposed 1970 census procedures, provided a basic source of data. Local agencies also made available certain data from their own records to enable testing of data handling techniques developed by the study.

In response to the established goals of the study, exhaustive research was carried out in the following areas:

Geographic base systems
Record matching
Computer mapping
Special tabulations of data
Special sample surveys of family health and area
    travel patterns
Local data user interests and needs.

The study was supported financially by the following federal agencies: Department of Commerce; Office of Civil Defense of the Department of the Army; Department of Health, Education and Welfare; Department of Housing and Urban Development; and the Department of Transportation.

The city of New Haven provided substantial facility and personnel support, and 30 local agencies cooperated in the study.

The results of the study, including documentation of the computer programs and other procedural guidance, are presented in a series of reports and computer packages. To date, the following titles listed below have resulted from the New Haven project. Further information on these titles can be obtained from the Publications Distribution Section, Bureau of the Census, Washington, D.C. 20233.

1. General Description
2. Computer Mapping
3. Data Tabulation Activities
4. The DIME Geocoding System
5. Data Interests of Local Agencies
6. Family Health Survey
7. Health Information System
8. Data Uses in Health Planning
9. Data Uses in Urban Planning
10. Data Uses in School Administration
11. Area Travel Survey
12. Health Information System II

Computer Program Packages

ADMATCH: An address matching system
DIME: A geographic base file system
GRIDS: A computer mapping system

In July 1969, the Southern California Regional Information Study (SCRIS) was established in Los Angeles, California. The study is jointly sponsored by the Bureau of the Census and the Southern California Association of Governments, an association of local and county governments in the Los Angeles area. SCRIS, of which the Census Use Study forms the Bureau's contingent, will attempt to transfer experience gained in New Haven to a larger

176

urban area, with a view to assisting census data users in all large urban areas in preparing for and using 1970 census data as it becomes available.

Appendix Q — Intergovernmental Seminar Program on Federal Statistics for State and Local Government Use

The Bureau of the Census established, in 1966, an Intergovernmental Seminar Program for state and local government officials. This action was taken in response to the recommendations of the 1965 National Governors' Conference and the 1966 National Conference on Comparative Statistics. As a major part of the program, the Bureau of the Census, in consultation with the Statistical Policy and Management Information Systems Division (SPMISD) of the Office of Management and Budget, developed a series of five day seminars on federal statistics for state and local government use.

These seminars focus on the kinds of statistical information and services available from the Census Bureau and other federal agencies, with emphasis on the types of state and small-area data that are of particular interest to those attending and that can be utilized by the states and local governments in their own programs. Information on current programs, plans for future programs, and some of the problems involved in the development of such plans are presented to seminar participants by representatives not only of the Census Bureau and SPMISD but also of other federal agencies.

The seminars also provide a marketplace for the exchange of ideas and for the discussion of problems and needs by the producers and users of statistical data. Ideas developed here are expected to be helpful in influencing the development of future statistical programs at all levels of the government. Seminar participants have the opportunity to meet with federal representatives individually on specific problems and to make valuable contacts with their counterparts in other similar areas. Many of them subsequently contact the Census Bureau for current information on state and small-area data. Moreover, comments made by participants during seminar discussions serve to stimulate improvements

177

in available services, in working relationships with federal agencies, and in statistical coordination among intergovernmental units.

Attendance at these seminars is by invitation to state, county, and city governmental units; regional, county and city planning agencies; and university research centers. Participants are not necessarily statisticians — many of them are planners, budget and data processing officers, economists, and administrators. The federal government assumes the cost of conducting the program and charges no fees for the seminars. Travel and subsistence costs are met by the participants or their organizations.

To date, 13 seminars have been held with a total of 332 participants representing 224 organizations: 94 participants from 47 state governments; 131 from 94 cities; 25 from 20 counties; 65 from 49 planning agencies; 13 from 10 university research members; and 4 from 4 other types of organizations.

The seminar program is planned as a long-range effort to bring participants up to date on new programs and developments. Invitations will continue to be extended to organizations which have not previously participated in the program, as well as to state and local governmental units which have been represented at earlier seminars.

Appendix R — The Federal Information Processing Standards Program of the National Bureau of Standards (NBS)

In the fall of 1965 the Secretary of Commerce established the NBS Center for Computer Sciences and Technology to carry out the Secretary's responsibilities under the Brooks Bill (Public Law 80-306, passed October 30, 1965). The Center provides leadership and coordination for government efforts in the development of voluntary commercial information processing standards, develops recommendations for federal information processing standards, performs required research and analysis, and provides scientific and technical support and consultative assistance in the field of computers and information processing to federal agencies.

Soon after the NBS Center for Computer Sciences and Technology was formed in 1965 and given the responsibility for federal standardization in this area, the Bureau of the Budget provided policy direction by stating that NBS would participate in the development of national voluntary standards to the extent that such activities were beneficial to the federal government. Also, NBS was given the responsibility of monitoring the participation of government representatives on the American National Standards Institute (ANSI) standardization groups to ensure that the interests of the entire federal establishment were present and protected in the field of information processing. The NBS Office of Information Processing Standards was established within the Center to handle this task.

The development and implementation of standards to meet federal requirements should, to the extent practicable, be consistent with corresponding national standards that are developed and approved by standards-making bodies such as ANSI, and international recommendations approved by the International Organization for Standardization (ISO).

Specifically, federal information processing systems must be compatible not only with each other, but also with those of state and local governments, the private sector of the economy, and those of other nations.

To further this objective, representatives of the NBS Center for Computer Sciences and Technology, along with representatives of other government agencies, actively participate in work of ANSI standardization committees. Much of this work is accomplished in ANSI Committee X3, Computers and Information Processing.

NATIONAL ASSOCIATION FOR STATE INFORMATION SYSTEMS (NASIS)

In March 1969, the Committee on Information Systems of the Council of State Governments met in Washington, D.C., and established a permanent organization of the states to provide for improved management of information systems. Prior to this meeting, the Committee on Information Systems had undertaken several major projects: the development of a model contract for the lease of ADP systems; the development of policy for state information systems; the sponsorship of two major reports on data processing in the individual states; participation in the Intergovernmental Task Force on Information Systems, and the sponsorship of a highly successful national conference of executives and legislative personnel interested in information systems.

In view of the Committee's successful accomplishments, a recommendation was made to the Council of State Governments that the Committee's functions be transferred to a larger body. Upon approval, the Committee was redesignated as the National Association for State Information Systems (NASIS), and became an affiliate of the Council of State Governments.

The National Bureau of Standards, in promulgating Federal Information Processing Standards, has established contacts with the 50 states through the NASIS. Copies of proposed and approved federal standards are provided to the state coordinators of the NASIS. The state coordinators may comment on the applicability of these standards within their state and local government, and these comments are considered before standards are approved for federal use. Also, the NASIS provides a liaison member to the Federal Information Processing Standards Coordinating and Advisory Committee.

As of January 1971, the following standards had been published or were under development:

Published FIPS PUBS

> CALENDAR DATA (FIPS 4)
> STATES OF U.S. (FIPS 5-1)
> COUNTIES OF THE U.S. (FIPS 6-1)
> METROPOLITAN STATISTICAL AREAS (FIPS 8)
> CONGRESSIONAL DISTRICTS (FIPS 9)
> COUNTRIES (FIPS 10)

In Coordination

> IDENTIFICATION OF INDIVIDUALS (Office of Management and Budget)
> GOVERNMENT AGENCY CODES

Under Development

> PLACE CODES (General Services Administration)
> TIME (National Bureau of Standards)
> TIME ZONES (National Bureau of Standards)
> NATIONAL DRUG CODES (Health, Education and Welfare)

HANDBOOK FOR DATA STANDARDIZATION (Office of
Management and Budget)
IDENTIFICATION OF ORGANIZATION (Internal Revenue)
SUBDIVISIONS OF COUNTRIES (State)
TELECOMMUNICATIONS (National Communications
System)
CIVILIAN PERSONNEL (Civil Service Commission)

A catalog of classifications and standard nomenclature systems
in detailed areas is also being planned.

Appendix S — **American Statistical Association Committee on Small Area Statistics**

On April 4, 1931, Professor William F. Ogburn, President of
the American Statistical Association, announced the creation of an
ASA Committee on Census Enumeration Areas. A primary charge
of the Committee was to develop the concept and use of census
tracts, as expressed in the keynote of its 1932 meeting, "To promote the development of the use of census tract data through the
exchange of the ideas and experiences of those persons promoting
the use of census tract cities."[1] Howard Whipple Green was appointed its first chairman. The highly successful movement to
develop census tracts is without question due to the energy of the
Committee and Chairman Green, the efforts of the Census Bureau
staff, and the resulting momentum generated in the work of hundreds of census tract key persons and now thousands of local
census tract committee members and other users of census tract
data. From only 18 tracted cities in 1930, the tracted area has
grown to include all standard metropolitan statistical areas and
over one hundred non-metropolitan tracted areas in 1970.

The emphasis was on census tracts and their uses almost exclusively for three decades. Many excellent papers at the annual
meetings of the ASA developed the various local and national uses
made of tract data in problems relating to health, welfare, housing,

---

1 The Census tract are small, relatively permanent areas into which large cities
and adjacent areas are divided for the purposes of providing comparable small
area statistics. Their use for planning in place of volatile political areas such as
wards was advocated as early as 1910.

city planning, utilities, churches, schools, merchandizing, mail advertising, and many other fields.

For a brief time in the early 1960's, the Committee's name was simply, "ASA Census Tract Committee." In recent years, the Committee's horizon has greatly widened in response to the escalation of the need for small area data and analysis. To reflect this wider view, in 1967 the Committee's name was changed to the "ASA Committee on Small Area Statistics," and its charge was correspondingly widened. "The ASA Committee on Small Area Statistics is concerned with the supply of statistics from federal, state and local sources for cities and counties and for areas within them, such as census tracts and other divisions; the establishment and development of statistical areas to serve analytical uses; the techniques by which data from various sources may be effectively brought together and made readily available; establishing the needs for such data and promoting their use; and with developing standards for the assembly and presentation of such statistics."

In carrying out this wider charge, the annual conferences of the Committee in recent years have sought to focus public and professional attention on numerous new developments in small area statistics — for example, local data banks and information systems, rapid retrieval computer packages, computer graphics, and federal grant opportunities for local data systems.

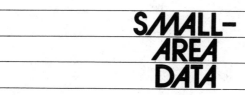

SMALL-AREA DATA

Part B

448-559 O - 71 - 13

Report on Intrastate Statistical Coordination

By
Herbert Alfasso

TABLE OF CONTENTS

185

INTRODUCTION

Decision-making in our federal system requires a supporting statistical base which accurately reflects conditions in each area and can be aggregated to produce comparable state totals and possibly national summations. As in other fields of human behavior, this objective has been widely acknowledged but rarely accomplished.

Several facts have served to increase the President's Commission's interest in this subject:

- Despite efforts by all federal administrations during the 1960's to improve federal-state relations in statistics, progress has been disappointingly slow.
- There is increased awareness at federal and local government levels that data on subnational areas — regions, states, counties, cities and even small areas within cities — are increasingly important as units of government assume greater

responsibilities for dealing with the nation's social and economic problems.

OBJECTIVES

The specific objective of this report to the Commission is to analyze and evaluate intrastate statistical coordination activities, with special attention paid to those which affect and/or are affected by federal statistical activities.

BACKGROUND

Federal Interest in Intrastate Statistical Coordination

There is a case for federal promotion of intrastate statistical coordination. All practices of coordinating agencies to rationalize and make more effective use of data through *joint* production are embraced within the concept "statistical coordination." The major areas in which an intrastate coordination program in each state would facilitate the efforts of individual federal agencies and the federal government as a whole are cited below:

1. Large and increasing amounts of money transferred from federal to state and local governments require considerable local area data for operational purposes. In fiscal year 1971, over $25 billion was transferred from the federal government to state and local governments as grants-in-aid.
2. Nearly every federal program has to be justified to members of Congress in terms of impact on the local constituencies they represent. Consequently, uniform measurements of the local impact of each program are a requirement in furnishing information to Congress.
3. The logistics of federal program operations alone require considerable local data. Ninety percent of federal employees are based away from Washington, D.C. Cost-benefit analyses of their activities call for comprehensive uniform state-local data.
4. It can be argued that where a single office in each state is responsible for establishing statistical standards, there is greater likelihood for development of interstate compara-

bility of statistical series. The prospect of achieving inter-state comparability of statistics in the recent past was generally considered a major benefit to be achieved by creating state statistical coordination offices.

5. A good deal of data which can be used by federal departments is accumulated as a by-product of state operations. However, these statistics often become available only under the impetus and guidance of a state statistical coordination office.

6. A state statistical coordination office can help expedite certain federal statistical programs, especially for those federal agencies which have no direct state counterpart.

Areas of Federal-State Coordination

Many critical areas where comparative statistics are required at national and local levels are currently effectively served through federal-state cooperative efforts, through the surveys and censuses conducted by the Census Bureau or other federal statistical agencies, or by local governments using standards established at the federal level.

1. *Programs run entirely by the federal government.* These include censuses and annual surveys. In addition there are statistics which emanate as by-products of essentially non-statistical federally-operated programs, such as internal revenue collection and social security.

2. *Programs administered by the state which are financed wholly or in part by the federal government.* These are the sources of data on agriculture, labor, certain highway programs, vital statistics, and welfare.

3. *Programs administered by the state or local government, with federal interest expressed mainly through technical assistance.* These include the State/Federal Information Exchange System (S/FIXS) of the U.S. Office of Economic Opportunity, and the State-Census Bureau County Population Estimation Program. There are also demonstration projects initiated at the federal level which are designed to develop computerized information systems. The current

development of such information systems is interesting and will be discussed more fully later in this report.

Recent Efforts to Improve Federal-State Relations and Intrastate Coordination

In February 1966, at the recommendation of the Executive Committee of the National Governor's Conference, the First National Conference on Comparative Statistics was held in Washington, D.C. It was a well-attended affair sponsored jointly by a host of organizations representing governors, mayors, cities, city managers and states, and organized by the Council of State Governments. One of the recommendations — and probably the most significant — was that each state develop an agency to coordinate statistical activities within the state and to serve as a channel to the federal government and to other states.

At that time, only a handful of states, including New York and California, had statistical coordination programs.

Although agreement for holding a National Conference on Comparative Statistics on an annual basis was universal, there were some problems in deciding which organization should bear responsibility for "guiding" the efforts. There was much feeling that the Advisory Commission on Intergovernmental Relations (ACIR) would be the most appropriate agency, but it declined. The Office of Statistical Standards (OSS), U. S. Bureau of the Budget, agreed to undertake this function but it was reluctant at that time to have the federal government assume leadership. The final agreement was that OSS would serve as secretariat, by organizing the annual conferences and generally providing the staff work, but the policy-making would evolve from the newly created National Conference on Comparative Statistics comprised of state and local officials.[1]

As a result of the 1968 Conference, efforts within states to establish statistical coordination offices increased. By the time the Second National Conference on Comparative Statistics was held in

1 The unwillingness to have federal leadership or even the appearance of it at the time, in this writer's opinion, has contibuted significantly to the lack of progress experienced in this field. The avoidance of federal "control" is largely forgotten now, but it probably had a detrimental effect on the effort to establish state statistical coordination units because there was no continuing pressure to initiate action while enthusiasm for intrastate coordination was still intense.

April 1968, more states had established such offices.

According to information furnished to the National Governor's Conference in August 1967, 27 states had established or were in the process of establishing state statistical coordination functions. But a survey conducted by OSS in 1968, just after the Second National Conference, showed that only 13 of these offices were in actual operation, four were still being organized and "ten had not replied." (Based on the surveys made in both 1968 and 1971, the number of functioning statistical coordination offices — frequently reported at 30 — appears to have been highly exaggerated.)

At the Second National Conference, the program included sessions on both "successes and problems of newly formed state statistical coordinating offices" and "some federal actions since the First Conference." The latter included mention of the Census Bureau Seminars for State and Local Government Officials (these one-week seminars, started shortly after the First National Conference, proved highly successful and have been continued); the OEO Federal-State Information Exchange System; the Census-State Cooperative Program for Developing County Population Estimates; and "some new services from the Bureau of Labor Statistics."

The writer would be remiss if he failed to mention the special role played by the Census Bureau in making a conscientious effort to carry out the recommendations made at the First National Conference on Comparative Statistics (and later reinforced by the Intergovernmental Cooperative Act of 1968). The recommendations pertaining to federal agencies included: (1) exploring the needs for consistent and comparable statistics at the state and local level, (2) fostering intergovernmental coordination to meet these needs, and (3) communicating statistical information useful for planning and evaluating many of the federal-state-local programs. The list of Census Bureau activities along this line is too long to repeat here, but it includes many other services in addition to its seminars, publications acquainting users with statistical information and services available from the federal government, and the Census-State Cooperative Program for Local Population Estimates.

Of equal importance, is the Bureau's helpful attitude toward state and local governments which encourages such officials to look to the Bureau first for many kinds of assistance including speakers for state programs, technical advice in carrying out surveys and general guidance on almost any problem in the statistical area.

The Census Bureau, of course, is unique in that it is the prime source for a broad variety of statistics, but nevertheless should be credited with carrying out the spirit of the suggestions made by the National Conference on Comparative Statistics. Unfortunately, the Census Bureau does not have the authority or the mandate to bring the entire federal statistical establishment together to foster improved federal-local relations.

INTRASTATE COORDINATION IN
ALL STATES — SUMMARY OF SURVEY

Introduction

To obtain data for this report, a mail survey of all states was conducted employing a questionnaire[2] to determine (a) whether a formal intrastate coordination function exists, (b) how and when it was established, (c) how it operates, and (d) its activities. For states with no current coordination activity, a question was asked as to whether plans exist for establishing formal procedures in the near future, and when such plans could be expected to be implemented.

This survey also constituted a followup to one conducted by the U. S. Office of Statistical Policy in 1968, after the Second National Conference on Comparative Statistics.

Among the findings of the 1968 survey were:[3]

- Of the 40 states which responded, some 13 had state statistical coordination functions in operation.
- Most state statistical coordination offices were new; only

---

2 Appendix includes sample letter sent to all states, questionnaire, and tables of responses to questionnaire.

3 This information was obtained from Roye L. Lowry, U. S. Office of Statistical Policy, who conducted the 1968 survey and who at that time was secretary of the National Conference on Comparative Statistics.

five were in operation prior to 1966.

- Most state statistical coordination offices were attached to planning or budget agencies. Two states relied solely upon interagency committees, two assigned the function to departments of commerce or economic development, and one associated it with data processing.
- Most statistical coordination efforts were authorized by a governor's executive order or by some form of administrative action. Five, however, had legislative authorization. The authority for statistical coordinating/standardizing ranged from "the most general to the highly specific."
- About two-thirds of the states which had statistical coordinating activities provided specific budgetary support.
- Most of the statistical coordination offices had some operating statistical responsibility. Half were responsible for producing a statistical abstract, half were responsible for producing an inventory of all state statistical reports, and some were responsible for producing certain financial or demographic information. Slightly under half had responsibilities for serving as a "clearinghouse" for statistics.
- Over half of the activities were related to efforts to develop state information systems.
- Four states related their statistical coordination/standardization activities to federal aid program reporting.
- Three states were able to use some federal aid money in developing their statistical coordination/standardization activity.
- Four states reported that their offices played a role in establishing professional qualifications for statisticians, or in developing training programs, to raise the professional qualifications of statistical employees in state agencies.

Summary of Results of the 1971 Survey

(Note: See Table of Responses in the Appendix. The 1971 survey is not directly comparable with the 1968 survey because in neither survey was there a 100 percent response, and the states responding were not the same.)

1. Thirty-seven states (including New York) responded to the

survey. Of these about 16 had some formal intrastate statistical coordination function. (The exact number having formal intrastate coordination functions is approximate because of definitional problems. At least one state considered OEO's S/FIX System a "formal" statistical coordination function (which it is not) and one or two states indicated that there was no such formal function, although descriptions of their activities indicated the contrary.)

2. Eleven of the 16 states were also engaged in setting standards for either municipal codes or statistical standards.

3. In addition to the 16 states with existing offices in May 1971, ten are planned for the future. The time-table of establishment is as follows:

Year	Number of States	
Before 1966	4	
1966–1968	5	
1969–1970	7	
Subtotal — offices existing in May, 1971		16
June–December, 1971	1	
1972–1973	4	
After 1973	2	
Date uncertain	3	
Subtotal — potential future offices		10
Total Offices — in operation or being planned		26

Thus, 26 of the 37 states responding to this survey have organized (or are planning to create) formal state coordinating functions. Three of the states said they are *currently in the process* of creating such an activity; others have plans for as late as 1974-75.

4. Most of the offices were established by either Governor's executive order or administrative action. Only four have some authority derived from legislation; and two of these four had their start through some sort of executive action.

5. Fourteen states operate through a permanent staff. Two operate solely through committees (a permanent committee

in California, and an ad hoc committee in New Jersey); Massachusetts operates through a "permanent" consultant group paid by HUD funds.

6. Eight states having offices with permanent staffs are attached to the state planning agency, another five are located in the state budget or fiscal office. The trend, however, appears to be to attach statistical coordinating offices to the planning agency. The placement of an office does not seem to be associated with state size or geography. Since location of the statistical coordination office within a state structure may be critical, this is an area for additional study. Materials reviewed for this study and discussions held with state officials indicate that there was, in some states, a good deal of concern over the very important location factor.

7. Most states operate the statistical coordination function with very few people. By far the largest is the State of Washington with ten professionals;[4] all the others have the equivalent of between one and four full-time professionals working on statistical coordination. (Iowa's office while existing is still unstaffed.)

In general the total number of *professionals* associated with statistical coordination *and* other related functions is not much greater than for the statistical coordination function alone. (There are some outstanding exceptions, however.) Although reliability of some of these figures may be questionable because of the definitional difficulties confronted by those completing the questionnaires, the trend is unmis-

---

4 It was learned by a telephone conversation, with the person heading the statistical coordination funcion, that the State of Washington has a very powerful role in the statistical operations of the State through control over the statistical outputs of state departments. For example, the staff has responsibility and authority to review such key statistics as school enrollment projections and revenue estimates. It has direct responsibility for the annual statewide population censuses which are the basis for the state's revenue sharing program. Further, it performs special statistical analyses in a number of functional areas for the head of the agency (Budget) and the Governor. Initiated in 1969, this office appears to be the most solidly founded of all such offices the writer is familiar with. In addition to its intrastate activities, the office also keeps abreast of all relevant Federal statistical activities as well as those in other states. It maintains liaison with federal statistical agencies only on an "as needed" basis.

takable —intrastate coordination is carried out with very small staffs and apparently is an "inexpensive" operation.

8. Ten major functions were reported to have been assigned to offices of this type:

   a. *Clearing questionnaires.*

   Only three of the 16 states said they reviewed and cleared questionnaires; two more said they either do it "on occasion" or "it is under consideration."

   b. *Publishing statistical or statistics-related materials.*

   Nearly all states issued publications as part of the intrastate coordination activity. The most popular publication is a state statistical abstract (10 states) with a newsletter or "statistical reporter" being a close second (8 states). Four states publish inventories of statistical series or statistical publications, and a few publish assorted other publications, including statistical guidelines, an economic report and "special" reports.

   c. *Coordinating EDP.*

   No state indicated that it combines EDP coordination with statistical coordination. Where coordinating computers is accomplished (as in New York and Washington), that function is carried out by another unit.

   d. *Developing management information systems.*

   This survey did not cover the question of whether statistical coordination is associated with management information systems, even though wording in one question used the term "management information systems." However, comments added to some questionnaires indicated that statistical coordination is frequently associated with developing state information systems.

   e. *Preparing population estimates.*

   At least ten states prepare population estimates as part of the statistical coordination function.

   f. *Issuing or promulgating standards.*

   Eleven states issue standards for municipal codes, including four which also issue statistical standards. Another three states issue statistical standards but not standards for municipal codes. (Although "statistical standards" was not defined on the questionnaire, based on other information, such standards typically include guidelines for conducting surveys and standards for presenting statistical materials.)

g. *Reviewing statistical budgets.*

Only three of the 16 states review statistical budgets. Surprisingly, one of these offices (Utah) is apparently *not located* in the State's budget agency (the other two are).

h. *Maintaining federal liaison.*

Despite the fact that one of the reasons given at the First National Conference on Comparative Statistics for creation of a central state statistical agency was to improve federal-state relations, four of the 16 states indicated that this was not part of their coordinating activity; another response was "only partially." But two of these four states are California and New Jersey, which operate solely through committees, and do not have the permanent staff necessary for this activity.

i. *Helping to secure federal data for state use.*

Eleven of the 16 states do some kind of "lobbying" or cooperative work with the federal government. But it appears as if much of it is for the summary tapes from the 1970 Census, and in one case it is done only through the Federal Statistics Users' Conference.

j. *Providing services to local governments and to non-governmental organizations.*

Only eight of the 16 states indicated they did any work with local governments or non-governmental organizations. Both "local governments" and "non-governmental organizations" were combined in one question. Judging from the comments elicited by this question, very few states have strong ties to local governments. Except for

197

Georgia and Hawaii, where there was a definite indication that the state central coordinating office works closely with local governments, the other states answering "yes" to this question appear to deal only minimally with local governments (answering occasional inquiries, distributing publications, etc.).

k. *Performing of other functions.*

Other functions performed by statistical coordinating offices include:

- doing socio-economic research
- developing an A-95/A-98 (Federal circulars) clearing house
- performing EDP systems work
- reviewing legislation for the Budget Director
- performing activity called "reports management"

In some cases, the functions listed above were cited as the major activity of the intrastate statistical coordination office.

9. **Summary**: As elicited by questionnaire responses, the most popular functions performed by intrastate coordinating offices are:

-- *Issuing publications* (statistical abstracts, newsletters)
-- *Maintaining federal liaison* for general informational purposes and to obtain federal data for state use (in many states, this seems to be limited to securing 1970 census tapes rather than the broad spectrum of other data which could be used by the state)
-- *Promulgating standards* — especially for municipal codes. This would imply that fostering computerized data systems is often related to the intrastate coordination function.

Conclusions Resulting from the Survey

The purpose of the survey was to provide some indication of the state of development of statistical coordination among states. The responses indicated that, since 1968, there has been "progress" in terms of *numbers* of states instituting formal state statistical coordinating activities. And more such progress can be expected in the future. But the writer cannot help being impressed at the small staffs involved, and the apparent subordination of "statistical coordination" to other functions, such as making population projections or establishing a census summary tape center. Although it has been demonstrated that such operational functions can strengthen the office and should be included with the intrastate coordination function, it appears that few states are (or can because of small staff sizes) perform in many of those areas which would benefit the federal government (as cited in the Background section of this report).

California and New Jersey, with their committees, both seem to be operating at a low ebb. The writer is familiar with the strong interest by certain individuals in New Jersey to create statistical standardization for codes of various types. But according to the reply received in this survey, after the Interdepartmental Statistical Standardization Committee promulgated a standardized identification code for counties and municipalities for the State in 1968, "A steering committee has met intermittently to deal with specific problems of interdepartmental coordination and jurisdictional questions, but very little formal work has been done." It does appear that permanent staff may be added – one position in 1971-72 – "for establishing standards for guiding all State agencies engaged in collecting and publishing statistical data or interpretive materials."

While many of the intrastate coordination offices show considerable vitality, few have substantial relations with the federal government other than the Census Bureau. On the other hand, involvement of the U. S. Office of Statistical Policy has been minimal since the Second National Conference on Comparative Statistics in 1968.

The other major federal statistical agencies which work with states tend to deal with their state agency counterparts directly, thus by-passing the central state statistical office. An exception is the U. S. Office of Economic Opportunity, which has instituted its S/FIX System in several states, usually in a central staff agency. However, this function is not inherently associated with the central state statistical coordination function: a number of states have

199

created federal-state "clearinghouse" to which the S/FIX System could logically be attached.

In summary, intrastate coordination is growing, but it is growing slowly and haphazardly. Without federal guidance, there appears to be little chance that intrastate coordination offices will either make estimates for small geographic levels or help accumulate data as a by-product of state operations. Even the benefit of having a single state statistical contact point which represents the entire state government may not be assured unless these offices are recognized, dealt with and helped by the federal agency in the best position to accomplish this.

DESCRIPTION OF INTRASTATE COORDINATION IN THREE STATES

The states selected for in-depth analysis were those which met the following criteria:

a. had been operating a statistical coordination program for several years,
b. were different from each other in the manner in which they functioned, and in their activities, and
c. were considered to have generally successful operations, and, as a practical matter, could be dealt with within the relatively short period of time available for doing this paper.

The three states ultimately selected were those which met the above criteria and with which the writer had had some prior familiarity — New York (in which he heads the statistical coordination function); California (which operates solely through a committee); and South Carolina (a "small" state in which the head of statistical coordination is also responsible directly for other functions).

The following observations are based on the intrastate statistical coordination activities of these three states.

a) Although each state operates intrastate coordination differently, and each has had some important successes, all currently have serious "problems":

- New York is encountering a fiscal crisis which may strongly affect the role and organization of intrastate statistical coordination.

- California's committee has no staff and currently views its role more narrowly than the other states (and than it apparently did in the past), thereby, "providing limited coordination efforts."[5]

- South Carolina's agencies generally lack well-staffed research-statistical units, thereby forcing the head of the statistical coordination office to focus on developing statistical proficiency within state agencies.

b) None of the states has any significant state-local statistical relationships.

c) While South Carolina's activities are growing and New York's are changing, California's appear to be static.

d) South Carolina and New York have much stronger state-federal ties than does California where cooperative efforts with federal agencies are conducted by individual departments. Furthermore, because South Carolina is considerably smaller than New York and California, more of its statistical activities are centralized. Consequently, the lack of standard federal policy with regard to federal requests for state statistics becomes more apparent in the smaller state. Of the three, South Carolina exhibits the greatest desire for federal guidance, although New York has frequently voiced its support for a more active federal role.

e) Computerized data systems are being developed in all three states.

The elements for establishing and operating an effective state statistical coordination office include:

a) Permanent professional staff and top level support within the state.

b) Competent leadership, particularly during the formative years. (It could be argued that any new function requires high level support and competent leadership. However, it must be emphasized that an activity which is "line" in nature, such as administering a tax collection system, either

---

5　Responses to letter and questionnaire from Mr. W. L. Parker, (then) Chairman of State Interdepartmental Research Coordinating Committee of California.

does not require or automatically gets the highest level of support. On the other hand, a staff function such as statistical coordination lacks the "essential service" quality and, being more vague and discretionary in nature, must have top level support and leadership to survive.)

c) Operation of related activities which support the coordination function, such as compiling a statistical abstract, preparing population estimates and forecasts, or reviewing agency statistical budgets.

For improved federal-state relations and the strengthening of intrastate coordination, the following federal activities or policies would be desirable:

a) Continuing contact with central state statistical coordination agencies to provide national direction. Governor West of South Carolina expressed this point well when he wrote, "Within a state comparability of information and data can only be secured by a central coordinating agency. Yet, there exists a need for coordination and uniformity among the states, which requires national direction."

b) Establishing a uniform federal policy on standards for state reporting. The fact that different federal agencies may require different sources for the same types of statistics (e.g., income) places unnecessary burdens on the intrastate coordination agencies.

c) Organizing regular meetings of state statistical coordinators to facilitate sharing of experiences. Considering the poor fiscal condition of many states and the precarious nature of many state statistical coordination offices, payment for expenses by the federal government (as is done for persons serving on federal advisory committees) would ensure the highest degree of participation.

d) The federal government should attempt to secure continuing support and involvement by ACIR, the Council of State Governments, the National Governor's Conference and other such organizations in development and improvement of state statistical coordinating agencies.

e) Federal requests for information or suggestions on federal statistical policies (not involving a specific federal-state program) should be sent to (or through) the central state statistical coordination office. This policy is being pursued at present by the U. S. Office of Statistical Policy (such as for SMSA definitions) and, to a lesser extent, by the U. S. Bureau of the Census. There are probably other agencies which might pursue this practice since so many statistical policies cut across agency lines.

f) The federal government should take the lead in helping states establish uniformity of statistics by making technical assistance available to statistical coordinating offices. The point is that federal agencies should be encouraged to help states in using sound techniques in new areas, as is being done in the Census-State-County Population Estimation program.

RECOMMENDATIONS

1. The federal government should play a leading role in encouraging and promoting intrastate statistical coordination by helping create such functions where they do not now exist, and by providing recognition, technical guidance, and other assistance for improving intrastate coordination activities where such functions do exist.[6]

2. The data needs of state governments should be given greater recognition than at present. This is consistent with current national policy to delegate many of the nation's problems to the state/local level. Meeting state data needs might require some adjustment of priorities of data production at the federal level.

3. Federal support of intrastate coordination should include the following activities:

    a. Maintain contact with state statistical agencies to provide information both on "what other states are doing," and on the status of federal activities and policies.

---

6 The Office of Statistical Policy has the authority to: (a) coordinate the many existing federal-state-local statistical cooperative efforts; (b) encourage increased federal-state cooperative efforts; and (c) develop a federal statistical policy with regard to local areas. Such a policy should help standardize information requested by federal agencies from local governments.

b. Organize regular meetings of state statistical coordinators to facilitate sharing of experiences and to obtain feedback from states on what the federal government might do to improve federal-state relations.

c. Secure continuing support of the Advisory Commission on Intergovernmental Relations, the Council of State Governments, the National Governor's Conference and other public and private organizations directly involved in current problems.

d. Send federal requests to states for information (not involving a specific federal-state program) to (or through) the central statistical coordination office.

e. Establish a training program on a 50-50 federal-state cost basis, to help states with weak research/statistical capabilities, as, has been done by the National Institutes of Health in training biostatisticians in the public health field. Of course budgetary limitations, and the costs and benefits of this form of training as opposed to other training programs, merit further attention.

4. In helping to establish or improve intrastate coordination activities, the federal government should be guided by the following considerations:

a. Intrastate coordination activities should include permanent staffs with the highest caliber leadership available, since quality of both staff and leadership are critical. The role of intrastate committees of directors of research and/or statistics should be limited to advice.

b. Intrastate coordination offices should be encouraged to conduct *related operational activities,* such as publication of a statistical abstract, preparation of population estimates and projections, and development of a central state data system.

c. While there is no single "best" agency to which the intrastate coordination function should be attached in all states, it should be located in a central staff agency, or, perhaps, the legislature. Since the "location factor" is crucial to the ultimate effectiveness of the intrastate coordination function, guidance should be offered to states on an individual basis as needed (or desired).

d. Central state coordinating agencies should be encouraged to foster access to information developed as by-products of on-going operations in state agencies generally. These statistics, which are useful immediately for *intrastate* purposes, should eventually be standardized, with federal guidance, for *interstate* comparisons where desirable and feasible.

CONCLUSION

Many of the suggestions made for improving federal-state relations include federal leadership or guidance of one type or another. While such leadership was not sought at the First National Conference on Comparative Statistics in 1966 (when the prevailing mood seemed to be for *interstate coordination without federal leadership*) this is not the case today. It is the writer's conviction, based on personal experience and discussion with federal and state officials, that statistical coordination among 50 states without federal leadership cannot be achieved. Statistical information is much too complex to be achieved by voluntary agreement between 50 independent jurisdictions. Furthermore, the federal establishment has the expertise for assuming leadership.

Earlier in this report, serious problems which currently exist in the three states were highlighted. Although these states are among the most successful in implementing intrastate coordination, it is quite possible that, within a short period of time, coordination activities might be eliminated or greatly reduced in all three. Among the reasons for the vulnerability of these activities are:

a) Computerized information systems may supplant the central statistical office. This substitution may result because of confusion by state policy-makers between ready accessibility to information and quality of information. Albert Mindlin, in a paper presented to the Intergovernmental Seminar on Federal Statistics for Local Government Use, October 1970, stated, "Professional statisticians, operating out of a central statistical office, can provide a sophistication to the

205

management and improvement of our urban environment simply not possible without such skills." Mr. Mindlin was suggesting a merger of computerization of data and quality control since he realizes, as do most federal statistical agencies, that the value of statistics depends not only on their timeliness (through development of statistical computerized data systems) but also on their quality (available only through professional statistical know-how).

b) Fragmentation of statistical policies by federal agencies. If reporting requirements of federal agencies for federal-state programs continue to differ, it will seriously weaken intrastate coordination efforts. Lack of federal coordination is evident in such projects as OEO's FIXS, which has no apparent ties with the work of the older Governments Division in the Bureau of the Census.

c) Lack of recognition by the federal government of state coordination agencies. If the federal government fails to recognize the existence and importance of state statistical offices, there is a strong likelihood that top state officials will not recognize their importance.

A final word on placement of a central statistical office within a state bureaucracy. In New York and South Carolina the units are located in the "budget office"; in California, in a committee reporting to the Governor. Obviously, because of its nature, it belongs in a central staff agency, but the value of locating it in a planning versus a budget agency cannot be determined from the study of these three states. At the present time, it appears that the best location for a central statistical office will differ from state to state.

The main problem of locating a central statistical office in a budget agency is that it will probably have little relevance to the functions of the rest of the agency and thus be quite vulnerable to forces of change. The main benefit is the possible "clout" gained from influence over the resources of state statistical offices. The advantage of locating the central statistical office in a planning agency is that its functions generally mesh well with the overall mission of such an agency. If, as is being done in some states,

206

planning and budgeting are combined, there may be little difficulty in determining the agency to which the function should be attached.

In some states, a case can be made for locating the central statistical office in the legislature. In all cases, strong relationships with legislative staffs will increase effectiveness.

APPENDIX

Appendix consists of:

1. Sample letter sent to all states.
2. Questionnaire sent to all states.
3. Table of responses to questionnaires regarding State Statistical Coordinating Activities.

April 16, 1971

The Honorable William A. Egan
Governor of Alaska
State Capitol
Juneau, Alaska 99801

Dear Governor Egan:

In August 1970, the President established a Commission of distinguished citizens to study the operations of the federal statistical system. The Commission, whose members represent a broad spectrum of nongovernment interests, has been requested to investigate the efficiency with which the federal statistical system operates and its responsiveness to public and private users.

The Commission is particularly interested in current federal-state cooperative efforts and in the manner in which they mesh with intrastate coordination activities. As you may know, acting on the recommendations made at the Second National Conference on Comparative Statistics, the Office of Statistical Policy in the U. S. Office of Management and Budget conducted a survey of state coordination activities in 1968. The enclosed questionnaire has been designed to update and supplement the information developed at that time. Your answers will provide the basis for recommendations regarding measures the federal government might take to promote coordination activities at all levels of government.

Since information about each state is vital to this survey, your response is very important. In addition to the completed questionnaire, please forward any descriptive materials including personal comments and suggestions which you feel should be considered by the Commission. Of course, if you wish, we will hold suggestions you make in confidence.

The Commission has a limited time in which to complete its activities. Therefore, I would appreciate it if you would complete and return the questionnaire by April 30, 1971.

If you have any questions or would like to discuss in greater detail any aspect of your state's program please contact me. I can be reached at (518) 474-5709.

Thank you for your cooperation. I look forward to hearing from you.

Sincerely yours,

Herbert Alfasso, Director
Statistical Coordination

Enclosure

Please return to:

Herbert Alfasso, Director
Statistical Coordination
New York State Division of
  the Budget
State Capitol
Albany, New York 12224

PRESIDENT'S COMMISSION ON FEDERAL STATISTICS

QUESTIONNAIRE: INTRASTATE STATISTICAL COORDINATION AND STATISTICAL STANDARDS

STATE OF _____

NOTE: 1. All questions, except No. 16, focus on statistical operations of State Agencies only.
2. Lengthy answers to specific questions (or relevant materials) should be appended to the completed questionnaire.

	Yes	No
1. A. Has your State established formalized procedures, staffing patterns or other arrangements for intrastate coordination of statistical activities?	☐	☐
B. If "YES": Does this activity include setting of statistical standards for intrastate usage?	☐	☐
C. If "NO": Are there plans for establishing formal procedures for coordination in the near future?	☐	☐

When? _____

IF THE ANSWER TO QUESTION 1. A. IS "NO" SKIP TO QUESTION 20. However, any information and materials on your State's current activities or plans in this general area would be helpful to this study. We will greatly appreciate any materials forwarded.
IF THE ANSWER TO QUESTION 1. A. IS "YES", PLEASE COMPLETE QUESTIONNAIRE.

2. In which calendar year was centralized coordination inaugurated? _____

3. By which type of action was it established?
   - A. Legislation ☐
   - B. Governor's action ☐
   - C. Other (please explain) ☐

   _____
   _____
   _____

4. Which of the following best characterizes the type of arrangement or unit that was given centralized responsibility for coordination of statistical activities? *If more than one is checked, please explain.*
   - A. Permanent staff or unit ☐ Name: _____
   - B. "Permanent" committee ☐ Name: _____
   - C. Ad hoc committee or temporary task force ☐ Name: _____
   - D. Other (please explain) ☐

   _____
   _____
   _____

5. To what agency or department is centralized coordination of statistical activities attached?
   (e.g., Budget, Planning Agency, EDP Office)

   _____
   _____

6. If there is a permanent staff involved with this activity:
   - A. How many professionals are on this staff?   Full Time: _____ Part Time: _____

   - B. Of these, how many professionals are devoted primarily to statistical coordination and/or standardization activities?   Full Time: _____ Part Time: _____

209

6. *(continued)*

    C. Please describe organizational arrangement:

_____

_____

_____

WHICH OF THE FOLLOWING ACTIVITIES ARE PERFORMED BY THE CENTRAL COORDINATING GROUP FOR YOUR STATE? *CHECK AS MANY AS ARE APPROPRIATE.*

7. Reviewing and clearing questionnaires or forms to be sent out by State Agencies for collection of data. ☐

8. Preparing publications for disseminating statistical data or other information among State Agencies, such as:
    A. Annual statistical abstract or yearbook for your State; ☐
    B. Periodical "Reporter" or "Newsletter" to State Agencies and others; ☐
    C. Other *(please describe)* ☐

_____

_____

9. Coordinating electronic data processing or management information systems: *(please describe)* ☐

_____

_____

10. Preparing population estimates or projections. ☐

11. Establishing and promulgating such standards as:
    A. Identification codes for municipalities *(cities, etc.);* ☐
    B. Techniques or standards for tabular, graphic, or statistical methods of presentation of data or research findings. ☐

12. Providing technical assistance to others in your agency or to other State Agencies: *(please indicate types of assistance and to whom furnished)* ☐

_____

_____

13. Reviewing State Agency statistical budgets. ☐

14. Maintaining liaison with the Federal government in relation to your State's position on Federal statistical policy questions: *(e.g., census frequency, SMSA definitions) (please describe)* ☐

_____

_____

_____

15. Coordinating or helping State Agencies to receive Federal data for State use: *(please describe)* ☐

_____

_____

_____

16. To what extent is service rendered to municipalities or non-government organizations? *(please describe)*

_____

_____

_____

210

17. In addition to activities checked, what other statistical coordination functions or standardization responsibilities are discharged? *(please explain)*

_____

_____

_____

18. Is there an appreciable portion of the group's time utilized for duties *NOT* related to statistical coordination or standards?

Yes ☐   No ☐

If "YES," *please explain:*

_____

_____

_____

* * * * * * * * *

19. Name of person responsible for statistical coordination activity:

Name _____ Title _____

Address _____ Telephone Number _____

_____
zip code

20. This questionnaire was completed by: *(if same as above, please write "same")*

Name _____ Title _____

Address _____ Telephone Number _____

_____
zip code

PLEASE RETURN TO:
Herbert Alfasso, Director
Statistical Coordination
New York State Division of the Budget
State Capitol
Albany, New York 12224

Table on Responses to Questionnaires Regarding State Statistical Coordinating Activities*†

State[1]	(1A) Formal Intra-Stat. Function?	(1B) Setting Standards?	(1C) or (2) When?	(3) How Established
California	Yes	No	1945	Gov.
Delaware	Yes	Yes	1970	Gov.
Georgia	Yes	Yes	1967	Gov.
Hawaii	Yes	Yes	1963	Gov.
Idaho	No			
Illinois	No[2]			
Indiana	No[3]			
Iowa	Yes	No	1969	Leg.
Kansas	No			
Kentucky	No			
Maine	No[4]			
Maryland	No			
Massachusetts	Yes	No	1967	Adm.
Michigan	No[5]			
Mississippi	No[6]			
Missouri	Yes	No	1967	Gov.
Montana	No			
New Jersey	Yes	Yes	1968	Adm.
New York	Yes	Yes	1964	Adm.
North Dakota	Yes	No	1970	
Pennsylvania	Yes	Yes	1970	Gov.
Rhode Island	Yes	Yes	1964	I. a.
South Carolina	Yes	Yes	1967	Gov.
Tennessee	No			
Utah	Yes	Yes	1969	Gov.
Vermont	Yes	Yes	1970	Gov.
Washington	Yes	Yes	1969	Leg.
West Virginia	No			

*See footnotes and abbreviations at end of table.

†Numbers in parentheses above the columns refer to question numbers on the questionnaire.

(4) Type of Arrangement	(5) Type of Agency Function is Attached	(6) Number of Professionals Total		(7) Clearing Questionnaires
		Total	Stat. Coord.	
Perm. Comm.	N.A.	None	None	Yes
Perm. Staff	Planning	1 P.T.	1 P.T.	No
Perm. Staff	Planning	2 F.T.	2 F.T.	No
Perm. Staff	Planning	3 F.T.	3 F.T.	No
Perm. Staff	Planning	1 F.T.		No
Consultant[8]	7/ Planning	8 F.T.	6 P.T.	No
	Budget	2 F.T.	1 F.T.	No
Info. system	Planning	3 F.T.	3 F.T.	No
Ad hoc comm.	N.A.			No
Perm. Staff	Budget	4 F.T.	4 F.T.	No
Perm. Staff	9/	10/		No
Perm. Staff	Planning	2 F.T.	1 F.T.	No
Perm. Staff	Budget	5 F.T.	2 F.T.	Yes
Ad hoc comm.	Planning	2 P.T.	1 P.T.	Yes
Perm. Staff	Budget	1 F.T.	1 F.T.	Yes
Perm. Staff	Budget	10 F.T.	10 F.T.	No

213

Table on Responses to Questionnaires Regarding State Statistical Coordinating Activities *(continued)*

	(8) Publications and Type	(9) Coordinate EDP?	(10) Prepare Pop. Est.?	(11) Type of Stand. Establ.
California	Stat. Abstr.	No	No	
Delaware	S.A.; Rpt.	No	Yes	Mun. codes
Georgia	Rpt.; Index	No	Yes	Mun. codes
Hawaii	Stat. Abstr.	No	Yes	11/
Idaho				
Illinois				
Indiana				
Iowa	Stat. Abstr.	No	Yes	
Kansas				
Kentucky	Reporter		Yes	
Maine				
Maryland				
Massachusetts	S. A.; Rpt.	Yes	Yes	Mun. codes
Michigan				
Mississippi				
Missouri		12/		
Montana	S. A.; Rpt.	No	No	
New Jersey		No	No	Mun. codes
New York	13/	No	No	Several codes
North Dakota				
Pennsylvania	Rpt.; Cat.	No	No	Mun. codes
Rhode Island	Reporter	No	Yes	Mun. codes
South Carolina	Ec. Rpt.; Rpt.	No	Yes	14/
Tennessee				
Utah	Stat. Abstr.	No	Yes	Stat. stand.
Vermont	Stat. Abstr.	No	Yes	14/
Washington	Stat. Abstr.	No	Yes	14/
West Virginia				

214

(12) Provide Tech. Assistance?	(13) Review Stat. Budgets?	(14) Maintains Fed. Liaison?	(15) Helping to secure Fed. data for State use?
Yes	No	No	No
Yes	No	Yes	Yes
Yes	No	Yes	Yes
Yes	No	Yes	No
Yes	No	No	No
Yes			Yes
Yes	No	Yes	Yes
Yes	No	No	Yes
	No	No	No
Yes	Partly	Yes	Yes
	No	Yes	Yes
Yes	No	Yes	Yes
Yes	No	Yes	Yes
Yes	Yes	Yes	Yes
Yes	Yes	Yes	Yes
Yes	No	Yes	No

Table on Responses to Questionnaires Regarding State Statistical
Coordinating Activities *(continued)*

	(16) Services to Local Gov't & non-Gov't	(17) Other Stat. Coord. Functions	(18) (19) Other non-Stat. Coord. Functions
California	No	Yes	No
Delaware	Yes	No	Yes
Georgia	Yes	No	Yes
Hawaii	Yes	Yes	No
Idaho			
Illinois			
Indiana			
Iowa			
Kansas			
Kentucky			
Maine			
Maryland			
Massachusetts	Yes	No	Yes
Michigan			
Mississippi			
Missouri			
Montana			Yes
New Jersey		No	
New York	No	Yes	Yes
North Dakota			
Pennsylvania	No	No	Yes
Rhode Island	Yes	No	Yes
South Carolina	Yes	Yes	Yes
Tennessee			
Utah	Yes	No	
Vermont		FIXS	No
Washington	Yes	Yes	No
West Virginia			

FOOTNOTES

[1]No tabulable responses were received from the following states:

Alabama	Florida	New Mexico	South Dakota
Alaska	Louisiana	North Carolina	Texas
Arizona	Minnesota	Ohio	Virginia
Arkansas	Nebraska	Oklahoma	Wisconsin
Colorado	Nevada	Oregon	Wyoming
Connecticut	New Hampshire		

[2]Has management information system unit which establishes standards for statistical reporting.

[3]Some activities exist for coordinating demographic data and development of economic information systems.

[4]Many agencies do much of the work on ad hoc basis.

[5]May be as a result of a reorganization.

[6]Possibly under reorganization and creation of a planning office.

[7]Department of Economic and Community Development and Budget Agency will jointly conduct function.

[8]Consultant group financed thru HUD's Section 701 funds.

[9]Tied in with U.S. OEO's FIX; questionable as a statistical coordination function.

[10]Operating with 2 professionals having non-statistical coordination activities.

[11]Municipal codes; Statistical methods

[12]All coordination functions are part of Census summary tape processing center.

[13]Statistical Abstract; Reporter; Technical Guidelines.

[14]Municipal codes; Statistical standards

ABBREVIATIONS

Adm. — Administrative actions
Cat. —Catalogue
Ec. Rpt. — Economic Reporter
EDP — Electronic Data Processing
FIXS — Federal Information Exchange System
F.T. — Full Time
Gov. — Governor's Action
I. a. — Interagency agreement
Leg. — Legislative
Mun. codes — Municipal codes
N.A. — Not Applicable
Perm. Comm. — Permanent Committe
P.T. — Part Time
Rpt. — Reporter
S. A. — Statistical Abstract
Stads. Estab. — Standards Established
Stat. — Statistical
Stat. Coord. — Statistical Coordination
Stat. Stand. — Statistical Standards
Tech. Guid. — Technical Guidelines

SMALL-
AREA
DATA

Part C

Geographic Coding

By
Robert E. Barraclough

TABLE OF CONTENTS

INTRODUCTION

Thanks are due to numerous people in federal, state and local government agencies who assisted in providing unpublished information.

Special thanks are due to those who reviewed the paper — particularly Dr. Joseph F. Daly, George L. Farnsworth, and William T. Fay, of the Bureau of the Census; Ernest M. Fisher, Professor Emeritus, Columbia University; and Dr. Wilbur B. Steger, CONSAD Research Corporation, Pittsburgh. Their valuable comments were most helpful.

This is a report on geographic coding in the United States with particular reference to federal, state and local governmental agencies. The report covers the following topics:

- background of developments in geographic coding
- current status of geographic coding in federal, state and local governmental agencies
- potential applications of geographic coding, including consideration of provision of small unit data not currently available

- recommended actions for federal, state and local governmental agencies to improve geographic coding
- costs and benefits.

Descriptions of a technical nature are provided in appendixes on: geographic base files, master enumeration district list and census maps.

BACKGROUND

Geographic coding, or geocoding as it is now commonly called, is the assignment of geographic codes (geocodes) to records in a data file to facilitate geographic ordering of data.

Development of Geocoding

Geocoding has been used for many years but in recent years it has assumed much greater importance. The principal reasons are:

- decreasing costs
- improved techniques
- increasing demands for data.

In the past two decades there has been a growing demand for data drawn from small geographic units, particularly to support analysis of "urban problems" which are increasing in complexity and scale. Geocoding is an essential step — in many cases the most important one — in the production of data organized by small geographic units.

Techniques for geocoding have improved with the introduction of methods based on the use of the computer and peripheral computing equipment. Manual geocoding processes have been superseded by computer-oriented processes. Many new computer analysis procedures have been developed which require geocoded data as an input. These improved techniques have permitted high-speed geocoding and geographic analysis of large volumes of data.

While techniques have been improving, there also has been a substantial reduction in unit costs both for geocoding processing and for the processing of geocoded data. As computer manufacturers are quick to point out, computing costs over the past decade have decreased by factors of 20 to 60, while computing speeds have increased by factors of 20 to 40.

A combination of decreasing costs, improved techniques, and increasing demands for data underlie most of the major developments in geocoding over the past twenty years. These developments are outlined below.

INCREASE IN STANDARD AREAS

The number of standard small geographic areas for which the Bureau of the Census has produced population and housing data has increased substantially in recent years.

The number of cities for which census tract[1] data were produced from successive decennial Censuses of Population up to 1950, was as follows:

Census	No. of Cities
1910	8
1920	8
1930	30
1940	60
1950	114

The approximate number of census tracts and blocks for which data were produced from Censuses of Population and Housing from 1950 on, was as follows:

Census	No. of Census Tracts	No. of Census Blocks
1950	12,000	500,000
1960	23,000	750,000
1970	35,000	1,500,000

Data for each census tract and block has to be identified by a unique number (a geocode) so that with the huge increases in the numbers of census tracts and blocks there has been a corresponding large increase in geocoding activity.

NEED FOR SMALLER AREAS

Many studies have shown that different results are obtained from analysis of urban problems when different geographic groupings of the data are used. For example, analysis of data grouped by census tracts may yield quite different results from analysis of the same data grouped by blocks.

---

1 Census tracts are small subdivisions with an average of about 4,000 persons. For further explanation see Appendix D.

Tracts are not homogeneous areas for all data items. For some analyses tract areas are too large. They conceal rather than reveal the data essential for analysis of some problems. Smaller groupings of the data reduce this problem.

Undoubtedly this factor has been partly responsible for the great increase in the number of standard small geographic areas for which data have been made available from the Censuses of Population and Housing. Additionally there has been an increasing tendency to retain data in disaggregated form (at the level of individual observations) and to assign geocodes to the data at this level. This provides maximum flexibility in geographic groupings of the data. And it has meant a substantial increase in geocoding activity. The precise scale of the increase is difficult to estimate.

INCREASE IN NON-STANDARD AREAS

As the numbers of standard small geographic areas such as census tracts and blocks increased, users realized that these units were not satisfactory for many purposes, and that there was a need to produce data for non-standard areas.

There has been a tendency to abandon earlier attempts to make do with standard areas. It is now accepted that the crazy quilt of nesting and conflicting administrative and analysis areas, typical of most urban regions, must be accepted as given, and that data must be available for all of the many different area systems involved, such as school districts, health districts, police districts, community action areas, poverty areas, traffic zones, and planning analysis areas.

New problems often require new area systems for analysis or administrative purposes. Changes over time often require changes in the boundaries of these administrative or analysis areas. Boundaries of some of the areas can be made to correspond with boundaries of established areas but in many cases this is not possible.

Statistics are not available on the numbers of non-standard geographic areas for which data have been made available. Until now, it is doubtful whether the numbers remotely approach the numbers for standard areas (in the future they may well exceed the numbers for standard areas). In any event it is clear that the increasing use of non-standard areas has caused a further substantial increase in geocoding activity. Each additional set of non-standard geographic areas has required the use of an additional set of geocodes.

INCREASE IN OTHER GEOGRAPHIC UNITS

There are now large numbers of files that contain data on small geographic units which are not small areas. These include files on the networks of streets, highways, airways, railways, waterways, gas transmission lines, gas distribution lines, oil lines, electric lines, telephone lines, water lines, and sewer lines. Data in these files are organized by nodes and links — that is, lines between nodes or points.

Much of the data in these files could be used more effectively if it were related to data on the characteristics of people served or affected which are often in the form of small area data. For example, highway data should be analyzed in terms of the characteristics of people served.

It is now accepted that there is a need for locationally identifying point and line data in such a way that they can be related geographically to other data on people, sites, and areas, permitting analysis of these data on an integrated, common, comprehensive, and geographic basis.

Again, although it is difficult to estimate the scale of the increase in geocoding activities that have resulted from geocoding line and point data, it is clear that the increase is significant.

USE OF COORDINATES

Use of the usual geocodes for small areas and other geographic units does not permit the computer to sense the location of these units on the ground. For example, numbers for census blocks, tax blocks, census tracts, health districts, police districts, or numbers for links or nodes in networks, give no clue as to the actual location of these geographic entities. The only means by which it is possible to indicate locations is by use of coordinates such as latitude-longitude.[2] They are used in much the same way as a navigator uses latitude-longitude to fix the position of his aircraft or ship.

---

2   A note is included in Appendix D on the types of coordinates that can be used for different geocoding applications.

When coordinates are used as supplemental geocodes to the usual geocodes for areas, lines or points, a huge potential is tapped for geographic manipulation of data by computer. When individual observations are identified by the coordinates for the location of the observation, the possibilities for geographic manipulation of the data are virtually unlimited. Some of the more important capabilities that result from identification of the data by coordinates are discussed below.

The advantages of coordinates have been demonstrated in a large number of applications, and it is now widely accepted that any data which has locational significance should be geographically identified by coordinates as well as other geocodes.

The reduction in costs realized by measuring coordinates through automatic digitizing equipment has made the use of coordinates much more feasible.[3] Prior to the extensive use of this equipment for geocoding in the urban data field (five to ten years ago) coordinates were measured by hand – a laborious and costly process. The full effects of more recent innovations, such as electronic light pens, automated line-following equipment, and "interactive" techniques using displays on cathode ray tubes, have yet to be felt in the urban data geocoding field.

There are no statistics available to indicate the volume of geocoding activity that has resulted from the use of coordinates, but again undoubtedly it has been considerable.

STREET ADDRESS MATCHING

Computerized techniques for matching street addresses have made it feasible to geocode large numbers of files containing such data. Examples of these files include records of hospital patients, welfare recipients, health services, students, vehicle registrations, travel surveys, and business establishments.

Additionally directory files containing street addresses for a given population can be geocoded by these processes. This provides a rapid and economical means of geocoding census or survey data. For the 1970 Census of Population and Housing, for example, a directory file containing street addresses for some 60

---

3 Automatic digitizing equipment permits rapid measurement of coordinates for locations of points from maps, aerial photos and other such documents. The coordinates are automatically inserted into machine-readable records.

percent of the population (in urban areas) was geocoded by this method.

Efficient techniques for computerized street address matching have been developed fairly recently. The full impact of these techniques on geocoding activities has yet to be felt, but already there are indications that it is likely to be considerable. The subject is discussed further below.

GEOGRAPHIC ANALYSIS

As geocoding tools and techniques have been improved, computerized methods for geographic and other computerized analytic procedures using geocoded data as input have more than kept pace. For example, there have been notable improvements in techniques for computer mapping, automatic plotting, and other methods of graphic display of data (all of which depend on input data identified by coordinates). There have been improvements in techniques for simulating traffic flows over networks, and for forecasting land use distributions.

These improvements in the techniques for the use of geocoded data naturally have resulted in increased demands for such data. This has stimulated increased geocoding activity but it is difficult precisely to assess the size of the increase attributable to improved techniques.

Recent Advances in Geocoding

The most significant development in geocoding has occurred only in the past two years. This is the establishment of uniform geographic base files for most of the country's metropolitan areas.

The geographic base files are maps in computer form. They consist of records containing locational information on all "segments" in a region. A segment usually consists of a portion of a street length between two intersecting streets (for example, the portion of Washington's Connecticut Avenue between L Street and M Street). The locational information contained in segment records for an urban region usually consist of street name, range of addresses, node numbers for the intersections at each end of the segment, coordinates for the intersections, and codes for the areas

229

on either side of the segment (blocks, census tracts, police districts, and planning analysis areas).

Additional codes can be added to the segment records for points (the intersections or nodes), lines (the segments), or areas (the areas lying either side of the segment). Thus a geographic base file may contain comprehensive locational information for a region. Since the information on points, lines and areas is incorporated in a geographic base file in such a way that it is completely interrelated, a geographic base file permits geocoding of point, line and site or area data on a common, integrated and comprehensive basis.[4]

When a geographic base file is stored in a computer, it can be programmed to use the file in much the same way as we use a map, but at much faster speeds. Ways in which the geographic base files may be used are discussed below.

Summary

The major developments in geocoding over the past two decades include the following:

. a huge increase in the number of standard small geographic areas for which population and housing data have been produced

. realization of the need for smaller groupings of data for analysis of urban problems, and the advantages of retaining data in disaggregated form

. increased use of non-standard geographic areas for analysis and administrative purposes

. development of files of data on networks and points in addition to files of data by small areas

. realization of the advantages of coordinates and increased use of coordinates in the urban data field

. utilization of computerized street address matching procedures for geocoding data files containing street addresses

. significant improvements in computerized procedures for geographic analysis and other procedures requiring geocoded data as an input

---

4 The nature and development of geographic base files is described in greater detail with illustrations in Appendix A.

. development of geographic base files for most of the country's metropolitan areas

There is every indication that past trends encouraging increased geocoding activities will continue in the future. Recent developments have set the stage for the next decade and it appears certain that advances still to be exploited will result in much more geocoding activity in the future.

CURRENT STATUS OF GEOCODING

The current status of geocoding may be described under four headings:

federal government
state government
local government
intergovernmental cooperation.

As far as possible geocoding is described at the level of government which is using it, regardless of the funding level. Thus geocoding carried out by local government agencies under programs largely funded by federal agencies are described under "local government." Activities involving substantial cooperation between different levels of government are described under "intergovernmental cooperation."

Federal Government

BUREAU OF THE CENSUS

The Bureau of the Census has geocoded more data than all other federal agencies combined. The Bureau even maintains a separate organizational entity for its geocoding activities – the Geography Division. The Geography Division determines the boundaries of geographic areas in the collection and presentation of statistics, devises geographic identification coding schemes, prepares maps, has the prime responsibility for the development of geographic base files, and performs on a contract basis special tasks involving geocoding and related activities.

The 1970 Census of Population and Housing required more extensive geocoding activity than any previous census. The num-

231

ber of small geographic units involved was roughly:

35,000 census tracts
250,000 enumeration districts and "block groups" [5]
1,500,000 blocks.

Not only places of residence but also places of work were geocoded to the block level in the 1970 census. This was made possible for the first time because street addresses for places of work were enumerated in the 1970 census. Places of residence for rural areas were geocoded to the enumeration district level, and places of work to less refined geographic levels. (Geocoding at one level implies geocoding at other levels. For example, geocoding at the block level implies coding at the block group, enumeration district, census tract, place, city, county, SMSA, state and other levels.)

The level at which the data are geocoded is not necessarily the level at which the data are published or otherwise made available. More data are available for larger than for smaller areas. For example, more data are available at the census tract than at the enumeration district or block level. But with so much urban data geocoded at the block level it is possible to obtain (at cost) a much wider variety of standard and non-standard small geographic groupings of the 1970 census data, subject to the constraints of confidentiality and sample variability, than was possible from previous censuses. These geographic groupings also may be either by place of residence or by place of work.

Thus the 1970 census represents a significant advance in geocoding activities and special geographic tabulation capabilities. Also it has provided a completely new set of data based on place of work. This includes journey to work data, employment data and data on other socio-economic characteristics of workers by place of employment, such as income, age, sex, family size, housing, and education.

Another important product from the 1970 Census of Population and Housing, judged in the light of its geocoding content, is the Master Enumeration District listing (MEDlist). It is a listing of all enumeration districts and block groups with geographic codes

---

5 Enumeration districts and block groups are small areas with an average of about 800 persons. For further explanation refer to Appendix D.

for higher level geographic areas. It contains coordinates for population centroids of all enumeration districts and block groups. It contains area and place names corresponding to the geographic codes used on the statistical summary tapes of 1970 census data (which are available to the public). And it contains population and housing counts for enumeration districts and block groups, from which congressional districts and other area totals may be compiled for congressional and state redistricting and other purposes.[6]

A further product of the 1970 census important for its geocoding content is maps. Three series were produced: metropolitan maps, county maps and place maps. Together these maps show boundaries and codes for all geographic areas used in the 1970 census.[7]

For other censuses — such as the censuses of manufactures — business, construction, transportation, and governments — geocoding has so far been much less refined than for the Censuses of Population and Housing. But there are indications that data obtained in some of these censuses in the future could be geocoded at a finer level. The Bureau has recently requested funds for advance planning and testing of a computerized address directory of all U.S. business firms and their establishments. This would facilitate finer geographic coding of data collected in the censuses of manufactures, business, construction and transportation. Data from these censuses could be geocoded on the same basis as the data from the Censuses of Population and Housing, permitting for the first time geographic correlation of data from several different censuses on a small area basis.

For the Censuses of Transportation the PICADAD system of geographic identification has been used. This system permits easy calculation of straight-line distances between origins and destinations on a coordinate basis, but at a coarse geographic level.

OTHER FEDERAL AGENCIES

Generally federal agencies other than the Bureau of the Census have not been directly involved in geocoding activities below the

---

6   The contents of the MEDlist are shown in Appendix B.

7   Examples of these maps are contained in Appendix C.

state level. Some of the significant exceptions are noted below:

- The Department of Commerce's Office of Business Economics prepares wage data by Standard Industrial Classification, for counties, from state unemployment insurance files. There are future plans to prepare employment and unemployment data from the same source.
- The Department of Housing and Urban Development prepares data on housing programs at the locality or place level.
- The Internal Revenue Service prepared data on gross income for 1966 by three – and five – digit ZIP code areas. Similar data is being prepared for 1969. There are some problems with these data. Actual boundaries of ZIP code areas are not well mapped, often are only known by local postmasters and change from time to time. There have been unsuccessful attempts to prepare geographic converter files. The Office of Business Economics has plans for preparing such a file for aggregation of ZIP code areas to counties.
- The Department of Labor's Bureau of Labor Statistics prepares employment data based on a national sample for SMSA's. Some work has been done on obtaining employment and related data in selected cities on a sample basis for smaller areas (poverty areas). The Department of Labor's Manpower Administration produces data on manpower training programs for counties.
- The Social Security Administration (OASI) prepares data on benefits by types, for counties.

Some federal agencies have made arrangements for preparing special small geographic aggregates of census data which are useful for their program purposes. Usually this is accomplished by first preparing a geographic converter file at a tract, pseudo-tract, enumeration district or block level. For example:

- The Office of Civil Defense (OCD) and Office of Emergency Planning (OEP) made arrangements with the Bureau of the Census in 1960 for updating and revision of a National Location Code (NLC) that was first developed in 1956 as a basis for preparing computer estimates of damage from nuclear attack. The NLC contained universal coordinates for

234

the population centroids of 43,000 Standard Location Areas, and such other geocodes as were necessary to permit insertion of the coordinates into census data files. The Standard Location Areas consisted of census tracts in tracted metropolitan areas and other small areas elsewhere. The Bureau of Public Roads — now a part of the Department of Transportation's Federal Highway Administration — obtained copies of the census data files after the coordinates were added for use by state-urban transportation planning agencies.

. In 1970 the Office of Civil Defense made arrangements for the Bureau of the Census to prepare a special file containing universal coordinates for the population centroids of enumeration districts and block groups. There are a total of 250,000 such areas. Coordinates were added to the MEDlist mentioned earlier to facilitate aggregation of population and housing data by special areas for a number of purposes.

. The Department of Health, Education, and Welfare's National Center for Educational Statistics recently made arrangements with the Bureau of the Census to develop national geographic converter files to permit assembly of 1970 census data by school districts (or pseudo school districts where existing school districts are abnormally large). Creation of the converter file involves assigning geocodes for school district areas to files containing block and enumeration district codes. In some cases even these small units must be split to achieve conformity with school district boundaries. Several uses of the converter file are envisaged. One is to develop improved allocation of federal and state educational funds to school districts on the basis of income, age and other data. Another is to provide a frame for stratified sampling of school districts.

. The Department of Transportation's Federal Highway Administration recently made arrangements with the Bureau of the Census to prepare computer programs for tabulations by traffic zones of data of interest to urban transportation planning studies. Under this arrangement urban transportation studies pay for actual tabulation costs, and pre-

235

pare block-to-traffic-zone converter files.

These tendencies in geocoding represented by the efforts of OCD-OEP, HEW and DOT, evidence interest at the federal level in national data sets by non-standard geographic areas that can be used interchangeably by federal, state and local government agencies. They indicate clearly that data by standard census geographic areas are not sufficent for all purposes, that there is need for national data sets by non-standard geographic areas, and that there is need for geographic identification of the data by coordinates.

State Government

In the past the geocoding practices of state government have varied widely from one state to another, and even from one agency to another within the same state. There have been few attempts to coordinate geocoding practices within states or among states. The most common practice has been to geocode data to municipality, county or SMSA levels, but this has seldom been done on a consistent basis through all states. Varying systems of geocoding are used and data are coded at different levels in different states. A notable exception is the state unemployment insurance records. These are geocoded consistently in all states. The records contain street addresses of firms, and county codes of establishments.

State plane coordinate systems have been established on a standard basis for many years in all states but they have not been used widely for geocoding data.[8] They have been used considerably in mapping and in engineering or cadastral land survey applications.

More recently state governments have shown a growing interest in geocoding as a part of their general efforts to computerize state government activities and to develop state-wide information systems.

. Wisconsin has geocoded highway network data on a state-wide basis. The Wisconsin HINDI system is one of the best examples of state computerized highway network files.

---

8 All state plane coordinate systems are tied to latitude-longitude (many are based on Transverse Mercator projections, others are based on Lambert Conformal projections). The unit of measurement is feet in all cases.

There is a number of others; many are being developed for statewide planning purposes and/or maintenance operations purposes.

. Indiana is geocoding accident reports on a statewide basis. The Indiana geocoding system is coordinate based. Many other states are working on the establishment of improved methods for geocoding accident data. The Federal Highway Administration has prepared draft reports relative to standards for reporting locations. Some of the systems provide for combining accident data with highway, vehicle and driver data.

. Michigan is developing family health surveys for some seven metropolitan areas on a coordinated basis. Geocoding will be standard for all health surveys. It will be at the street address and block level so as to provide for flexibility in assembly of homogeneous geographic areas.

. Texas is developing a method for ordering data by school district areas. This appears to be similar to — if not a duplication of — the geographic converter file being developed by the Bureau of the Census for HEW's National Center for Educational Statistics.

. New York is considering identification of all land parcels by coordinates. Consideration has been given to the use of a single statewide system of Universal Transverse Mercator (UTM) coordinates. Because of its size the New York state plane coordinate system consists of four separate zones each with different origin points. Use of the UTM system will simplify data processing and geocoding.

One of the most interesting current developments in geocoding at the state level is represented by work under way in California. A comprehensive statewide geographic base file is being built containing boundary coordinates and other geocodes for all standard census areas and other small political subdivisions. It is a higher level geographic base file than those for metropolitan areas (described above). Full use is being made of existing geocoding materials available from the Bureau of the Census including census maps and the MEDlist. The file is being developed initially for state legislative redistricting purposes but is expected to serve other purposes. (No similar effort has been reported for other states.)

On the whole, however, although there is increasing interest in geocoding at the state level, efforts to date do not appear to have matured to the point where states are considering comprehensive geocoding systems for coding all state data on a common integrated basis.

Local Government

Significant geocoding has been performed at the local government level within the urban metropolitan transportation planning agencies.[9] In more than 200 metropolitan areas comprehensive transportation planning data on transportation facilities, travel, socio-economic characteristics, land use, and employment, were collected. These have been used extensively for transportation land use and other planning functions. Within each metropolitan area the data were geocoded on a common integrated basis — more recently at the block level — to facilitate relating one set of data to another. The transportation studies recognized the need to relate several interdependent sets of data of varying geographic bases. These included data by sites on the activities and socio-economic characteristics of people, firms and institutions; data by sites on the origins and destinations of flows of persons and goods; data by sites and areas on the socio-economic characteristics of travellers; and data by links and nodes on the transportation networks and terminal facilities.

The transportation studies in the roughly 200 metropolitan areas were not all performed at one point in time. For example, the studies for Detroit, Chicago, Pittsburgh, and Buffalo were started in 1953, 1956, 1958 and 1960 respectively. Innovation was encouraged and improvements in geocoding systems and techniques were made from one study to the next.

---

9 The bulk of the funding to support urban metropolitan transportation planning agencies was made available through the states from the Bureau of Public Roads — now a part of the Department of Transportation's Federal Highway Administration. Some funding for some areas was supplied under HUD planning programs. State and local government matching funds approximated one-third of the total funds.

Virtually all major improvements in geocoding techniques were introduced through transportation studies. These improvements included use of coordinates (in 1947), address coding guides (in 1952), machine mapping (in 1956), network coding (in 1957), cathode ray tube displays of daily travel (in 1958), automatic data plotting (in 1960), automatic digitizing (in 1963), and street address matching (in 1969). The urban transportation studies were responsible for the development of geocoding techniques to a highly sophisticated level.

The urban transportation studies also introduced analysis techniques that depended on the input of data with different geographic bases (sites, links and nodes) which were geocoded on a common integrated basis. These included computer techniques for simulation of flows through networks (in 1957), and for ordering data by decreasing geographic detail with increasing distance from successively selected points (in 1967).

Geocoding has been performed by other local government agencies such as city planning agencies, but the level of sophistication and volume of geocoding achieved in these efforts has not equalled the achievements of the urban transportation planning agencies. In areas where multi-purpose metropolitan Councils of Governments (COGs) have been established, it has been the metropolitan transportation planning element within the COG that has established the comprehensive geocoding system and performed the geocoding of data with different geographic bases.

Intergovernmental Cooperation

The recent development of geographic base files is the most important example of intergovernmental cooperation in geocoding activities. As shown in the illustration below geographic base files are now being developed in more than 200 metropolitan areas. The geographic base files embody not only all the sophistication in geocoding techniques developed by the urban transportation planning agencies, but also additional features. As described earlier, the files have been developed at the street segment level and produced on a standard basis throughout the country.[10]

---

10 A detailed description of content and a description of the method of development of geographic base files is contained in Appendix A. A description of

OVER TWO—HUNDRED SMSA'S ARE PARTICIPATING IN THE ACG/DIME IMPROVEMENT PROGRAM

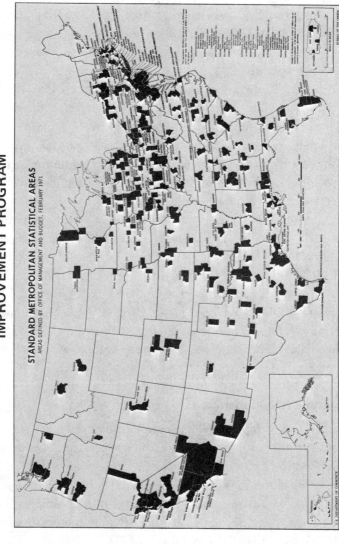

Figure 1: Geographic distribution of geographic base files now being developed. (The ACG/DIME Improvement and Program is briefly described in Appendix A.)

Source: U.S. Bureau of the Census

The geographic base files, as completed, will be available to government and private agencies at the cost of reproduction. The files will be completed by early 1972. The total cost of the geographic base file program through June 1971 was approximately $18 million — about $15 million for the development of the files and their associated maps, and about $3 million for research and development of tools designed to assist users in geographic base file applications.

About half the funds for the program have been provided by the Bureau of the Census which has prime responsibility for the development of the files and associated maps, and for research and development of tools to facilitate use of the files.[11] The balance of the funds have been provided by other federal agencies (including DOT, HUD, and HEW), as well as a large number of state and local government agencies. Thus the program has enjoyed strong support at all levels of government.

Summary

At the federal level, the Bureau of the Census has geocoded more data than all other agencies combined; more for the Censuses of Population and Housing than for other censuses; and more for the 1970 Census of Population and Housing than for earlier censuses.

For the 1970 census not only places of residence in urban areas but also places of work were geocoded to the block level. Twice as many blocks (about 1,500,000) were included as in the 1960 census. The number of standard geographic groupings of data will be much greater than for previous censuses, and the potential for non-standard geographic groupings is several times greater than for previous censuses. The quality and quantity of geocoding tools is also greater than for previous censuses. Notable examples are the maps for metropolitan areas that show boundaries and designations for blocks, tracts and other census subdivisions, and the

(Footnote 10 Continued)
the Metropolitan Map Series (MMS) which were used as a basis for development of the files is contained in Appendix C.

11 Research and development of the tools to facilitate use of the files has been carried out through the Bureau's Census Use Study. The Census Use Study had depended on intergovernmental support and cooperation. Additionally there has been support from the private sector.

computer files for the whole country that show geocodes, coordinates, and population and housing counts at the enumeration district or block group level.

Data from the other censuses, such as the censuses of manufactures, business, construction, transportation and government, have not been geocoded to the same fine level as data from the Census of Population and Housing. This could be feasible if the Bureau obtains funds to test development of a computerized address directory of all U.S. business firms and their establishments.

Generally speaking, other federal agencies are not performing significant geocoding activities because as a rule they are not involved in producing small area data. Data geocoded below the state level are usually geocoded to SMSA or county levels. But there are exceptions — for example IRS has geocoded data to three - and five - digit ZIP code levels. Also some federal agencies have made arrangements for development of geographic converter files for grouping census data into non-standard geographic areas, such as school districts and traffic zones.

At the present time state government agencies are not heavily involved in geocoding activities. Data are mostly geocoded at municipal, county or SMSA levels — seldom at small area levels. Also practices vary widely from state to state and within states. There is evidence of growing interest in several states in improved methods of geocoding but this has not reached the point where these states are committed to plans to geocode all data having locational significance on a common integrated basis.

At the local government level there has been significant geocoding activity. This has largely occurred within the 200 or so urban metropolitan transportation planning agencies. Large volumes of data — on the use of land, travel and the socio-economic characteristics of travellers, and transportation networks and terminal facilities — have been geocoded on a common integrated basis, more recently at the block level. Extensive use has been made of these data in transportation, land use and other planning functions.

Many important innovations in geocoding urban data and the use of geocoded data were introduced by the transportation planning agencies. These include use of coordinates, geographic coding guides, cathode ray tube displays, computer mapping, network coding, automatic plotting, automatic digitizing, simulation of traffic flows through networks, and automated street address matching. Geocoding tools and techniques were developed to a highly sophisticated level. Because the transportation planning studies were carried out at different points in time geocoding was not performed on a standard basis.

In the past two years intergovernmental cooperation has produced the most sophisticated set of geocoding tools. Geographic base files have been produced for almost all metropolitan areas on a uniform basis at the street segment level. They were developed by the Bureau of the Census with strong support and cooperation from other federal agencies, and state and local government agencies.

POTENTIAL APPLICATIONS

Potential applications of the geographic base files, described above, are considered under the following headings:

. organization of data geographically
. geocoding of data files
. primary uses of geocoded data files
. data on areas versus persons
. some further uses of geographic base files

Organization of Data Geographically

Finding effective solutions to our urban problems depends in large measure on having good information on the intensity, distribution and local impact of these problems. For each metropolitan area, well organized, comprehensive, integrated information systems are needed that can effectively support policy making, planning, implementation and evaluation — at all levels of government.

. decision makers need to be able quickly to develop policies in response to problems.
. planners need to be able to continuously develop proposals and plans as a basis for policies.
. administrators need to be able to effectively implement the plans and policies on a day-to-day basis.

243

decision-makers, planners and administrators need to be able to evaluate continuously plans and policies to determine whether they are in fact solving the problems they are intended to solve, and to determine whether the policies and plans are being properly implemented.

Metropolitan information systems are needed that can bring maximum useful information to bear on particular problems for particular locations.

The quantities of information produced by small geographic units have increased rapidly in recent years. The precise dimensions of these quantities are not known, but it is clear that they are indeed large. Nevertheless, when information is needed for particular problems within a metropolitan area, it is seldom readily available. Usually considerable time and effort is required to assemble and organize the information. For example, the metropolitan transportation planning agencies spend 30 percent to 50 percent of their budgets on collection and organization of data, and in many cases take two to three years to accomplish this work.

For each metropolitan area, data files are generated by many different agencies at the federal, state, and local level. The total result is a patchwork of uncoordinated information systems and data files, characterized by fragmentation, gaps and duplication. There have been many attacks on different aspects of the problem in different areas but taken as a whole they have not been effective. There is an urgent need to organize the existing *ad hoc* information systems and data files in each metropolitan area into comprehensive, integrated information systems that can furnish pertinent data continuously on a timely basis.[12]

One of the most important aspects of the problem of organizing data for metropolitan information systems is the geographic aspect. The geography of a metropolitan area has been referred to as the platform for human activities. Geographic organization of

___

12 A notable experiment presently under way is the USAC project under the leadership of HUD with support from other federal agencies. The program provides for the development of integrated municipal information systems. Five cities are being used for the development of operational systems; procedures developed in these areas are expected to be transferrable to other areas.

metropolitan data provides the means for relating the data on activities, and facilities for these activities, to the "platform."

When the data are effectively organized geographically it is possible to bring together several different types of information for each small area for analysis and presentation in reports and displays for decision-makers, planners and administrators. Data from federal sources, such as census data, can be effectively combined with data from state and local government sources. In the long run geographic organization of metropolitan data can result in significant increases in efficiency in assembling information for policy making, planning, administration and evaluation. It can also lead to significant cost savings by reducing duplication of efforts in data collection and handling, and by reducing costly *ad hoc* data operations.

The geographic base files described above provide the basis for comprehensive geographic organization of metropolitan data on a common integrated basis. They provide the means for making readily available large quantities of data by small geographic units that are at present inaccessible – either totally or only to particular agencies. The base files provide the means for effective geocoding of wide varieties of data having locational significance.

Geocoding Data Files

The availability of geographic base files (and computer programs that facilitate geocoding) permit geocoding of metropolitan data files at high speed and low cost. This substantially increases the potential applicability of geocoding and the potential provision of small unit data that is presently not available.

One of the most important types of computer programs developed recently for geocoding is based on street address matching.

STREET ADDRESS MATCHING

Geocoding procedures used up to now have been slow.

. three addresses per manhour was the average rate for manual geocoding from maps
. thirty addresses per manhour was the average rate for manual geocoding from printed address coding guides

245

The new computer street address matching procedures are much faster. Rates as high as one million addresses an hour have been attained with procedures such as ADMATCH, which was developed recently by the Census Use Study of the Bureau of the Census.

The ADMATCH procedure requires two inputs: first the data file to be geocoded (containing street addresses); and second the appropriate geographic base file (containing ranges of addresses, geocodes, coordinates as described above). The procedure involves computer matching of the street addresses in the data file to the pertinent range of addresses in the geographic base file, and insertion of geocodes and coordinates in the data file. Unmatched addresses are rejected and listed. They are then reviewed by an analyst who determines whether with minor modifications it will be possible to reprocess the records to effect a match, or whether it will be necessary to geocode the addresses manually.[13]

The extent to which procedures such as ADMATCH can be applied, and the quantities of geocoded data that can be made available by these means, will depend, however, on costs. The costs of geocoding will depend largely on the volume of "rejects" that have to be geocoded manually. The volume of such rejects depends on the quality of the addresses in the data file being geocoded. Tests conducted by the Bureau of the Census and other agencies indicate that from 5 percent to 30 percent of total records in a data file may be rejected. The Bureau's Census Use Study is conducting further tests now to determine the costs of geocoding by ADMATCH and other procedures. Results will be available later this year. Meanwhile, considering the dramatic difference in geocoding speed between the old and new methods, it appears certain that future geocoding costs will be dramatically reduced.

It also appears certain that vast numbers of data files containing street addresses, which could not be feasibly geocoded under the old procedures, will become prime candidates under the new procedures. These files exist at all levels of government:

.   at the federal level there are the files of the Social Security

13 ADMATCH procedures are documented in several Census Use Study publications listed in the bibliography; other publications are being prepared and should be available shortly.

Administration (OASI) and the files of the Internal Revenue
Service.

. at the state level there are unemployment insurance record
files, motor vehicle registration files, and driver permit files.

. at the local level there are files for property tax assessment,
building permits, zoning applications, housing violations,
welfare recipients, health services, school children, travel
surveys, and accident records.

Business establishments, utility companies and other private
institutions also have large data files that contain street addresses.
The new geocoding procedures could be applied to them to provide geocoded data files for business applications (such as market
analyses and studies on location of outlets), or for governmental
applications.

OTHER GEOCODING PROCEDURES

The geographic base files can also be used as a basis for geocoding by simpler and less costly procedures. These procedures
can be used where data files already contain special geocodes.
They can be used to geocode property tax assessment data files
that already contain tax block numbers (the tax assessor's special
geocodes). By building a correspondence table showing the corresponding tax block numbers for the census block numbers in the
geographic base file, and adding the tax block numbers to the
geographic base file, it is possible to assign census block numbers
and other geocodes from the geographic base file to records in the
property tax assessment file.

Similarly geocodes from the geographic base file can be inserted into a highway inventory file after a correspondence table
has been developed that shows the corresponding link numbers
(used in the highway inventory file) for the link numbers that
appear in the geographic base file. The same process can be applied
to insert geocodes from the geographic base file into a file containing data on traffic accidents where the information may be
geographically identified in terms of intersections or nodes.

By extension of this process it is possible to add all the special
geocodes used by different agencies within a metropolitan area so

247

that the geographic base file becomes a comprehensive geographic converter file capable of geocoding all types of data on a common integrated basis, not only by street address matching procedures, but also by:

- point or node matching
- link matching
- area matching

The quantities and types of data that can be geocoded by these procedures will vary from one metropolitan area to another, but considering, for example, property tax assessment files alone, these methods of geocoding potentially could make large quantities of data much more widely available.

Primary Uses of Geocoded Data Files

Important initial uses of geocoded data files will no doubt be those for which costs are low, utility is high, and procedures are simple and widely available. The following categories of uses appear to have all of these qualities and therefore will most likely constitute the most important primary uses of geocoded data files:

- aggregations by standard and non-standard areas
- aggregations by regular polygons
- aggregations by irregular polygons
- computer maps and other graphic displays.

AGGREGATIONS BY STANDARD AND NON-STANDARD AREAS

Aggregations of data are frequently needed by standard and non-standard areas for a variety of purposes at various levels of government. For a larger metropolitan area, aggregates may be required for such standard and non-standard areas as:

- census tracts
- unincorporated areas
- supervisorial districts
- councilmanic districts
- senatorial districts
- congressional districts
- court districts
- statistical areas
- planning areas
- tax assessment areas
- community action areas
- traffic zones

248

- school districts
- power districts
- water districts.

- police districts
- welfare districts

Assuming data files have been geocoded so as to contain geocodes for all of these areas, aggregates of the data can be produced by simple procedures. The volume of processing would tend to be high in large metropolitan areas because of the size of files and the number of standard and non-standard areas involved. But processing costs would be relatively low.

Aggregates for standard and non-standard areas can be used for a wide variety of purposes, including analysis, ranging from simple comparative analysis to factor analysis, input to forecasting and other planning models, day-to-day administration, program evaluation, and reports and graphic displays for policy makers and the general public.

AGGREGATION BY REGULAR POLYGONS

When data files have been geocoded so as to contain coordinates, simple low-cost procedures can be used to prepare a variety of aggregations by regular polygons such as:

- grid squares
- rings
- sectors.

It is also possible to produce aggregations consisting of combinations of these regular polygons. For example, data for a metropolitan area can be aggregated by one-fourth square mile units, which in turn can be aggregated to one square mile units, and then to a series of sectors and rings of varying sizes. These can be centered on the central business district of the metropolitan area. It is even a simple matter to arrange for a series of aggregations of increasing area with increasing distance from a point or a series of points within the metropolitan areas. Coordinates permit a great degree of flexibility in data aggregation.

Because regular polygons have constant area, aggregation by these units imparts to geographic analyses the same type of regularity and consistency present in time-based analyses where constant units of time are used (months, years, decades, etc.).

This makes aggregation of data by regular polygons particularly useful in examining the structure of a metropolitan region or a series of metropolitan regions. Areas can be standard from one part of the metropolitan regions to another, and from one region to another. The distribution of a variety of characteristics over the surface of the region(s) can be examined on a uniform area basis. Densities are automatically expressed without the need for further computation, as is necessary in the case of standard and non-standard areas (which vary in area size). For example, if the data are aggregated to units of one square mile (grid squares), the totals automatically express densities per square mile. It is thus possible easily to compare the variations in the distributions over the surface of a region(s) of a wide variety of characteristics — such as number of residents, income, employment, automobile ownership, education, daily travel, pollution, health, land uses, and floor area. Also relationships between these characteristics can be easily derived.

Aggregation by regular polygons permits the coordination and integration of a wide series of analyses conducted by independent agencies at different levels of government for different points in time. The past, present and future of different aspects of the region(s) can be sized, scaled, and estimated on a consistent area basis. A large number of analyses for operations, management, planning, policy making and program evaluation purposes can be easily integrated.

AGGREGATION BY IRREGULAR POLYGONS

Coordinates in the data files also provide the basis for aggregation of data by irregular polygons. These can include aggregations by standard and non-standard areas. At present, however, these can be accomplished more simply and at less cost by the methods referred to above (using the geocodes for the standard and non-standard areas). Therefore the aggregations by irregular polygons referred to here are those which do not conform to standard and non-standard areas.

The size, shape and location of the irregular polygons can be almost infinitely varied. Also there is no need to define the boundaries of the irregular polygons at the time of geocoding (there is also no need to define the boundaries of regular polygons at the time of geocoding but this is necessary for standard and non-standard areas). This feature makes aggregation by irregular polygons useful for applications where the boundaries of the areas of concern are not known in advance, or may have to be changed over time.

An example of this type of application is the examination of alternative alignments for a proposed highway. Given a series of centerlines for the alternative proposed alignments, data can be aggregated for areas defined in terms of a fixed distance either side of each center line. The characteristics of each alternative area can then be compared — population, the number and quality of housing units, business establishments, assessed valuations, open land and parks within each area. Engineering data, such as quantities of cut and fill, can also be aggregated. Comparative analyses based on the data aggregates for each alternative area can be used as a basis for preparing reports and recommendations for decision-makers, the persons affected, and the general public.

There are many other applications where similar types of aggregations are useful. For example, in examination of alternative areas for urban redevelopment, locations of mass transit routes, airports, cultural centers, shopping centers, university extensions, and community action areas.

Costs are low for preparing the aggregations, and procedures simple where the types of areas are not complex — as in the example cited above for examination of alternative highway alignments. Procedures would be less simple and costs could be higher where more complex areas are involved. For these cases, use of "point-in-polygon" or "polygon-in-polygon" techniques may be indicated. Simply expressed, these techniques depend on determination of whether or not given points or areas lie within given polygons. Locations of the points or areas are expressed in terms of coordinates in the data files, and locations of the boundaries of the polygons to which the data are to be aggregated are expressed in terms of coordinates in separately-developed files. However, with further use and development of these techniques it is possible that even the costs for these procedures will be lower in future.

251

COMPUTER MAPS AND OTHER GRAPHIC DISPLAYS

Computer maps and other graphic displays can be used in literally hundreds of different applications throughout government and industry — at local, state and national levels. Potential uses are increased several times when the displays or maps can be delivered rapidly and at low cost using simple procedures, which is possible when coordinates are inserted in data files as they are geocoded. The data files can then be used as input to any of several inexpensive computer mapping or graphic display procedures.[14]

Computer mapping procedures that can be used now include:

. GRIDS
. SYMAP

Display devices that can be used now include:

. character plotters
. pen plotters
. "geospace" type plotters
. cathode ray tubes

These devices and procedures can be used for preparing large quantities of hard-copy maps or displays, showing different characteristics for metropolitan or other areas at different scales. Data values can be represented in terms of colors or various black-and-white shadings; they can be for standard or non-standard areas, or regular or irregular polygons; they can be represented by actual values or symbols, or by simple lines or contours; and they can be printed or displayed with or without background information (for example the street network, boundaries for areas, natural features).

Cathode ray tube devices can be used on an interactive basis for operations, management, planning, or policy making purposes to determine rapidly answers to "what-if" questions. For example, an existing transportation network can be displayed. An operator can

---

14 These procedures are in essence the reverse of the automatic digitizing process referred to earlier. Coordinates are "read" from the machine records and the values in the records (or symbols for the values) are automatically printed, plotted, or otherwise displayed. The procedures are described in numerous publications, some of which are cited in the bibliography. A good general description is contained in the Census Use Study publication "Computer Mapping."

make changes in this network representing proposed future additions to the transportation network. The effect of these changes on the future land development pattern can be forecast and displayed. This future pattern can be then compared to a display of a *desired* future land development pattern. The process can be repeated until a satisfactory future transportation network is arrived at.

Admittedly, present use of these interactive planning methods is limited because costs are relatively high and computer software has been developed for only a small number of applications, but it appears likely that there will be increased use of such aids in the future. Meanwhile, in the near future a large variety of hard-copy displays can be produced rapidly at low cost, using simple procedures and devices now in common use.

It is possible to prepare at low cost a uniform series of metropolitan atlases based on the 1970 census data. This could significantly enhance understanding of the structures and problems of our metropolitan areas at all levels of government. Mapped data can be much more readily grasped than tabulated data (although both are necessary). The maps could at a relatively small additional cost show not only 1970 conditions, but also changes between 1960 and 1970. A wide variety of changes could be shown, including changes in the structures of income distribution, racial segregation, housing conditions and the labor force. Changes in employment and journey-to-work patterns could also be shown but this would involve additional expense because the 1960 data are not available on the same fine geocoded basis as 1970 data.

Data on Areas Versus Persons

One of the underlying features of many of the uses of geocoded data described above is the matching of data by areas (or geographic correlation of the data), placing data from several sources on the same geographic basis to facilitate comparisons of values for different characteristics from one place to another, and to facilitate the development of relationships between the characteristics on an area basis.

One school of thought that enjoys considerable support stresses the limitations of comparing characteristics on an area basis, particularly the characteristics of persons. Adherents of this view stress the importance of obtaining data on a person basis and advocate the use of either small sample surveys, computer matching of individual person records to amass person data from a variety of source files, or a combination of these methods. They point to the danger of the "ecological fallacy" inherent in geographic correlation of data (where characteristics for an area are erroneously ascribed to persons within the area).

These arguments deserve careful consideration on a case by case basis. It is important to weigh the costs, feasibility and effectiveness of obtaining data on a person versus an area basis in each particular case. In some cases data on an area basis will not be an effective substitute for person data, and in other cases it may be. In some cases, comparison of analysis results from data obtained on both bases will be the only means of settling the question.

There are, however, some serious practical problems that should be considered in regard to obtaining data on a person basis — particularly in obtaining such data by computing matching of individual person records from a variety of sources. One is the problem of invasion of privacy, which has received increasing attention over the past decade. The actual and potential abuses by government and industry of dossiers on individuals is a very real problem for society today and will continue to be a serious problem in the future. Data matched on an area basis is not subject to this type of abuse.

Another problem is that of cost and feasibility. Experiments have shown that matching of person data on the basis of characteristics of persons (because of the absence of person identification numbers) can be costly and unreliable. Matches that do occur are in fact in many cases erroneous.

Although it is not advocated as a panacea, it is much simpler to match data by areas than by persons, and it is often an eminently satisfactory substitute for a number of reasons including confidentiality, feasibility, reliability and cost.

Some Further Uses of Geographic Base Files

The geographic base files can be used in a number of ways besides those already described. Some of these are beyond the

254

subject of geocoding, but should be taken into account in considering the total potential benefits of the geographic base files. Some may become more important in the future than the geocoding applications. It is difficult to judge because relatively little work has been done in most of these areas compared to that already accomplished in the area of geocoding.[15] These further uses are considered under the headings:

- spatial analysis
- adjacency analysis
- network analysis
- automated mapping systems

SPATIAL ANALYSIS

Various spatial analyses can be performed using the geographic base files, with or without geocoded data files, as input to a number of computer procedures which are already in wide use. Use of the coordinates in the geographic base files or the geocoded data files, or both, is essential to these applications.

Centroids of areas can be computed by specifying the geocode(s) for the areas or by describing the boundaries of the areas in terms of nodes, coordinates or street names and address ranges. Centroids of routes can be computed by specifying names of geocodes for the routes, or beginning and ending points, and points of major change in direction of the routes. Centroids for groups of points can be similarly computed.

Calculation of centroids is useful in a variety of applications where it is important to know the focal points of characteristics of areas, routes or clusters of points, or where it is useful to represent the location of an area, route, etc. by a single point. One important application is in computer mapping or other graphic displays. Data values or symbols for characteristics can be shown at the centroids of the areas and routes they pertain to.

Distances can also be computed. Air-line distances can be computed simply by specifying two points; route distances can be computed by specifying points of change of direction in routes;

15 Some of these potential applications are described in publications cited in bibliography. The best general description to be found in the Census Use Study publication "The DIME Geocoding System."

shortest paths can be computed by specifying origin and destination points for each path, and using a "shortest-path" algorithm.

Computations of this sort have been widely used in the past for computing lengths of trips (analysis of trip lengths is an important phase of metropolitan transportation planning analysis); for computing routes for salesmen, delivery men, trash collection, meter reading, and postal delivery; and for computing distances of customers from stores, distances of children's places of residence from schools, and patients' places of residence from clinics.

Areas of polygons can be computed by specifying the geocodes for the polygons or by describing the boundaries of the polygons in terms of nodes, coordinates or street names and address ranges. These calculations can be used in several applications, such as density computations for determination of the incidence and intensity of crime, wealth, poverty, retail sales, automobile ownership, floor area, and for determination of boundaries of component units in areal systems (police districts, school districts, neighborhood action areas) where size of area is one of the criteria.

Calculations of centroids, distances and areas are the primary elements in spatial analyses and form the basis for more complicated spatial analyses. The spatial analyses in turn can provide the basis for other applications some of which are described below.

ADJACENCY ANALYSIS

The geographic base files also may be used for adjacency analysis. Adjacency tables can be developed for a set (or sets) of areas represented in the geographic base file, showing for each area the geocodes of adjacent areas; these can then be added to the geographic base file to provide the basic input for a variety of adjacency analyses, with or without geocoded data files.

For example, adjacent areas can be agglomerated until a stipulated size limit is reached. The limit may be in terms of total area, total length of segments, numbers of persons, numbers of persons of certain characteristics, or combinations of these. This technique has been used for development of alternative districting proposals, as in the State of California's legislative redistricting, and for school desegregation purposes as in Santa Monica, California. It may be used similarly for developing police patrol beats, delivery routes, and health clinic areas.

Adjacent areas that contain similar characteristics also can be agglomerated to develop homogeneous clusters. The clusters may be used to define areas for planning or administrative purposes, or to determine areas requiring action programs to lift them toward community standards.

NETWORK ANALYSIS

The geographic base files constitute network files for each metropolitan area; the network of streets and highways for the metropolitan region are described in a connected manner. Intersections of street segments are identified by unique node numbers so that it is possible to tell which segments "depart" from a given node. Given a particular segment and a direction of travel along the segment, the computer can consider which of several "branches" may be taken to depart from the segment. In this way using the geographic base files as input to a network analysis procedure the computer can consider a variety of paths through a region. For example given the "shortest-path" algorithm and the time or distance required to travel along each segment, the computer can compute and describe the shortest time or distance path from point A to B. A number of similar and related procedures for network analysis have been developed and used extensively for several years.

These procedures can be used for a variety of applications. For example, they can be used as an adjunct to those already described for computing appropriate routes for salesmen, delivery men, meter reading, trash collection, and snow removal. They can be used for advance testing of proposed mass transit routes or improvements to the road network, and to evaluate proposals for new bridges, tunnels or expressways (these applications are based on simulating the flow of traffic through the network). And they can be used for traffic or emergency vehicle (police, fire, ambulance, etc.) routing and for determining the shortest routes for a vehicle to follow in order to pick up or deliver passengers or goods at a number of locations (this could be useful in such proposed future vehicle systems as "Dial-a-Bus").

Network analysis in conjunction with other types of analyses can also provide the basis for determining locations, areas and networks that meet specified conditions. As such it forms a valuable tool for a variety of planning applications. After analysis of existing facilities in terms of pre-set standards for distances customers or clients should travel, size of area to be served, and numbers of persons to be served, it can be used to determine appropriate locations for additional fire stations, police stations, schools, branch banks, department stores, shopping centers, and other facilities. Areas that are poorly served can be quickly determined, as well as appropriate locations for new facilities.

The network features of geographic base files may be used for a large variety of analyses. Use of some of these methods, however, depends on adding data to files: data on segment travel time, numbers of lanes, parking restrictions and timing for traffic signals. This may require considerable time and effort depending on the condition of existing network data in the metropolitan area. In the long run it appears that this would be more than offset by the benefits from operations and planning uses of these data.

These benefits would no doubt be enhanced by placing all network data for metropolitan areas on a common basis – data on the physical characteristics and use of the road network including data on traffic accidents, together with data on the networks of water, sewer, gas, electric and telephone lines. Uniform organization of all types of network data, using the geographic base files as the common structuring tool, could eventually lead to significant cost savings in the development and use of procedures (and in the interchange of data) for operations, management, planning and policy making purposes in both industry and government.

AUTOMATED MAPPING SYSTEMS

Using graphic display devices such as those already described, it is possible to produce maps automatically from a geographic base file. The Census Use Study of the Bureau of the Census, using a "geo-space" plotter, has produced experimental maps which show street outlines, census tract boundaries, designations, and census block numbers. A map of New Haven, Connecticut was printed in a matter of minutes by this method.

The Bureau is also experimenting with methods of updating and maintenance of the geographic base files using as source material local maps and aerial photographs. The use of newly developed semi-automatic line-following equipment to speed the input process has also been considered.

Experiments such as these eventually could lead to an operational automated mapping system, although the present indications are that this is probably several years away.

The development of such a system would revolutionize present mapping methods. Instead of maintaining maps in file drawers, the maps could be kept in computer storage. Retrieval routines could provide for "live" displays or hard-copy maps for any area, at virtually any scale, showing selected information in a variety of formats. The maps could be transmitted over telecommunications channels to remote locations, including moving vehicles. Inputs could be received from remote locations, including remote sensing devices. The system could become as flexible and as sophisticated as the present computer systems which have superseded our old methods of manual bookkeeping.

It has been suggested that a map could be transmitted "over-the-air" to a telephone, electric or gas utility repair crew in the field; they could effect repairs and then transmit information on repairs and changes completed; this information could be automatically entered into the "base map" in computer storage and into a reporting system for maintenance and engineering improvements.

Also it has been suggested that information for urban regions could be placed in computer storage in map form, in a series of layers. Each layer would represent a separate layer of information — geological structure, soils, topography, vegetation, landscape, sewers, water lines, telephone lines, transportation facilities, vehicle buildings, open land, persons, socio-economic characteristics, firms, and retail sales. Different layers of information could be retrieved, analyzed and compared by computer in much the same way as overlay maps are now compared by eye. Results of comparative analyses could be displayed and printed in many different ways at high speeds. Synoptic views of regions could be made available. Kinetic views of past and alternative future possibilities for the region could be displayed.

These sorts of developments are exercises in imagination at this time. Before they can become reality, many technological developments, institutional changes, experiments and studies, including cost-effectiveness studies, will be necessary. Also it is possible that when such systems are developed they may be only remotely connected with the present forms of geographic base files. But the geographic base files represent a start along the road to some form of automated mapping system of the future, and the potential development of improved methods of handling map-type data in the future should be considered in assessing the total potential benefits of geographic base files.

Summary

The geographic base files for metropolitan areas provide a basis for a number of potential applications that can result in significant increases in the quantity of data by small geographic units in the future, and in wider uses of existing and potentially available data.

The geographic base files provide the basis for the first time for comprehensive geographic organization on a common integrated basis of a wide variety of different types of data for our metropolitan areas — data from all levels of government and industry, data for different points in time, data on different geographic bases (areas, points, and networks), and data on a wide variety of different subjects.

They provide the basis for new methods of geocoding data on a consistent basis for all metropolitan areas — including computerized matching on a street address, node, link and area basis. Comprehensive geographic converter files can be developed, using the geographic base files as a standard basis, and these can be utilized in conjunction with the newly-developed computerized procedures to geocode large quantities of data at costs that it appears almost certain would be significantly lower than previous geocoding costs. Just how much lower will be known shortly when studies at present under way are completed.

The geocoded data files can be used for a number of purposes but the primary uses initially will most likely be to develop products that can be produced at low cost which have high utility. These would probably include a large variety of aggregations of data by standard and non-standard areas and by regular and irregular polygons; also a large variety of computer maps and other graphic displays. These products would be useful in numerous operations, planning, policy making and program evaluation functions. For example, a series of metropolitan atlases could be produced at low cost from 1970 and 1960 census data showing present conditions and changes in such areas as income distribution, racial segregation, adequacy of housing, labor force, employment and the journey to work. These could be used at all levels of government and industry for a number of different purposes.

Further potential uses of geographic base files include numerous applications in terms of spatial analyses, adjacency analyses, network analyses and automated mapping systems. These applications could in the future prove more important and more cost-effective than the other types of uses referred to above that will be easily feasible in the short run. In any case these applications (some of which extend beyond geocoding) should also be derived from the geographic base files in the future.

The potential applications of geographic base files are just emerging. They are not yet mature. Developments over the past three to five years have been highly significant and they indicate the potential for significant new developments in the next three to five years. The rate of change and improvement in this area appears to be gathering momentum. It appears to be highly important to provide for a new level of effort, leadership and coordination to ensure that emerging developments do in fact become a satisfactory platform for the development and use of the metropolitan information system of the future.

RECOMMENDATIONS

The central recommendation of this report is that a national geocoding system be established. Other supporting recommendations are considered under two headings:

261

- national geocoding system
- other recommendations

National Geocoding System

The development of the geographic base files for metropolitan areas, and procedures for use of these files, represents a major breakthrough in geocoding technology. The files also can be applied to many areas beyond geocoding.

Up to now tasks that required maps as a basic input have been largely performed by manual methods. Now with the geographic base files as input these tasks can be performed by computer methods. The power of the computer permits performance of these tasks with much greater efficiency. It also permits undertaking many tasks that would not have been feasible using manual methods.

Significant increases in efficiency result in both the production and use of maps that are part of an overall system. Similarly significant increases in efficiency will result both in the production and use of geographic base files that are part of an overall system. The geographic base files provide a foundation for a national geocoding system, somewhat akin to a national mapping system.

Further actions are necessary to develop a complete national geocoding system. Provisions for ensuring appropriate organizational and institutional changes — as well as the supply of sufficient resources to accomplish this objective — are of primary importance.

Recommendation 1: NATIONAL GEOCODING SYSTEM

Action should be taken at an early date to establish an appropriate organizational and institutional framework for the development of the national geocoding system, using as a basis the geographic base files already developed for metropolitan areas. Sufficient resources should be provided for this purpose.

It is recommended that the Office of Management and Budget provide leadership in the development of the national geocoding system. Federal, state and local government agencies that will be involved in the development and use of the system should be represented, along with private user groups.

Other Recommendations

Given an appropriate organizational and institutional framework and sufficient resources, a number of specific actions will be necessary to ensure full development and use of the national geocoding system. Recommendations on a number of important specific actions are furnished below. A first order of business of the new "agency" that is established pursuant to Recommendation 1 above, however, should be to prepare a *comprehensive* set of objectives and tasks for development of the national geocoding system.

Recommendation 2: UPDATE AND MAINTENANCE

It is recommended that a study be initiated to report on methods of providing continuing funding and establishing responsibilities for updating and maintenance of geographic base files.

The study should include consideration of all potential resources and funding mechanisms, including:

. inter-agency agreement
. designation of a single federal agency with full responsibility for securing funds
. not-for-profit corporation

The study should include consideration of funding problems and estimated costs for several years in advance.

Also it should include careful consideration of the possibility of funding future updating and maintenance by fixing charges for copies of original files and updated files so as to provide for amortization of costs (with due allowance for concessions in charges to governmental agencies which have participated in the updating and maintenance efforts or otherwise shared these costs.)

It is recommended that the Office of Management and Budget provide leadership for the initiation of the study and for ensuring that an effective updating and maintenance system is established and funded. Federal, state and local government agencies concerned with the implementation of the system should be represented as well as governmental and private user groups.

448-559 O - 71 - 18

Recommendation 3: HOUSE NUMBERING

It is recommended that a study be initiated to report on methods for developing and implementing a national standard house number assignment system.

Most rural areas and a few urban areas (particularly at the fringes of metropolitan areas) are not now using house numbers. Continuing urbanization is leading to conflicting house numbering schemes with duplicate street names and overlapping address ranges.

It is recommended that the U.S. Postal Service provide leadership for both the initiation of the study and for implementation of the recommended house number assignment system. They should ensure adequate representation of governmental agencies and private industry at national, state and local levels as well as the general public. The study should include consideration of improvement of the ZIP code system — particularly to provide maps of ZIP code areas and to reduce the frequency of changes in ZIP codes.

Recommendation 4: STANDARDS

It is recommended that action be taken to establish at an early date comprehensive standards on street addresses, geographic codes, geographic base files and related matters including updating and maintenance procedures.

This action is essential to avoid proliferation of geographically incompatible data. Early action will result in greater savings than would otherwise be possible, will increase opportunities for use of data on a geographically integrated basis, and will facilitate interchange of information between different private and governmental agencies at local, state and national levels.

Again, it is recommended that the Office of Management and Budget provide leadership and ensure effective action. Federal, state and local agencies which produce or use data for small geographic units should have a major role in developing the standards. The interests of private user groups should be represented. Also the interests of groups upon whom reporting burdens fall.

Recommendation 5: CENSUS GEOCODES

It is recommended that the Bureau of the Census take the necessary actions to ensure that standard census geocodes are inserted into all basic record files of all future censuses and surveys conducted by the Bureau.

The geocodes to be inserted should be at the finest possible geographic levels (to the extent feasible), and should be accompanied by appropriate coordinates.

Recommendation 6: BUSINESS ADDRESS DIRECTORY

It is recommended that the Bureau of the Census be strongly supported in its request for (fiscal 1972) funds to provide for the advance planning and testing of the development of a computerized address directory of all U.S. business firms and their establishments.

The eventual development of this directory would greatly facilitate rapid automatic geocoding of many types of data derived from the various economic censuses (manufactures, business, etc.) on the same fine basis as data from the Censuses of Population and Housing. This is particularly important in view of the Bureau's present consideration of the feasibility of conducting an annual series of censuses of business, manufactures, and other business — related areas.

It is planned to include in the directory each firm's name, mailing address, industry code, and size code. Provision should also be made for including locational address where this differs from mailing address. Also consideration should be given to inserting standard census geocodes in the directory or a related file, so as to facilitate geocoding of data from the economic censuses.

Recommendation 7: RESEARCH AND DEVELOPMENT

It is recommended that means be found of substantially increasing the resources devoted to research and development of computerized methods of applying geographic base files (and geocoded data from local, state and federal sources) to various urban and rural problems.

Commendable progress has been made but research and development efforts should be accelerated to develop a comprehensive battery of computerized methods for application of geographic base files, and geocoded census and other data, to problems in housing, health, education, welfare, transportation, crime, poverty and other fields.

These computerized methods should be developed at the earliest date possible and sufficient resources should be made available to effect rapid transfer of these methods to local, state and federal government and private agencies which have interest in the development and utilization of these methods.

Recommendation 8: EXTENSION OF FILES

It is recommended that a study be initiated to recommend the best methods of extending geographic base files to provide full coverage on a uniform basis of all areas beyond the present urban coverage.

The study should include consideration of priority areas such as: a) metropolitan areas not so far covered; b) coverage of remainder areas of SMSA's; c) coverage of small urban areas; d) coverage of metropolitan interstices, such as between Baltimore and Washington; and e) coverage of remaining places and rural areas. The study should include consideration of improving files for those areas which have only partly completed geographic base files (e.g., areas which have only Address Coding Guide files). The study should also include consideration of problems, costs, benefits, funding and it should develop a recommended workable program.

Recommendation 9: STREET ADDRESS FILES

It is recommended that a study be initiated to identify and describe national, state and local data files that can be usefully and readily geocoded on a standard basis, using such techniques as street address matching, to provide additional small unit data now available, as well as wider use of these data.

The study should include consideration of problems, costs, manhours, and schedules. It should include descriptions of potential applications for each type of file following geocoding, and it should include recommendations on the most effective means of introducing standards for street addresses, geographic codes, and geographic coding practices in private and governmental agencies at local, state and national levels (these recommendations should include consideration of inserting standard geocodes into the files identified).

Files of agencies such as the following should be considered in the study:

- Social Security Administration (OASI)
- Internal Revenue Service
- state unemployment insurance agencies
- motor vehicle registration agencies
- property tax assessment agencies
- accident report agencies
- crime report agencies
- health and vital statistics agencies
- building permits agencies
- utility companies
- welfare agencies
- transportation planning agencies

The above list is by no means exhaustive and a first task of the study should be to develop as complete a list as possible.

Summary

The recent development of geographic base files for metropolitan areas, and procedures for their use, represent a major breakthrough in geocoding, and provide the basis for a national geocoding system. It is recommended that action be taken to establish an appropriate organizational and institutional framework for, and to provide sufficient resources for, the establishment of a national geocoding system.

It is also recommended that action be taken in a number of specific areas, including:

- updating and maintenance of geographic base files
- development and implementation of a national standard house number assignment system

- establishment of appropriate standards for street addresses, geocodes, and related matters
- insertion of standard small area census geocodes and coordinates into all future census and survey data files
- development of a national computerized address directory for U.S. business firms and their establishments
- research and development of procedures for increased use of geographic base files to assist in providing solutions for urban and rural problems
- extension of the geographic base files for metropolitan areas eventually to provide full coverage of the whole country
- identification and description of data files that contain street addresses, and that could provide small unit data that is not now available.

Provision for development and maintenance of a national geocoding system on an ongoing basis would give explicit recognition to significant emerging developments. It would provide a means for further coordinated development of geographic base files, procedures for the use of the files, and a number of related activities that would substantially increase potential applications of the files to urban and rural problems. And it would provide a proper basis for the geographic organization of metropolitan and state information systems that can be used at national, state and local levels.

COSTS AND BENEFITS

The total cost for development of the metropolitan geographic base files was stated earlier as approximately $15 million.

It is difficult to provide fully reliable cost estimates for extension of these files to cover the entire country without further detailed study. However, these costs are tentatively estimated as being on the order of $4 to $5 million, assuming extension in rural areas would be at the enumeration district level for the most part. Similarly it is difficult to estimate costs of annual updating and maintenance of these files without further detailed study. But tentatively these costs are estimated as being on the order of:

- $1.5 to 2 million annually at the federal level
- $1.5 to 2 million annually at the local level

These estimates are for updating and maintenance *after* development of a full national geocoding system covering the U. S.

Thus the total costs for the initial development and annual updating and maintenance of files for the complete national geocoding system are *tentatively* estimated as follows

    metropolitan areas (already spent) . . . $15   million

    outside metropolitan areas . . . . $4 to 5 million

    updating and maintenance (annually) . . $3 to 4 million

Costs for research and development of procedures for use of the geographic base files and geocoded data files can, of course, vary considerably depending on the scope of the program. Past expenditures have totalled approximately $3 million. An expenditure at the level of $1 million annually for four to five years would probably be sufficient to fund a research and development program that would yield most of the more cost-effective procedures.

Benefits are much more difficult to estimate. What is the value of a map? Who can tell all the uses it might be put to? Who can say what costly errors might have been made if the map were not available? Similarly what is the real value of geocoded data and the analysis, maps, displays and reports that can be produced from data that are well organized geographically? Satisfactory quantitative answers can not be provided for these questions. Yet it is these answers that are needed properly to assess benefits.

Another way of considering the benefits of information, however, is to consider the economic stake involved and to weigh the costs of information against this. The stake is indeed large. The total expenditures that might be affected in operations, planning, policy making or other uses of geographically well-organized metropolitan and state information systems are not known. But if they were, they would certainly be expressed in terms of billions of dollars. The cost of a national geocoding system is indeed small by comparison. As a result of investing in the development of a national geocoding system, the chances are high that sufficient costly errors would be avoided to offset investment costs many times over.

Another way of gauging benefits is to consider whether given tasks can be done for a lower unit cost as a result of a given capital investment, and over what period do the cost savings equal the investment. Reliable estimates of unit costs for geocoding using the recently developed new methods are not yet available. The Census Use Study has some studies under way but results are not expected until late 1971. Additional studies are needed to determine the total volume of geocoding that was feasible under old methods (and the total cost), and the total volume of geocoding that would be feasible using the new methods (and the total cost). At present no such studies are contemplated.

Meanwhile, as stated earlier, it is expected that the recently developed procedures will eventually lead to significant reductions in unit costs for geocoding because of dramatic increases in speed possible with these procedures (preliminary studies show order-of-magnitude increases in speeds are possible). There is every reason to believe that the additional expenditures necessary to complete the national geocoding system would result in substantial cost savings, and that over a relatively short period these cost savings would exceed the amount of the expenditures (considering geocoding applications alone). A further way of gauging the merits of the expenditures is to take some of the special applications, and to consider whether it would pay to develop a complete national geocoding system for one or two of these applications alone. Again this would require further detailed study. But again it is expected that such studies would show quite favorable results. For example, it appears that potential use of the complete national geocoding system in the transportation field alone (for continuing urban transportation planning and state-wide transportation planning) would more than justify the expenditures involved.

In conclusion, it is expected that further study would show a high benefit to cost ratio for additional expenditures that would be necessary for a) extension of the recently-developed geographic base files so as to provide for a complete national geocoding system covering the entire U.S.; b) updating and maintenance of the national geocoding system; and c) research and development to provide for procedures for the use of the system.

Appendix A - **GEOGRAPHIC BASE FILES**

Geographic base files are maps in computer form. They are placed in computer storage to permit the computer to identify and manipulate data geographically. The computer can even use geographic base files to trace routes in much the same way as we use street-highway maps to find our way when travelling through areas that we are not familiar with.

Geographic base files consist of a number of machine readable records in a file. Each record contains locational information for a segment. Usually a segment consists of the portion of a street between two intersections. The basic information contained in a segment record consists of street name, range of addresses, node numbers for the intersections, coordinates for the intersections, block numbers for the blocks on either side of the street segment, local jurisdiction area codes for such areas as health districts, police districts, and school districts; and analysis area codes for such areas as planning analysis areas, traffic zones, poverty areas, etc. Additional codes can be added for all significant points, lines and areas in a region. Since in the geographic base file each point and line is identified in terms of the areas that it is common to, and vice versa, the geographic base file provides a means for identifying all types of point, time and area data on a common comprehensive geographic basis.

There have been several approaches to the development of geographic base files but the one that will undoubtedly be most widely used in the future is the Dual Independent Map Encoding (DIME) approach.

"Dual Independent" refers to the fact that each segment is described by specifying its two end nodes and its right and left blocks. With each node and block uniquely identified the computer can construct two independent "networks," one based on nodes, the other based on blocks. These can then be matched. Mismatches signify errors. When errors are corrected, coordinates for each node are added to indicate the terrestrial position of each node.

DIME type geographic base files have been almost completed for more than 200 metropolitan areas. Two methods have been used. In the first method the DIME files were produced directly from Census Metropolitan Maps supplemented by local address reference material. In the second method DIME features such as node numbers and left and right block indicators were added to Address Coding Guide (ACG) files. Both methods have been described fully in numerous publications — most of which were issued by the Bureau of the Census.[16] The basic method is described in simple illustrations at the end of this appendix.

The second method was used for the 140 largest Standard Metropolitan Statistical Areas (SMSA's), where the 1970 Census of Population and Housing was conducted by mail. Address Coding Guide (ACG) files were developed for these areas to facilitate conduct of the mail census. The first method was used for the remaining smaller SMSA's, where the census was conducted by enumerators. ACG's were not prepared for these areas.

Regardless of which method was used the end result will be basically the same. Standardized DIME type geographic base files will be developed for more than 200 metropolitan areas. These files will be available as completed, later this year in late 1971 and early 1972. Prices will be nominal.

The full complement of geographic base files are being developed by the Bureau of the Census with the support of local, state and federal governmental agencies.

Applications of the files have been developed and will continue to be developed by the Bureau's Census Use Study with similar local-state-federal support.

Particularly striking is the number of agencies that have participated in the funding of the development of the files and the funding of the research and development of tools that can be used in geographic base file applications.

Dime type geographic base files have been produced only for urban areas so far. The basic method used for urban areas is illustrated in the following pages.

The DIME technique may also be used for preparing compatible DIME type geographic base files for rural areas. Street address

---

16 Many of the publications are listed in the bibliography at the end of the report. An example of a Census Metropolitan Map is included in Appendix C to this report.

information, appearing in DIME files for urban areas, would be
replaced by rural highway designations; census tract and block
numbers would be replaced by other area codes.

A GEOGRAPHIC BASE FILE IS A DESCRIPTION OF AN AREA (STREETS, INTERSECTIONS, GEOGRAPHIC CODES, ADDRESSES) IN COMPUTER READABLE FORM

Figure 1: Geographic Base Files

The standard street map is a simple, graphic device we use daily for relating
ourselves, other people, known and unknown places to the overall spatial
environment. Map data can be recorded in computerized files to permit the
computer records in urban-regional data files to be associated with their geographical locations in much the same way as a map allows us to relate to our
physical surroundings. Information files designed to relate data with their
geographical locations are called geographic base files.

Source: Figure 1 and the following figures in this appendix appeared in "A
Geographic Base File for Urban Data Systems," System Development Corporation, Santa Monica, California, 1969.

Legends for the figures were adapted from the text of the same publication —
in some cases with considerable modification.

273

THE DUAL INDEPENDENT MAP ENCODING (DIME) APPROACH, DEVELOPED AT THE NEW HAVEN CENSUS USE STUDY, REPRESENTS URBAN GEOGRAPHY AS A PATTERN OF BOUNDARIES AND AREAS

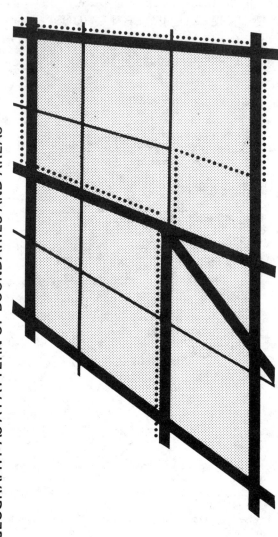

Figure 2: The DIME Approach

The DIME approach combines street address information with information which describes the street-highway-boundary network. A DIME geographic base file is essentially a file of segment records, where a typical segment is a portion of a street length defined by intersecting streets. Segments may also be such things as natural features, railroad tracks, local jurisdictional area boundaries, and the like. The basic feature of a DIME file is that each node (intersection), segment (street length), and block (area bounded by segments), are uniquely identified.

A DIME FILE IS A COMPLETE LIST OF BOUNDARY SEGMENTS CONTAINING:

Street Name

Street Address Ranges

Street Intersections

Intersection Coordinates

Census Tract and Block Codes

Local Jurisdiction Codes

Figure 3: Information in a DIME File

A basic DIME file contains for each segment in the urban region locational identifying information such as the street name, address ranges on the left and right block face, numbers and coordinates for the nodes at the beginning and end of the segment, census tract and block codes for the two block faces; and any local area codes that were added at the time of preparation such as codes for police, fire, health and school districts, or analysis area codes for planning analysis areas, traffic zones, poverty areas and so on. Additional codes can be added to the basic DIME file for areas, lines (segments), and points (nodes), at any time later.

FOR EACH STREET SEGMENT

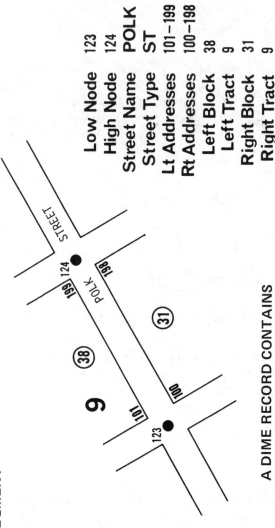

Low Node	123
High Node	124
Street Name	POLK
Street Type	ST
Lt Addresses	101–199
Rt Addresses	100–198
Left Block	38
Left Tract	9
Right Block	31
Right Tract	9

A DIME RECORD CONTAINS

Figure 4: DIME Record Contents

A single record in a geographic base file developed by using the DIME technique describes a segment — usually a street segment. All the information necessary to locate the segment, associate addresses with it, associate it to surrounding blocks, and associate it with census tracts or other areas is included in the initial record. Local jurisdiction or other area codes added at the time of initial preparation are also included. Coordinates are added in a subsequent step. Additional codes for areas, lines (segments), and points (nodes) may be added at any time later.

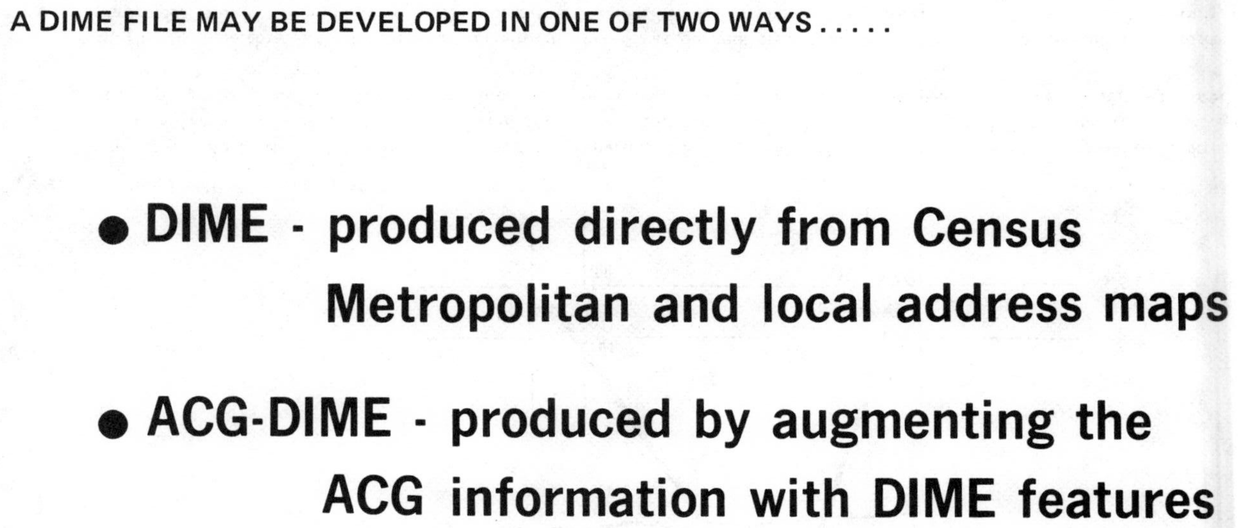

A DIME FILE MAY BE DEVELOPED IN ONE OF TWO WAYS......

● DIME - produced directly from Census Metropolitan and local address maps

● ACG-DIME - produced by augmenting the ACG information with DIME features

Figure 5: Alternative Methods of Developing DIME Files

DIME type files are now almost completed for over 200 metropolitan areas. Two basic methods were used. In the first method the DIME file was produced directly from the Census Metropolitan Maps supplemented by local address reference material. In the second method DIME features such as node numbers and left and right block indicators were added to Address Coding Guide (ACG) files. Regardless of which method was used the end product will be basically the same.

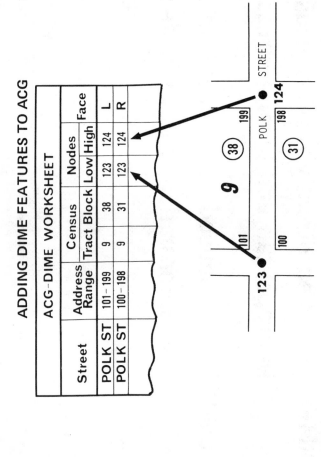

ADDING DIME FEATURES TO ACG

ACG-DIME WORKSHEET

| Street | Address Range | Census | | Nodes | | Face |
		Tract	Block	Low	High	
POLK ST	101–199	9	38	123	124	L
POLK ST	100–198	9	31	123	124	R

Figure 6: Adding DIME Features to ACG

This is an illustration of the second method of preparing DIME files. The Census Bureau generated a geographic street listing for those SMSA's for which ACG's had been developed. Additional data elements were encoded to convert the ACG to a DIME geographic base file. These features included node numbers associated with each end of a block face, as well as left and right block face indicators for blocks adjacent to the segment.

In the first method all the information shown above was derived from Census Metropolitan Maps and local address reference materials, and was encoded on a segment rather than a block face basis. Thus for the segment shown above only *one* line of information would have been encoded by the first method.

Appendix B - MASTER ENUMERATION
DISTRICT LIST (MEDList)

The Master Enumeration District List (MEDlist) is a listing of 1970 census geographic codes and population and housing counts for all enumeration districts and block groups in the country. Since Congressional district and other area totals may be compiled from the MEDlist, it is an important tool for Congressional and state redistricting.

The MEDlist is also an important tool for utilizing the 1970 census summary tapes. It provides a means of associating the names of counties, minor civil divisions (MCD's) or census county divisions(CCD's) and places with the geographic identification codes found on the tapes. (Similar information is provided in the Geographic Area Code Index.)

The types of geographic codes found on the MEDlist are shown in Attachment 1 and a glossary of terms in Attachment 2.[17] Additionally coordinates are included for the population centroids of enumeration districts and block groups.

---

17 Source: Attachments 1 and 2 were extracted from publications of the Bureau of the Census.

Attachment 1

1970 CENSUS OF POPULATION AND HOUSING
MASTER ENUMERATION DISTRICT LIST (MEDlist)

State: Michigan Frame No. 001 0

(1) 1970	(2) 1960	(3) Fed. Std. County	(4) County of tab.	(5) CC.	(6) MCD/CCD	(7) Place Code	(8) Desc.	(9) Size	(10) SCA	(11) SMSA	(12) Urbanized area	(13) Tracted area	(14) Prefix	(15) Code	(16) SEA	(17) ESR	(18) CBD	(19) Area name	(20) Tract Basic	(21) Suffix	(22) Blk. grp.	(23) ED Code	(24) Suffix	(25) Urb./rural	(26) Ward	(27) Cong. dist.	(28) Housing	(29) Pop.
26	34	121		1														MUSKEGON									49831	149493
26	34	121		1	090					5320		5320	1	34062	06	050	1	Ravenna TWP	0029			0442		1		09	650	2102
26	34	121		1	090	2275	4	02		5320		5320	1	34062	06	050	1	Ravenna Village	0029			0443		1		09	250	801
26	34	121		1	090		7											Remainder of MCD (or CCD)									400	1301
26	34	121		1	095	2345	4	06			5320	5320	1	34062	06	050	1	Roosevelt Park City	0022					0		09	633	2578
26	34	121		1	095												1	Roosevelt Park City	0022					0		09	633	2578
																	1				1			0		09	200	885
																					2					09	312	1175
																					3					09	121	518
26	34	121		1	110		7			5320		5320	1	34062	06	050		White Hall TWP									581	1930
																	1		0030			0404		1		09	30	90
																	1		0036			0405		1		09	40	125
																	1		0037			0406		1		09	72	150
																	1		0038			0407		0		09	60	130
																	1		0040		1			0		09	165	625
																			0040		2					09	214	810

Note: Explanation of column heading abbreviations: Federal Standard County; County of Tabulation; Central County Code (CC); Minor Civil Division (MCD)/Census County Division (CCD); Place Description; Standard Consolidated Area (SCA); Standard Metropolitan Statistical Area (SMSA); Universal Area Code; State Economic Area (SEA); Economic Sub-Region (ESR); Central Business District (CBD); Block Group; Enumeration District (ED); Urban/Rural; Congressional District.

Attachment 2

Master Enumeration District List — Glossary of Terms

1. 1970 STATE — FEDERAL STANDARD STATE CODE
2. 1960 STATE — 1960 CENSUS STATE CODE
3. FED. STD. COUNTY — FEDERAL STANDARD COUNTY CODE
4. COUNTY OF TAB. — COUNTY OF TABULATION
5. CC — CENTRAL COUNTY CODE
6. MCD/CCD — MINOR CIVIL DIVISION OR CENSUS COUNTY DIVISION
7. PLACE CODE
8. PLACE DES. — PLACE DESCRIPTION
9. PLACE SIZE CODE
10. SCA — STANDARD CONSOLIDATED AREA
11. SMSA — STANDARD METROPOLITAN STATISTICAL AREA
12. URBANIZED AREA
13. TRACTED AREA
14. UNIV. AREA PREFIX — UNIVERSAL AREA CODE LEVEL
15. UNIV. AREA CODE — UNIVERSAL AREA CODE
16. SEA — STATE ECONOMIC AREA
17. ESR — ECONOMIC SUB-REGION
18. CBD — CENTRAL BUSINESS DISTRICT
19. AREA NAME
20. BASIC TRACT CODE
21. TRACT SUFFIX CODE
22. BLK/GRP — BLOCK GROUP
23. ED. CODE — ENUMERATION DISTRICT CODE
24. ED. SUFFIX — ENUMERATION DISTRICT TYPE
25. U/R — URBAN/RURAL CLASSIFICATION
26. WARD CODE
27. CD — CONGRESSIONAL DISTRICT
28. 1970 HOUSING COUNTS
29. 1970 POPULATION COUNTS

Appendix C - **CENSUS MAPS**[18]

Three kinds of maps were produced for the 1970 census.

1. *Metropolitan Map Series (MMS)*

For the urban core portion of each standard metropolitan statistical area, a set of standardized maps was prepared showing all political and statistical areas, and their boundaries, recognized in the census. These map sheets are approximately 18 inches by 24 inches in size and are at a scale of 1 inch equals 2,000 feet. They contain street and street names and all census-recognized boundaries down to the city block level. This map set contains a large block numbered area in the central portion of the urbanized area which does not contain enumeration districts (ED's) and may recognized by the absence of ED boundaries and numbers. This area is known as the "computer list" area for which addresses, recorded on computer tape, were used for the mailing of census questionnaires. For the area in which computer list enumeration methods were used, unpublished data are available by block groups rather than by ED. Census boundary symbols and area identifications and a portion of the map for Springfield, Ohio appear at the end of this appendix. Data for areas beyond the county tie-in line boundary are not shown on these maps but are shown on the county maps.

2. *County Maps*

For the areas lying outside the boundaries of the metropolitan map coverage areas, principal reliance was placed on the county maps issued by the highway departments of the states. Census enumeration boundaries were superimposed on these maps. They are generally at a scale of one-half inch to the mile with sheet sizes of approximately 18 inches by 24 inches. The Blackford County, Indiana map is typical of the county map series. A portion of this map appears following those for Springfield, Illinois metropolitan map. These county maps also contain a list of the places for which place maps have been prepared.

---

18 The basis for the information contained in the text of this appendix is *Availability of 1970 Census Data for Congressional and State Redistricting, House Report No. 91-1024,* U.S. House of Representatives, Washington, D.C., U.S. Government Printing Office, 1970.

3. *Place Maps*

These maps usually are reproductions by the Census Bureau of maps which have been acquired from other sources and show enumeration district and other boundary features. They are at scales ranging from 400 to 1,000 feet per inch and include both incorporated and unincorporated places. The map for Montpelier, Indiana (one of the places in Blackford County, Indiana) is typical of the place map series (see portion of map following that for Blackford County, Indiana).

The availability, content and cost of the above maps are discussed in greater detail in *Data Access Description* CG-1 and Summary Tape User Memorandum No. 27. Orders for the map sheets can be placed with Geography Division, Bureau of the Census, Washington, D.C. 20233.

1970 CENSUS BOUNDARY SYMBOLS AND
AREA IDENTIFICATIONS

UNITED STATES ——————— MEXICO	International
WASHINGTON ——————— OREGON	State
DE KALB CO. ——————— STEELE CO.	County or equivalent area
▬·▬·▬·▬	Incorporated Place
NOBLE	Incorporated Place Name
NOBLE✳	Incorporated Place coextensive with Minor Civil Division or Census County Division
—x—x—x—	1960 Incorporated Place boundary where different from January 1, 1970 boundary
●●●●●●●●	Ward or equivalent area
16	Ward Number
OOOOOOOO	Congressional District
15	Congressional District Number
▪ ▪ ▪ ▪	Minor Civil Division or Census County Division
Rock Twp.	Minor Civil Division or Census County Division Name
▬▬▬▬	Urbanized Area Limit
▬ ▬ ▬ ▬ ▬ ▬	Unincorporated Place
DALE	Unincorporated Place Name
▲ ▲ ▲ ▲	County Tie—In (Beyond this line ED boundaries are shown on other maps.)

1970 CENSUS BOUNDARY SYMBOLS AND AREA IDENTIFICATIONS

   Census Tract

586

Census Tract Number
(Numbers greater than 9500
identify block numbering areas
where no census tracts exist.)

Enumeration District
(Other boundaries are also ED boundaries. The
ED boundary symbol is shown only where it
does not coincide with other boundaries except
that it always appears to separate the computer
list area from the ED area.)

ED 50   Enumeration District Number

S -ED 45   Special Enumeration District Number

Special Enumeration District for
which no boundary is shown
(Usually a special type of dwelling,
e.g., institution)

245   Block Number

223*

Asterisk indicates that this block number
is repeated on an adjacent map sheet or
elsewhere within the block

Features crossed by these "Fish—Hooks" are
not block boundaries

Arrow is used to connect identification label
to an area that is too small to contain the label.

Inset Map Limits

Outer limit of block area
(Symbol is shown only on sheets needed to
indicate the report in which block statistics
appear.)

Central City
(Used where needed to clarify extent of
incorporated place)

Detail From
1970 CENSUS METROPOLITAN MAP
Springfield, Illinois Area

For boundary symbols and area identification, see preceding two pages

Additional Detail From
1970 CENSUS METROPOLITAN MAP
Springfield, Illinois Area

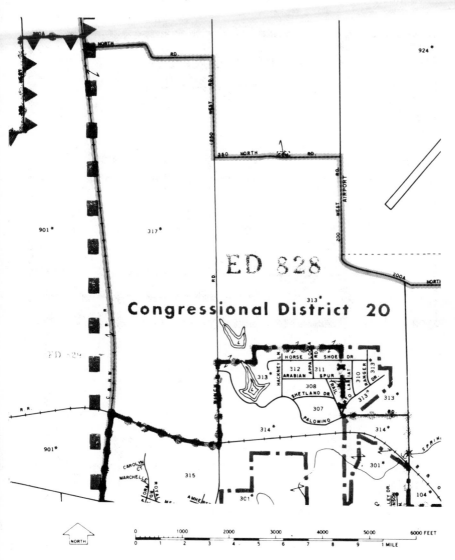

For boundary symbols and area identification, see preceding pages

Detail From
1970 CENSUS COUNTY MAP
Blackford County, Indiana

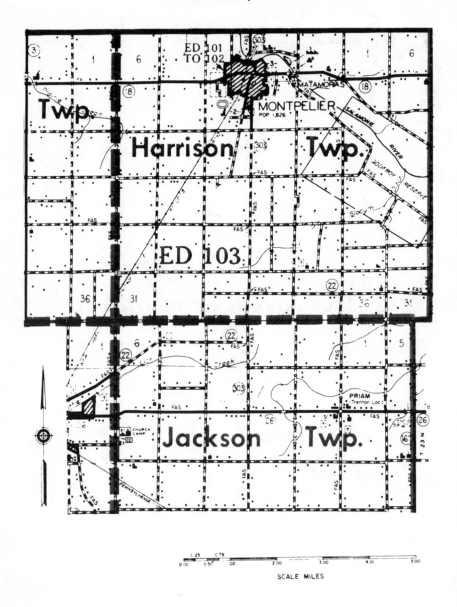

SCALE MILES

Detail From
1970 CENSUS PLACE MAP
MONTPELIER
Blackford County, Indiana

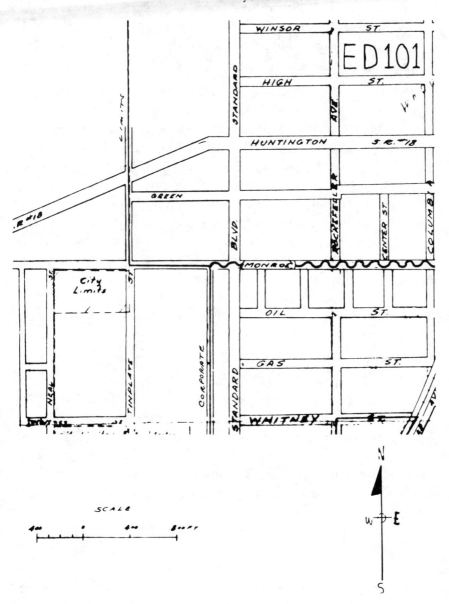

Appendix D - SPECIAL TERMS

While every effort was made to avoid use of technical terms in the report this was not feasible throughout. The terms "census tract," and "enumeration district" or "block group" often puzzle people not familiar with census operations. These are explained below.[19] Also a note is included on these types of coordinates used for different geocoding applications.

Census Tracts

Census tracts are small subdivisions with an average of about 4,000 persons, which have been established in every standard metropolitan statistical area (SMSA). Their boundaries normally are streets and other readily identified features, such as streams, and also the legal boundaries of municipalities. Maps of all census tracts are published by the Bureau of the Census. An SMSA consists of a city of 50,000 or over, the county in which it is located plus any adjoining counties which are closely integrated with it, as by commuting. For example, the SMSA for Washington, D.C., includes the District of Columbia, Montgomery, and Prince Georges Counties in Maryland, the cities of Alexandria, Fairfax and Falls Church, and the counties of Arlington, Fairfax, Loudon, and Prince William in Virginia. Census tracts have been established for this entire area.

Enumeration Districts and Block Groups

Enumeration districts (ED's) are small areas with an average population of about 800 persons. They have been established as administrative units for the control of the census work and have boundaries which are easily recognized on the ground. ED's also recognize the legal boundaries of cities, townships, and counties. Maps of ED's are published by the Bureau of the Census. In the larger metropolitan areas, where the census was taken by mail, "block groups" were used in place of ED's. Block groups are subdivisions of census tracts with an average population of about 1,000 persons.

---

19 Source: *Availability of 1970 Census Data for Congressional and State Redistricting, House Report 91-1024,* U.S. House of Representatives. Washington, D.C.: U.S. Government Printing Office, 1970.

Coordinates

The type of coordinate system used for geocoding purposes depends on the application. The system must of course fully cover the area of concern – the country, state, metropolitan area, etc.

For national data systems universal coordinates are used – for example latitude-longitude or Universal Transverse Mercator coordinates. For urban-regional data systems local coordinates may be used – for example state plane coordinates or an arbitrary system of coordinates. To facilitate wider use of urban-regional data the local coordinates should be convertible to universal coordinates by simple computations. This is possible with state plane coordinates or any arbitrary system of local coordinates which is defined or definable in terms of universal coordinates.

BIBLIOGRAPHY

Alexander, Robert. "Coupling Satellite Information with Urban Development," 25th National Conference of Association for Computing Machinery, New York, 1970.

Association for Computing Machinery: Proceedings of 23rd National Conference. Princeton, New Jersey: Brandom/Systems, Inc., 1968.

"Availability of 1970 Census Data for Congressional and State Redistricting." House Report No. 91-1024, U.S. House of Representatives. Washington, D.C.: U. S. Government Printing Office, 1970.

Barraclough, Robert E., "Mapping and EDP," *Proceedings of the Annual Meeting of the American Society of Planning Officials,* Toronto, Canada, 1965.

Barraclough, Robert E., and Clarke, Donald J. "Geographic Identification and Area Measurement by a Semi-Automatic Method," *Proceedings of the Conference on Improved Highway Engineering Productivity,* Boston, 1965.

Barraclough Robert E., and Rosenberg, Paul. "The AULT System – for Automatic Location Identification and Land Area Measurement," *Photogrammetric Engineering,* XXXII (September, 1966), 842-8.

Berry, Brian J. L., Morrill, R. L., and Tobler, W. R. "Geographic Ordering of Information: New Opportunities," *The Professional Geographer*, (July, 1964).

Bisco, Ralph L. (ed.). *Data Bases, Computers, and the Social Sciences.* New York: John Wiley and Sons, 1970.

Brounstein, Sidney H. "Some Concepts and Techniques for Constructing and Using a Geographically-Oriented Urban Data Base," *Journal of the Socio-Economic Planning Sciences* (1968).

Census Tract Manual. Washington, D.C.: U.S. Bureau of the Census, 1966.

Census Tract Papers. (Series GE-40.) Washington, D.C.: U.S. Bureau of the Census, 1968.

Census Use Studies. (Report Nos. 2, 4, 5, 7, 9, 10, 12, 13, and 15.) Washington, D.C.: U.S. Bureau of the Census, 1963-71.

Chicago Area Transportation Study, Final Report, Volumes I, II, III. Chicago: Chicago Area Transportation Study, 1959-60.

Colvocoresses, A. P. "A Unified Transverse Reference System," *Proceedings of the Tri-State Conference on a Comprehensive Unified Land Data System (CULDATA)*, University of Cincinnati, Cincinnati, Ohio, 1966.

Dial, Robert B. "Street Address Conversion System," Seattle, Washington: University of Washington, Urban Data Center, 1964.

Directory of Federal Statistics for Local Areas — Guide to Sources, Washington, D.C.: U.S. Bureau of the Census, 1966.

Dueker, Kenneth J. "Spatial Data Systems." Evanston: Northwestern University, Department of Geography, 1966.

Dueker, Kenneth J. and Horton, Frank E. "Urban Change Detection Systems: Status and Prospects." Study supported by U.S. Geological Survey. University of Iowa, Iowa City, Iowa: Institute of Urban and Regional Research, forthcoming.

"Evaluation of Data Requirements and Collection Techniques for Transportation Planning." Report by Creighton, Hamburg Inc. Washington, D.C.: National Cooperative Highway Research

Program of Highway Research Board, forthcoming.

Fasteau, Herman H., and Minton, George. "Automated Geographic Coding System." (1963 Economic Censuses: Research Reports, No. 1.) Washington, D.C.: U.S. Bureau of the Census, 1965.

FRIS: A Spatial Information System — A Pilot Study. (Series of Reports.) Sundbyberg, Sweden: Control Board for Real Estate Data, 1970-71. (Address is Vintergatan 1, Box 123, 172-23 Sundbyberg 1, Sweden.)

Gaits, George M. "Thematic Mapping by Computer," Journal of the British Cartographic Society, (June, 1969).

Garrison, William L., et al;. "Five Papers on Remote Sensing and Urban Information Systems." Illinois: Northwestern University, Department of Geography, 1966.

Gearhart, Burton C., and Littschwager, John M. "Legislative Districting by Computer," Behavioral Science (September, 1969).

"Geographic Base File: Address Coding Guide Improvement Program" (Supervisor's and Coder's Manuals.) Washington, D.C.: U. S. Bureau of the Census, 1970.

"Geographic Base File: Census Non-Mail Areas." (Supervisor's and Coder's Manuals.) Washington, D.C.: U.S. Bureau of the Census, 1969.

"A Geographic Base File for Urban Data Systems." Santa Monica, California: Systems Development Corporation, 1969.

"Geographic Coding Instructions." (Supervisor's and Coder's Manuals.) Washington, D.C.: U.S. Bureau of the Census, 1967 and 1968.

Highway Research Record. (Report No. 194.) Washington, D.C.: Highway Research Board, 1971.

Jaro, Matthew A. "Grid Related Information Display System (GRIDS)." Proceedings of American Statistical Association, Detroit, December, 1970.

MacLachlan, K. A. "The Coordinated Method of O and D Analysis," Proceedings of the Twenty Ninth Annual Meeting of the Highway Research Board, Washington, D.C., 1949.

Nordbeck, Stig, and Rystedt, Bengt. "Computer Cartography Point in Polygon Programs," Lund, Sweden: C. W. K. Gleerup, 1967.

Pisarski, Alan E. "Geocoding Transportation Data." Unpublished paper, Washington, D.C., 1969.

"A Proposal for the Geographic Base File Maintenance Program." Washington, D.C.: U. S. Bureau of the Census, 1971.

Schneider, Jerry B. "Solving Urban Location Problems: Human Intuition Versus the Computer," *Journal of American Institute of Planners* (March, 1971).

"Some Applications of ACG/DIME Files in Transportation and Regional Planning." Unpublished report by Creighton, Hamburg, Inc. for Department of Transportation, Washington, D.C., 1970.

Southern California Regional Information Study. (Series of Reports.) Los Angeles, California: Southern California Regional Information Study, 1970 and 1971.

"The State Coordinate Systems." (Special Publication, No. 235.) Washington, D.C.: U. S. Coast and Geodetic Survey, 1945.

"SYMAP V, Users' Reference Manual." Cambridge; Laboratory of Computer Graphics, Harvard University, 1968.

Tobler, Waldo R. "Automation and Cartography," *The Geographical Review* (October, 1959).

Tobler, Waldo R. "Automation in the Preparation of Thematic Maps." Presented at the Technical Symposium of the International Cartographic Association, Edinburgh, 1964.

"Universal Transverse Metcator Grid" (TM5-241-8). Washington, D.C.: Department of the Army, 1958.

"Urban and Regional Information Systems." Study by Systems Development Corp. for U. S. Department of Housing and Urban Development. Washington, D.C.: Government Printing Office, 1968.

Urban and Regional Information Systems Association, Proceedings, Kent, Ohio: Kent State University, 1967, 1968, 1969, and 1970.

294

Use of Address Coding Guide in Geographic Coding — Case Studies, Washington, D.C.: U. S. Bureau of the Census, 1970.

Use of Census Data in Urban Transportation Planning. (Special Report, No. 121.) Washington, D.C.: Highway Research Board, 1971.

448-559 O - 71 - 20

CHAPTER 4

HOW MUCH DO AGENCIES KNOW ABOUT ERROR STRUCTURE?

By

Harry Grubert

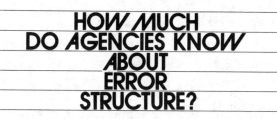

HOW MUCH DO AGENCIES KNOW ABOUT ERROR STRUCTURE?

TABLE OF CONTENTS

The extent to which federal data producers have investigated the error structures of their statistics is an important indicator of how well the statistical system is functioning. Analyses of error and its components can aid producers in determining how accuracy can best be improved and inform users how the data can best be used and help them decide whether further expenditure on improvements would be worthwhile. This essay reports on a Commission survey in which various federal statistical series and periodic surveys were selected and the producing agency was asked to submit information it had on the series' structure of errors.

Although there was considerable variation, both for different statistics in the same agency and across agencies, the responses to the survey showed disappointingly little knowledge of error structure. Sampling errors were estimated for most statistics based on probability samples, but there were, with only a few exceptions, very few analyses of response and other nonsampling errors, even in cases in which, because of long recall or the use of incomplete records, these were likely to be substantial. In judgment samples, estimates of error frequently were based on comparisons with a universe total or benchmark that is periodically available, but there seemed to be little interest in the accuracy of the bench-marks themselves (which in some cases are probably subject to the same nonsampling errors as are the samples.) Furthermore, in going through the agency submissions, it was possible in a few cases to think of improvements in concept and design or ways of measuring error which would not have been difficult to adopt.

This is not to say that every series should receive an intensive analysis exemplified by the few thorough submissions in the survey. The next section will attempt to clarify the benefits of error measurement and how they may be expected to depend on the way the data are used, the uncertainty about possible error in view of the nature of the response and the way they are processed, the extent to which an increase in expense might affect a reduction in whatever error is found, and so on. The feasibility of error analysis is also only one element in the decision on how the series should be designed. For many of the statistics in the survey, however, it was not really necessary to make very precise calculations, even if they were possible, in order to conclude that more analysis of error would be beneficial.

Some responses to the Commission's survey indicated that a high level of error analysis is possible. As agencies expand their study of error and its components, the statistical system as a whole will benefit because it will become clear under what conditions certain kinds of error tend to arise and how they can be dealt with. It will therefore be easier to identify areas of potential weakness and concentrate on strengthening them.

WHY ANALYSIS OF ERROR STRUCTURE CAN BE USEFUL

The benefits of error analysis arise from several sources. If the error structure is known, improvements in the data can be made most efficiently, and in fact, reductions in error may be possible without additional cost. The user can also benefit by having a more precise idea of the level of error for otherwise whatever level of accuracy there is may be wasted. For example, data may in fact be accurate but a user may not give it much credence for fear that it is unreliable. More information on error may also enable the user to sharpen the inferences he makes from the data. Moreover,

302

once the characteristics of the data are better known, users can make more informed judgments on how important a further improvement in error would be to them and producers may be in a better position to know how much reduction in error could be achieved, if more resources were devoted to it.

There is a number of ways in which analysis of error can be useful in improving a statistic. For instance, it may lead to the following kinds of change:

a. *Correction for constant bias.*

An example is the correction for housing starts not covered by permits in permit-issuing areas. Anticipations data also frequently have known biases as predictors of actuals and corrections are made, as in the Office of Business Economics survey of sales and inventory expectations.

b. *Questionnaire redesign which results from knowing that certain responses are unreliable.*

The greater detail in types of income now requested annually in the Current Population Survey is an attempt to aid recall, and close the large known discrepency from benchmark totals. The planned use of five quarterly interviews in the forthcoming Consumer Expenditure Survey is partly an effort to deal with "telescoping" effects which have been discovered in surveys involving long recall.

c. *Increased education of enumerators where they are important contributors to response errors.*

For example, Census has found that, in the area part of the housing starts survey, telling the enumerator to vary his route in his successive monthly canvasses of an area reduces the number of starts missed.

d. *Reallocation of the sample in response to knowledge of constituents of error.*

e. *Switch to a new sampling frame or the use of a combination of two frames if a substantial part of the universe is being missed.*

The periodic crime victimization survey now being planned is a response to evidence that a great deal of crime is not reported to the police.

It is clear that the most useful analyses of error frequently are the by-product of agency control systems designed to spot deterioration in performance. A detailed knowledge of error is, therefore, part of the whole process of carefully designing a data collection process in the first place and controlling its output subsequently. A determination to find more about error sometimes also requires the adoption of new procedures, such as probability sampling, which may reduce the error as well as generate more information about it.

Improvement is, of course, also possible without any very precise analyses of error. In particular, in the early stages of a series it may be easy to identify weak areas such as clear gaps in the sampling frame, or to think of sensible bases for stratification.

As noted above, error analyses can also be useful by making possible more informed judgments on whether further resources should be devoted to improving a series. Similarly, knowledge of error begins to make it possible to decide about the trade-off between timeliness and precision. One example of cases in which the *capability* of analyzing error would be useful is offered by agencies who solve the problem of error by waiting for complete response from the whole population, which may take a very long time. If they made the effort to analyze the effect of nonresponse or even estimate sampling error, it might become clear that the data could be made much more timely without giving up much accuracy.

Apart from possible data improvements which may result, knowledge of the amount of error alone, even if the error is not reduced, may be valuable to the user. Although there is really not much information on how statistics are used and what losses are incurred by users if it turns out they have made errors in judgment, it may help clarify things to look at a few simple examples. These will illustrate how the interest in error structure can vary and therefore may clarify just why knowing error is useful. In these examples, we will assume that existing error cannot be reduced and the only question is the importance to the user of knowing its size. We will neglect, for the moment anyway, the question of constant bias.

Consider, as an example, data on population, used in the decision to build retail outlets, or data on the number of pre-school children, used to plan school facilities. As long as the number provided is an unbiased estimate of the actual value, how interested is the user in knowing the standard deviation? That is, would he do anything different if he knew the error and how much better off would he be? We can gain some insight by starting with the extreme case in which knowing the error doesn't help because it doesn't affect decisions. This happens if two conditions are satisfied. The first is that the marginal profit (or marginal cost) of an action with respect to different states of the world (e.g., how the marginal profit of a slightly larger store varies for different true levels of population) is linear. In such a case the marginal profit averaged over all outcomes is just equal to the marginal profit with mean population. The second is that the decision-maker cannot control his exposure to risk by taking different courses of action.[1] Knowledge of the error becomes important as one moves from this special case by introducing:

a. Asymmetrical changes in the marginal effect of an action as the true value of the variable moves around its expected level, as would be the case, for example, if the costs of overbuilding are much higher than the sacrifice in profits from underbuilding. Similarly, if the marginal benefit of a given change in the money supply at a rate of inflation of 4 percent is much different from the average of the marginal benefits at 2 and 6 percent, as it probably is, then knowing the error is useful.

b. The ability to choose alternative actions with different amounts of risk. For example, the decision-maker may be considering alternative unrelated investments or different ways of building a given facility whose profits are more or less sensitive to errors in estimating population. In these cases knowing the magnitude of error may be important because it affects the relative risk of the alternative policies.

Another example which illustrates the value of knowing the

---

1 This is the old Theil-Simon result on quadratic objective functions and certainty equivalance. This can be found in H. Theil: *A Note on Certainty Equivalence in Dynamic Planning,* "Econometrica," pp. 346-349.

amount of data error can be found in the theory of estimation with errors in the variables.[2] Consider the standard example of estimating the linear relationship between X and Y, each of which are measured with error. Whether or not the extent of this error is useful in estimating the relationship depends on the question one is asking. Does one want to know the relationship between the "true" (unobserved) values of X and Y or does one only want to *predict* the (true or observed) level of Y given that one has *observed* a level of X?

An example in which the relationship between the "true" values of X and Y is of interest might be the use of a cross-section of schools to find how much school performance would be improved if all schools increased a certain educational input by a given amount. Here one is interested in the effect of changing the mean of the distribution of X itself, rather than predicting what will happen if one draws from the current distribution.

If the user wants to know the relationship between the true values of X and Y, it is well known that the least squares estimate of b, the coefficient of X, is downward based if X is measured with error. If the sample is very large, the estimate of b tends to

$$\frac{1}{1 + \dfrac{\sigma_u^2}{\sigma_x^2}}$$

of its true value where σ_u^2 is the observational mean squared error associated with X and σ_x^2 is the variance in the true value of X. The reason for this bias is that high observed values of X must on the average be higher than their true value because one of the ways of being observed at a high level is to have an error in the positive direction. It is clear that the knowledge of σ_u^2 can be used to improve the estimate of b.

On the other hand, if one is interested only in predicting the (true or observed) level Y if X is observed, the knowledge of σu^2 is unnecessary, for a straightforward application of least squares on the observed values will yield consistent predictions. That is, if one

---

2 This discussion of estimation with errors in the variables is adapted from J. Johnson, *Econometric Methods,* McGraw-Hill 1963.

is only interested in prediction, the true values of X do not play any role.[3] Furthermore, decision-makers who use predictions may not require error analyses of the type dealt with here. They will usually have a record of past forecast error of which data error is one of the components and a direct analysis of data error may, therefore, be unnecessary from their point of view.

The cost of making accurate estimates of error, nonsampling error in particular, may also vary a great deal. This depends on available records, on the existence of independent totals or benchmarks, on the existence of an alternative sampling frame that can be used periodically as a check, and so on. A complicating factor is that the magnitude of error and the cost of finding it tend to be positively associated. For example, responses based on personal recollection of expenditures are likely to be unreliable and also difficult to check in order to discover how unreliable.

The ability to make error estimates is only one of the considerations that enter into the choice of how to produce the statistic itself. In the Commission's survey, one of the common responses by agencies was that their only estimate of error was made by periodic comparisons with population totals or benchmarks. That was so because the series are generated by taking judgment samples of large respondents which are linked to earlier population totals. This may be a reasonable procedure in a low turnover industry which is dominated by large producers even though it restricts the error studies that are possible.

Summing up some of the points of this section, we conclude that the effort devoted to studying error should depend on:

a. The uncertainty about possible error in view of the nature of the response and the way it is processed.
b. The way data are used in terms of decisions and inferences.
c. The cost of making assessments of error.
d. The possible sources of error whose contribution can be identified and possibly be reduced.

---

3 We have been assuming that the σu^2 is constant over time. If it is not and its variation is known, this could presumably be used in improving predictions. If the error is known to be low, the forecast could be different from one with a high error.

e. The extent to which an increase in expense might affect a reduction in whatever error is found. This determines the extent to which the current level of error may be inappropriate.

HOW THE STATISTICS IN THE SURVEY WERE SELECTED AND THE FORM OF AGENCY RESPONSE

The statistics in the survey are all produced by agencies covered by the Coordinated Statistical Budget. That budget does not include the statistical activities of the National Bureau of Standards or of the National Oceanic and Atmospheric Administration.[4] The sample was chosen by Professor Stanley Lebergott who initiated the study. Apart from the Bureau of the Census and Bureau of Labor Statistics these statistics were drawn from a list of series and periodic surveys by Steven Klein of the Commission Staff in consultation with the Statistical Policy and Management Information Systems Division (SPMISD) of the Office of Management Budget. An effort was made to select important surveys about which agencies would be expected to be best informed. In some agencies no surveys were particularly earth shaking in which case typical surveys were selected. Taking the study as a whole, it should be biased, if anything, toward a favorable conclusion of how much is known about error.

Responses were in the form of letters from senior agency officials together with the enclosure of any existing studies. It was frequently necessary to make further inquiries for clarification or for studies that may have been overlooked.

DETAILED SUMMARIES OF AGENCY RESPONSES

In this section agency responses to the Commission's survey are summarized. In the summaries we will concentrate on the kinds of errors that are likely to be found in each statistic described. For example, response error is probably not very important in reporting something like the number of tons of bituminous coal produced every month. The summaries will in most cases also include

---

4 See Section F of *Special Analyses, Budget of the U.S. Government, 1972.*

a brief description of how the statistics are calculated because this indicates what the sources of error are likely to be and conveys some information on how carefully a survey has been designed.

Since knowledge of error structure can't really be separated from the whole process of designing and producing statistics, it will be necessary at times to comment on whether the statistics are constructed in a sensible way or whether data gathered are really useful in answering the pertinent questions.

A common difficulty in assessing how much an agency knows about errors is vagueness in what a statistic is supposed to represent. Sometimes the error structure of statistics with respect to a given definition may be known, but whether the definition is really a useful representation of reality cannot be determined in the conventional error analysis framework.

One area in which agencies may be emphasizing the wrong measurement is the frequent concern with errors in the *level* of a variable when changes may be of primary importance. When error studies are referred to in the summaries, they will always be for the level unless specifically stated otherwise. In the case of successive independent samples, the user could presumably calculate the sampling error in the change from the sampling errors of the levels but the fact that they are not displayed for the user may reflect an incorrect orientation in the program. The same is true in the frequent use of comparison with a benchmark in which the discrepancy is almost always expressed as a percentage of the level although it would usually be more interesting to have it as a percentage of the change between benchmarks. The Bureau of the Census does publish the sampling error of changes as well as levels for labor force statistics in the Current Population Survey and for retail sales, both of which are based on rotating samples, with resulting nonindependence in the errors of successive levels.

Although one cannot be certain whether level or change is of primary concern in specific cases, it is clear that change is frequently at issue. In assessing the effect of a change in some policy, an analysis in terms of change is often the most desirable. Even when level is important, e.g., in the calculation of the gap between full employment output and the actual level, change can still be important because the correlation between successive changes can be used to forecast future levels.

The attempt to reduce response error by redesigning questionnaires, etc., may be an example of the conflict between accuracy in level and accuracy in change. The redesign of the annual income questions in the CPS has reduced the shortfall from universe totals but it may have increased the error in the estimates of change in particular categories. The conflict may also arise in the allocation of a sample because, for example, the variance in level for big firms may be high but not the variance in their rate of change.

It should be remembered in reviewing the detailed summaries that the structure of errors may be complex. Errors can include:[5]
  a. Sampling error
  b. Constant bias over all units
  c. Variable component of bias which is constant for each unit but varies from unit to unit with mean zero. This bias may be correlated with the true value of the observation, e.g., the variable bias in responses on level of income bias may be positive for low income individuals and negative for high income ones.
  d. Fluctuating component of measurement error which varies as repeated readings are taken from a given unit.

Enumerator error can enter into any of these last three components. The number of enumerators and how they are used will of course affect the distribution. Whether or not a given error falls into one category or another may also depend on the time frame considered.

Bureau of the Census

RETAIL SALES (MONTHLY)

This series is based on a combination of a list and an area sample, both rotating, in which the area sample is used to fill in stores not present on Social Security employer lists (about 7 percent of total sales). Enumerators are used only for the area segment. The Bureau of the Census submitted estimates of sampling errors for the level, monthly change, and the change from the year

---

5   This categorization can be found in several basic texts such as W. G. Cochran *Sampling Techniques* Wiley, 1963.

ago month for total retail sales. They also submitted a copy of the results of a 20 percent area recheck program which gives (a) the percent of listing errors by enumerators who may miss or incorrectly include an establishment, (b) the percentage of the area sample for which imputations are necessary because of failure to get a report, (c) the completeness and accuracy of information on the report form itself, (d) the number of errors made by the Washington office in determining which establishments should be in the area sample.

However, this elaborate checking program failed to signal the extreme error in 1969 in which about 2 percent of retail sales were somehow lost, with a very substantial impact on the estimated growth of sales. The discrepancy was discovered by users of the series, such as the Office of Business Economics (OBE), and Census has only recently come to acknowledge the error. OBE concluded something was wrong in the first half of 1969 because, among other things, the Census figures on gasoline and service stations seemed inconsistent with independent shipper information on gasoline sales and because the growth in food sales per employee was far different from earlier trends.

Apparently the error was due to incorrect decisions as to which members of the rotating *area* panel that were scheduled to return to the sample had in the interim appeared in the Social Security lists. This source of error was not included in the recheck program.[6]

Retail sales are estimated in a mechanically very complex process in which not only are there both area and list frames but, in addition, establishments may change their status as they are carried forward in a panel. The possibility of mechanical errors may have been underestimated in choosing the sampling plan and certain mechanical details were apparently overlooked in the error checking process.

This episode also points to the value of using departures from

---

6   This paragraph is based on a conversation with a member of the Census staff.
   However, the recheck document received by the Commission does claim to
   include "skip list" errors. It may be that the real source of the 1969 error is
   still a mystery. It is difficult to believe that errors in the skip list could
   account for a full two percent in retail sales.

historical relationships with other data as signals for closer scrutiny of a series. As one of the OBE staff noted, if segments in which there is high turnover such as restaurants start to change in an unusual way compared to other parts of the universe, a closer inspection of the accuracy of the sampling frame should be initiated.

UNEMPLOYMENT RATE (TOTAL AND NONWHITE)

The Census submission on *labor force* statistics derived from the CPS was very thorough with a number of special studies and a useful summary under the headings of source of error, source and frequency of information, method of release to the public, and method of control. This is a series with a long history of congressional and executive interest and has been the subject of a great deal of scrutiny. The submission included information on:

a. *Sampling error for major labor force items.*

This is a strict probability rotating sample. Also included in the submission were copies of memoranda describing the way standard errors are computed and the sources of reduction in standard error from 1944 to 1964.

b. *Undercoverage*

The labor force figures published are ratio estimates based on independent totals on age, sex, and color so that the principal source of undercoverage error results from the undercount in the census itself. A (BLS) study on the effect of the census undercount on certain components of the labor force was included in the Census package. Coverage checks are also made in the reinterview program in which a random subsample of each interviewer's assignment is redone by the staff twice a year.

c. *Noninterview errors*

Noninterview rates vary from three to six percent during the year. Two of the special studies report on intensive efforts to determine the effect of noninterviews.

312

d. *Nonresponse (i.e., items left out on the questionnaire).*

This rate is very low and consequently no study has been made of their effect on estimates.

e. *Response biases*

Interviewer biases are (partly) detected in the reinterviews by experienced interviewers. Since labor force participation cannot be checked with a "true" number, response bias studies have consisted of various tests of the sensitivity of the responses to changes in procedures such as the use of different interviewers each month, or the use of different questions. There has also been an estimate of "rotation group bias" which results from a household's being interviewed in several successive months.

f. *Response Variance (partly included in sampling error estimates).*

Estimates on response variability again are based mainly on the reinterview program. Correlated errors are now being computed using 1966 data in which a random sub-sample of total CPS was conducted by a different staff of interviewers.

g. *Processing errors*

Census has computed error rates in Film Optical Scanning Device for Input to Computer (FOSDIC), the microfilm document reading system. These are very low and no effect on the statistics is calculated.

MANUFACTURERS INVENTORIES (MONTHLY)

This series is based on a "chunk" or judgment sample, with some representation of smaller companies, which is linked to universe totals available in the annual survey or census of manufactures. The responses are subjected to the usual edit checks such as reasonableness in relation to shipments and orders, unusual changes in inventory to shipment ratios and consistency with outside series, such as the Federal Reserve Board (FRB) index of industrial production. Sharp month to month changes are scrutinized for changes in accounting procedures. Respondents are also invited to report changes in accounting methods in a special part of the form. However, Census has not undertaken a systematic study of the consistency of accounting procedures over time.

The only calculation of error presented was in the form of discrepancies between year ending values for the series and the benchmarks that become available from either the annual survey or census of manufactures. The discrepancies appear small in terms of levels. The Bureau of the Census did not submit a comparison in terms of changes and the comparison is not completely obvious because apparently the series is not benchmarked annually and it is therefore not clear just what differences are to be compared.

Furthermore, this may be a case where the benchmark itself has substantial error. Firstly, fiscal year reporting is permitted so that the inventory figure received from a respondent is not for the end of the calendar year. Census could not provide information on the frequency of fiscal year reporting. Secondly, there is no systematic checking of records to estimate accounting consistency from year to year.

FAMILY INCOME FROM CPS (NUMBER BELOW $3,000 AND OVER $25,000)

Information was submitted on:

a. Sampling errors for the percentage of families having incomes of less than $3,000 and more than $25,000. These errors are very low, but given the very large response biases they are not in themselves very informative.

b. Nonresponse ratios and the characteristics of income of nonrespondents. In the 1970 CPS income collection, at least one component of income information was not reported for about 14 percent of all families. Missing items were imputed from responses by families with similar economic and demographic characteristics who did report those items.

c. Comparison of income aggregates (by type of income) with benchmarks produced by OBE. There is consistent underreporting with the discrepancies varying from small (in terms of percentages) for wage and salary income to large for property income. Although some of the discrepancies appear to be small as a percentage of total income, the understatement of public assistance and social security income is, for example, substantial compared to the "poverty gap."

Income reports based on the CPS have not been adjusted for known understatements. There is a very recent publication by Census which tries to correct the high side of the distribution using the Internal Revenue Service (IRS) data. There is also some unpublished work on mechanically "jacking up" each income reported by a constant percentage (for that item) so that the total will conform to the benchmark.

d. *Response Variances and Biases.* These reports are mostly a product of the CPS reinterview program and the CPS – Census match program in which response variation to all of the CPS items were estimated. However, Census has engaged in very little experimentation with different types of reporting schemes, such as more frequent than once a year interviews for certain types of income. The most interesting information becoming available on the effect of different reporting techniques is a by-product of income maintenance experiments now in process. One study has found that, for the poverty population under study, more frequent and longer interviews resulted in substantially more recollection of income receipts.

In summary, the income part of CPS seems to have been neglected compared to the labor force portions. This is not surprising, since income is not an area in which the contractor, BLS, has a major role. However, the income responses *are* used to construct some socially very important statistics such as the number of families in poverty (which recent evidence suggests may be seriously overstated). This is apart from the conceptual problem of using only cash income, neglecting sources of income-in-kind such as food stamps and owner-occupied homes.

HOUSING STARTS (MONTHLY)

The housing start universe is split into two parts of which the largest contains those areas which issue housing permits. For permit-issuing places, the housing start estimate involves two basic steps. First, an estimate of the number of housing units for which permits have been issued each month is made from monthly reports by a large (accounting for over 90 percent of total permit authorized construction) sample of permit offices. In the second step, a sample of housing permits is taken at the end of each month, and the enumerator checks what percentage of them are started in that and succeeding months; i.e., a series of ratios is calculated giving the percentage of permits issued in each of the previous months that resulted in a start in the past month. This distribution of ratios, stratified by region and type of structure, is then applied to the relevant estimates of permits issued in each of the previous months.

For the non-permit-issuing part of the universe there are also two steps. First, in a sample of 95 areas (CPS primary sampling units which are counties or groups of counties), a detailed list of starts in the non-permit portion of the area is obtained from visits with utilities, lending institutions, etc., who may be expected to have expert knowledge in the area. These are then verified. Finally, a sample of small land areas is drawn and compared with the lists to estimate the number that have been missed.

All the sampling in this series, done for convenience, is a subsample of CPS primary sampling units and this program benefits from the monitoring of the quality of CPS interviewers. However, no estimate is made of enumerator error or response variability.

Sampling errors for the level of housing starts are computed by region, type of structure and Standard Metropolitan Statistical Area (SMSA) versus non SMSA. Census has also selected a sample of starts in permit-issuing places by direct observation and tried to locate permits for them. The resulting estimates of the (small) percentage of starts not covered by permit is used to adjust the series. Furthermore, since interviewers go to a sample of permit offices to select a sample of permits each month, it is possible to estimate the discrepancy between permits actually issued and the number reported by that office. The final quality check reported was an independent determination of the number of apartments completed in 1969 in the course of the Market Absorption Survey.

316

CONDITION, VALUE OF OWNED HOME, DURATION OF VACANCY AND CONTRACT RENT IN THE 1960 CENSUS OF HOUSING

Gross rent and duration of vacancy were based on a 25 percent sample of housing units and some of the tabulation for condition and value were also based on the same sample. The 1960 Census volumes contained sampling errors for these items.

In the case of missing or inconsistent responses, Census adopted the policy of assigning entries based on information reported for the housing unit or for a similar unit in the neighborhood. The rate of assignments necessary was given by state for each of the above items. However, no study was made of the error resulting from these imputations.

The 1960 evaluation program included an analysis of response bias and variation for the condition of housing questions. This was done primarily by reinterviews and indicated very inconsistent and also biased reporting. No evaluation of the other three items was performed in 1960 but the 1950 Census of Housing evaluation program did include gross rent and value of home tabulations.

An ambitious program of estimating biases in reporting value of home and gross rent is being planned for the 1970 Census. A sample of homes sold in 1971 is going to be matched with census responses. For gross rent, reinterviews and information from managers or owners are going to be used for the contract rent part and utility information for the remainder.

Bureau of Labor Statistics

EMPLOYEES IN NON-AGRICULTURAL ESTABLISHMENTS — MONTHLY

The principal source of error estimates for this series is comparison with an annual benchmark. The latter is computed from Unemployment Insurance, Social Security and also some special sources for industries not covered by either of these two programs. Sampling errors are not calculated because this is not fully a probability sample. The monthly estimates are made by linking changes for respondents to the previous benchmark level and adding a bias

317

correction based on previous benchmark adjustments. The sample, which now amounts to about 160,000 establishments, was expanded and redesigned in the early 1960's. Within each industry, the allocation of the sample among size strata was proportionate to the total number of employees in each stratum as indicated in a total universe count at a point in time. In view of the annual benchmarking, and the possibility that large establishments in certain industries are systematically more stable than small ones, an allocation based on changes rather than levels would appear more appropriate.

Apparently there is not much response error in this series. A BLS survey on reporting practices, published in 1957, found that reports were almost exclusively based upon payroll records. Checks found response errors to be slight.

When all responses are in, this series appears to provide a highly reliable measure of aggregate employment. A recent problem has been large differences between preliminary estimates based on about 50 percent of the sample and the final monthly figures based on the whole sample.

CONSUMER PRICE INDEX

Sampling errors for the change in the Consumer Price Index (CPI) are now calculated using a replication design that was part of the revision instituted in 1964. The 50 sample places used in the CPI were selected in what is regarded as the establishment of 50 strata and the selection of one primary sampling unit in each. Twelve of the strata contained only one SMSA each. In the BLS scheme "similar" cities in different non-certainty strata are paired and, in the minimum replication design, strata variances are estimated from the difference in price change in the two cities with a different item sample used in each city. An extended plan is used in some city pairs in which the two item samples are used in each city. In each of the certainty cities two outlet samples, each with a different item sample, are used in the minimum design, and in the extended one, the two item samples are used in each of the outlet samples.

The outlets used are not described as being pure probability samples. They were originally drawn from composite lists and are changed only when a unit drops out and is replaced by a "similar" outlet. There is no effort to rotate the sample and represent new entrants. The item samples are drawn from a consolidated list of 812 in 52 strata which are based on the 1960 Consumer Expenditure Survey with periodic updating.[7] No information was presented on enumerator error, except to the extent that is reflected in the estimate of sampling error.

The sampling errors estimated have turned out to be very low. This may, in part, reflect an improvement in the sample that was a by-product of the replication scheme. It may be true that even mean squared errors are dominated by the "nonstatistical" procedures that have been the subject of much complaint. Real estate taxes are included in the CPI although presumably some increases in local taxes finance better public services. Another example of controversial procedures is the estimation of housing costs by assuming that every home owner repurchases his home at current prices *including* current interest charges.

WHOLESALE PRICE INDEX

No quality information of any kind was submitted. The Wholesale Price Index (WPI) is based on a judgment sample of producers who report their sales price for specified items. In some cases, prices on organized exchanges are used. There is widespread feeling and some evidence that the WPI does not reflect prices actually paid.[8]

CONSUMER EXPENDITURE SURVEY (1960-1961) ITEMS IN TWO SPECIFIED URBAN AREAS

BLS reported that sampling errors were not computed for individual cities. They were computed for four regions and for the urban U. S., using differences between city pairs in a procedure similar to the one used in the CPI. BLS reports that a city's CPI weights are usually not based exclusively on the Consumer Ex-

---

7   BLS continues the practice of only sampling from Tuesday through Thursday.

8   Stigler, G. and Kindahl J. *The Behavior of Industrial Prices,* National Bureau of Economic Research, 1970.

penditure Survey (CES) sample for that city but include varying amounts of judgment pooling with similar cities. The response rate of urban consumers, after substitution of alternates, was 79 percent. An (incomplete) table giving characteristics of nonrespondents is given. Since family names were not recorded, the only direct checking of response error was comparison, for a subsample, of responses on gas and electric expenditures with utility records. The only other item presented which sheds some light on likely response error is the percentage of urban families who used records in reporting specific expenditure categories. This material could presumably have been combined with the utility information to find the effect of the use of records on response error. The utility data could have been used to estimate a relationship between response error on the one hand and the use of records, the variability of expenditure over time, their importance in the total budget etc. on the other. Since information on use of records includes most items, one could have made much broader estimates of response reliability.

The reliability of the 1960-1961 CES data is described in a *forthcoming* BLS bulletin, part of which was submitted in draft to the Commission.

Bureau of Mines

IRON ORE PRODUCTION – MONTHLY

All statistics on iron ore production are based on "total voluntary response, within a practical interval of time, to systematic canvass of the industry." Until recently, no limit was placed on the time taken to respond. Eventually, all the data comes in for, apparently, "coverage approaches 100 percent in terms of tonnage." The main problem with this series has not been accuracy but timeliness. This may be a case where improved statistical capability would make it possible to consider less conservative strategies.

MONTHLY BITUMINOUS COAL PRODUCTION

The initial monthly estimate of coal production is based primarily on loading information from the Association of American

320

Railroads and the Corps of Engineers for Canals, and is revised about two months later on the basis of reports from state mine inspection agencies. There is an annual canvass of the whole industry at the end of the year so that evaluation of the earlier estimates can be made.

MAN-HOURS WORKED IN BITUMINOUS COAL MINES — MONTHLY

Estimates are based on linkage of information supplied by all mines employing 20 men or more to an earlier universe total. There is eventually a benchmark total for the whole year when the annual canvass of the universe is made. Apparently there have been checks on the accuracy with which the universe is identified and coverage has been found to be high.

Civil Aeronautics Board

ORIGIN-DESTINATION (O-D) SURVEY OF AIRLINE PASSENGER TRAFFIC

This is a survey in which every ticket (including those issued by foreign carriers) with a number ending in "O" gets reported by the first domestic airline which lifts any part of it. The whole trip given on the ticket is recorded and in the summary tables published, the data are presented in a number of different ways, e.g., a person with a round trip ticket is counted as one passenger for some purposes and as two passengers for others.

The Civil Aeronautics Board (CAB) submitted a *Sample Design and Reliability* statement which was prepared for the O-D survey as it was performed prior to January 1, 1968. These have not been updated although the survey has apparently been redesigned. The pre-1968 data submitted included standard sampling error tables for different estimated levels of passenger flows. These sampling errors were (conservatively) estimated by assuming that tickets were randomly selected from the whole population of airline tickets.

Although internal documents describing problem areas in the O-D samples were submitted, there were no estimates made of response or other non-sampling error. These problems included

321

incomplete reporting of long itineraries, undercoverage of traffic fed into the domestic system, various forms of incomplete reporting, and inconsistent procedures used by different airlines.

Federal Bureau of Investigation

UNIFORM CRIME REPORTS – MONTHLY AND ANNUAL

This is a program in which all local law enforcement agencies are asked to report the number of criminal offenses known to the police and the number of crimes cleared by arrest. The main control of the quality of the statistics takes the form of scrutinizing the reasonableness of changes over time. Whenever it is determined that an agency's data in successive intervals are not comparable because of changes in reporting procedures the data are not included in calculation of the national trend for the period.

The shortcomings of this system have been described in detail by the Commission on Law Enforcement and Administration of Justice (1967) and the following remarks are based on that description.

There are errors even within the present frame, i.e., only reported crimes. Although the Federal Bureau of Investigation (FBI) makes instruction manuals, etc., available to local agencies, it has apparently made no attempt to test response variation by sampling records among different agencies. The Commission on Law Enforcement and Administration of Justice reports that one state has successfully instituted an audit system for insuring conformity to uniform definitions. This data noncomparability across different agencies limits the accuracy of cross-sectional studies that try to determine the causes of crime.

The Crime Commission also reports that the response rates by local agencies on arrests are much lower than response rates for criminal offenses. Apparently a good national estimate could be made if the responses that do come in were properly stratified and the strata were weighted by known population distributions.

There are also errors due to unreported crimes. The Crime Commission funded and reported on the *first* national victimization survey which found (if this method itself is reliable) that most property crimes and almost half the crimes of violence are not reported. A periodic victimization survey is now being planned at the Bureau of the Census.

Federal Reserve Board (FRB)

INSTALLMENT CREDIT HELD BY
COMMERCIAL BANKS – MONTHLY

A new sample was instituted in January 1970 and no testing of the results has been undertaken. A report on the design and selection of the sample was submitted. The choice of sampling plan was based on the within stratum population variances in the June 1968 call report submitted by all banks, apparently including non-member and non-insured banks. However, this seems to be the wrong basis for selection because, in view of the fact that the series will be benchmarked to the June call report every year, the choice of sampling plan should be based on the variance in *changes* not levels. The changes could have been calculated from two successive annual call reports. This is apart from the question of whether, even without benchmarking, changes should be used as a basis for the design.

MANUFACTURING CAPACITY UTILIZATION

This series is based largely on a McGraw Hill survey of capacity and utilization rates. It also makes use of the FRB index of industrial production and the OBE-SEC series on plant and equipment expenditures. The resulting series is of admittedly uncertain quality. The FRB has no control over the McGraw Hill input and produces the series at very low expense. Forecasters who use it will have experience with how well it performs in a forecasting context and may require no direct measurement of error. Since the FRB is itself a typical user of this series, its judgment on whether a greater effort to study error is worthwhile may be reliable. There are apparently steps underway to reduce dependence on the McGraw Hill data.

Housing and Urban Development

MONTHLY STATISTICS ON MORTGAGE TRANSACTIONS AND COMMITMENTS

This is a new program and, since it identifies gross flows, is reputed to be an improvement over earlier net figures. Housing and Urban Development (HUD) coordinates and packages information from surveys operated by other government agencies and by trade associations, each of which specializes in a particular lender group. The letter to the Commission states that "in each case an appropriate analysis was prepared to measure the possible degrees of error." The manager of the program declined an invitation to provide more documentation of these error analyses. He also stated that it is not feasible to make checks from a sample of building permits or land titles on how much of the universe is covered.

Given the newness of the program, however, it may not be at the stage at which rigorous error analysis is really necessary to identify important areas for improvement. The program manager has taken steps to improve the coverage of some of the lender group surveys and seems aware that parts of his frame, such as mortgage companies, may be particularly weak. He is also taking steps to add new lending groups to the program.

Internal Revenue Service (Treasury)

STATISTICS OF INCOME 1968 – INDIVIDUAL TAX RETURNS

These statistics are based on 254,000 returns drawn in the field from all individual returns filed in calendar '69 with sampling rates based on adjusted gross income (AGI) or the largest income item if it exceeds AGI. Internal Revenue Service (IRS) submitted a number of documents on the quality of the data. These included (a) a section from Statistics of Income describing the sample and giving sampling errors for major classifications, (b) a description of the quality control of the manual abstraction of data from individual returns and a report on the error rate indicated by a reprocessing of part of the sample, and (c) a large manual describing about 40 different consistency checks used in the editing process.

This large volume of documentation may be misleading. There is, first of all, the problem of what these data are supposed to represent. The income statistics are based on reported income in a sample of all individual returns filed in 1969 except for amended returns and before audit. IRS does audit a special random sample of returns and, while one can see that they would not want to reveal their audit strategy, there doesn't seem to be any good reason why some aggregate distributions based on revision in reported income after audit are not included. Furthermore, IRS includes late returns on income before 1968 on the argument that this makes up for 1968 income that will be reported in returns filed after 1969 but they provide no information on the validity of this steady state assumption in view of changes in tax laws etc., over time.

The Office of Tax Analyses (OTA) in Treasury has extracted about 35,000 records from the total file and in preparing to make use of the data they found some disturbing problems.[9] One difficulty on several hundred returns was the apparent inconsistency between the data on AGI in the record and the weight the return was assigned. One extreme example was a return with dividend income of $130,000 and AGI of $135,000 which was assigned a weight of 1100 instead of 2.6. In a case like this, the return is eventually put in its proper AGI category when the tables are made but its erroneous weight is retained. The IRS justification for this, when they were asked about the OTA complaint, is that the return was originally misclassified in the field and a weight reflecting the sampling rate from the category it was drawn from is necessary for an unbiased estimate, for otherwise similar returns that were misclassified would not be adequately represented. However, the wrong weight could easily be due to an error in key punching the sample code and there is no reason why these errors should necessarily be unbiased.

Furthermore, even if returns are systematically misclassified in

---

9   The problems in the SOI records are described in a memorandum made available by the OTA.

the regional offices before the sample is drawn, it should be possible to find a procedure that would not require placing so high a weight on a return with such an untypically high percent of dividend income as the one referred to in the example. The unbiased estimator may have very high but reducible variance.[10]

Moreover, the IRS procedure on weights appears inconsistent. Most cases in which OTA found the weight inconsistent with the AGI data for the return had been assigned a much lower weight than indicated by the original sample code because various "anomalies" had been found. The effect of this procedure on the estimates is not reported.

OTA also found that 550 of the 35,000 returns it examined contained errors in the calculation of one or more of AGI, allowable deductions, taxable income, or tax under the assumption that the taxpayer always minimizes his tax liability. Presumably, this is after the 40 consistency checks had been made. Part of the problem may be the policy of not making use of amended or audited returns.

The conclusion seems to be that although IRS has a lot of information on the (apparently low) rate of error per data element in transferring data from a return to the Statistics of Income (SOI) file, this does not get translated into how much this contributes to errors in the estimates themselves. There also seems to have been no systematic study of the best way to deal with anomalous cases. It may be that we are imposing too high a standard on IRS, for, after all, the data may be adequate to the purpose for which it used and must be much more accurate than income data from other sources such CPS. The point here is not that accuracy should necessarily be increased but that the information provided on accuracy appears misleading. Furthermore, IRS seems to devote considerable effort to quality control and has both a mathematical statistics and a statistical techniques branch which foster expectations of high performance.

---

10 The tables in SOI incidate a high sampling error for dividends in the 100-200,000 AGI category, reflecting the particular weighting error.

Manpower Administration (Department of Labor)

EMPLOYMENT AND WAGES OF WORKERS COVERED BY UNEMPLOYMENT INSURANCE

These data, which come through state employment security agencies, represent a complete census of covered employers. Reports appear with a long lag because of delinquent returns and the editing of state reports. Although no validity study is reported, there are incentives to maintain accurate records because of the importance of establishing a worker's eligibility. It might be possible to get some idea of response error from the frequency (if available) with which records turn out to be wrong in processing claims.

CHARACTERISTICS OF THE INSURED UNEMPLOYED UNDER STATE PROGRAMS

This data is based on a sample of insured unemployed drawn by each of the state agencies with sampling ratios inversely related to the state's level of insured unemployment such that the absolute number of sample cases in a state is about 1200. Standard sampling errors by total level of insured unemployment and estimated number with a given characteristic are given. No analysis is presented of the possible response error by the Employment Service interviewer as he classifies the individual's occupation and industry attachment.

National Center for Health Statistics

MONTHLY VITAL STATISTICS REPORT (LIVE BIRTHS, DEATHS, INFANT DEATHS, MARRIAGES AND DIVORCES)

No error studies were submitted. These statistics are based on total counts or actual records submitted by state registration offices (or one of every two birth certificates which are numbered consecutively by the state) so there is no sampling error. Divorce figures are described as "crude estimates based on total counts by 42 states." Since some states only report marriage licenses, and not marriages performed, an adjustment based on observed differ-

327

ences is made. When the National Center for Health Statistics (NCHS) was asked about information on the completeness of state registration they submitted summaries of studies made by the Bureau of the Census on the coverage of birth registration in 1940, 1950 and 1970. The first two of these studies were based on matching all children below a given age (3 months in one case and 4 in the other) found in the Census with birth registration in state offices. The third study used children less than five years old in CPS households.

NATIONAL BIRTH SURVEY

This survey of mothers who have given birth in a given year is designed to collect information on past and expected future fertility together with certain demographic characteristics. The 1967-1969 survey has not yet been completely processed and the only submission received described the design of the 1964-1966 survey. Apparently the only change in the later survey is the addition of a few items to the questionnaire.

The sampling frame is the microfilm file of birth certificates submitted by the 54 birth registration areas. These certificates were systematically placed into groups of 1,000 records and one was randomly selected from each group. After the first mailing, there were two follow-up mailings and a final follow-up by a Bureau of the Census interviewer if the mother was a resident in one of the CPS primary sampling units. The final nonresponse rate was about 12 percent. Imputations for nonresponse were based on information such as the age of the mother on the original certificate.

National estimates are made by classifying responses by age of mother, race and birth order and weighting the cells by known national totals based on the whole certificate population. Sampling errors are estimated by repeating the procedure using 20 random half-sample replications. The half-samples were constructed by assigning each record systematically to 40 groups from which 20 random pairs were created. A half sample was created by randomly selecting one group from each pair. No other error analysis was performed.

328

Office of Business Economics (Department of Commerce)

QUARTERLY SURVEY OF MANUFACTURERS' SALES
AND INVENTORY EXPECTATIONS

Estimates of manufacturers' sales and inventory expectations are based on a panel of 1200 companies of which about 85 percent respond each quarter. Rather than being a probability sample, Office of Business Economics (OBE) describes it as a "chunk" sample, which is a judgment sample, made up primarily of large and medium sized firms. Sampling errors are not computed.

This is an example of a series where one is really only interested in its predictive value and one can make judgments on at least the average (over time) levels of bias and error by historical comparison with actuals or realizations. Experience with the inventory expectations series has led OBE to make bias corrections before publication. The actuals used for comparison are (after previous linking for levels) the manufacturers' book value figures produced by Census. OBE has not systematically studied whether the panel's expectations are much better predictors of its own (the panel's) actuals than actuals for all of manufacturing. This might be a guide to improvements in the panel.

SOURCES AND USE OF FUNDS OF FOREIGN
AFFILIATES OF U. S. FIRMS

The annual (1967 and 1968) data most recently reported for this series are only aggregates of data actually reported by a voluntary sample of major U. S. parent companies with no attempt to make universe estimates. A benchmark from a 1957 mandatory census of U. S. direct investments had been used for blowing up the sample for a number of years. A further census was taken for 1966 but this has only been tabulated for balance of payments purposes. The only quality evaluations reported are comparisons with data that are somewhat similar such as information on capital flows and earnings from a much larger mandatory survey of U. S. direct foreign investors and earnings in balance of payment reports. However, in each case there are significant definitional differences so that no very direct comparison can be made.

329

Office of Education (Health, Education and Welfare)

STATISTICS OF LOCAL PUBLIC SCHOOL SYSTEM FINANCES 1967-68 (ELEMENTARY-SECONDARY GENERAL INFORMATION SURVEY)

This survey is composed of a sample of about 1400 school systems selected from the Office of Education (OE) population of 19,600 operating systems as of fall 1968. Apparently it is the first in a series. The population was stratified into six enrollment size categories with differing sampling ratios in each. Sampling errors for the level of the important variables were calculated for each size stratum. The only other quality information submitted was a comparison with broad totals available from other sources. They included enrollment and personnel (by type) totals from an OE survey of state school systems, and enrollment totals from CPS.

OE recognizes that the kind of expenditure and personnel information requested is likely to have substantial response error. A validity study is being planned for fiscal 1972 in which responses will be constructed by OE staff from primary records in a sample of school systems.

Securities and Exchange Commission

WORKING CAPITAL OF U. S. CORPORATIONS (QUARTERLY)

This series is based on data taken from a variety of sources including the Interstate Commerce Commission (ICC) for railroads, Civil Aeronautics Board (CAB) for airlines, the Quarterly Financial Report for Manufacturing Corporations for manufacturing, and a voluntary sample of (primarily large) Securities and Exchange Commission (SEC) registrants for the remainder. It is linked, on an industry basis, to universe data that eventually become available from IRS in *Statistics of Income*. This series was watched with interest in 1970 because of fears of a corporate "liquidity crisis."

The only error estimates provided are the comparison with the IRS annual benchmarks from 1956 to 1967. Both the SEC sample and the IRS benchmarks may have errors due to changes in ac-

330

counting procedure and differences in degree of consolidation of affiliates. Because the SEC sample includes consolidated foreign affiliates, it is difficult to use other series as consistency checks.

HEW — Social and Rehabilitation Service

1969 AID TO FAMILIES WITH DEPENDENT CHILDREN (AFDC) SURVEY

This survey was made up of an approximately 1 percent of AFDC cases for which caseworkers were asked to respond. It is a basic source of information on the welfare population and its findings receive wide circulation. It appears to have many short-comings. First of all, the survey was incorrectly analysed and not very conveniently designed with respect to obtaining estimates of one of the most important questions about the welfare population: how long the average family receives public assistance once on the rolls. The results highlighted in the survey report are simply the median time since the most recent AFDC case opening of the then current AFDC population. However, since the AFDC population had been growing rapidly, this approach is misleading.[11]

The National Center for Social Statistics reported that no study of the quality of the data was conducted because of lack of funds, and apparently the Social and Rehabilitation Service has turned down a request for funds for this purpose in the 1971 survey. It is not clear why some of the funds allocated to the survey cannot be used to study the reliability of the data. The quality of the data is particularly open to question because for some responses, such as the family's prior welfare history, the case worker had to consult agency records and it is not clear that these are adequate because of mobility, etc.

Statistical Reporting Service (Agriculture)

ANNUAL HARVESTED ACREAGE SERIES

This is the second stage of an annual two stage process of

---

11   The AFDC report states that the "typical AFDC family was not a long term public assistance case" which is correct for the 1969 population. It may be much different when the wave of new entrants to the program is over. It might be possible, even with the design, to make some estimates of duration using information on the growth of the welfare population overtime.

which the first part is an enumerated survey in June of planted acreage. Because of redesign following a large error in the 1951 cotton crop estimate and a resulting Congressional investigation, this area probability sample now appears carefully constructed with the use of aerial maps etc.[12] The harvested acreage estimate is based on a post-harvest mail survey to the sample enumerated in June but nonrespondents are not followed up. Therefore, the only direct estimates of total error are based on the quinquennial censuses of agriculture.

Sampling errors and the results of reinterviews are available in the June part of the survey and the Statistical Reporting Service (SRS) believes that planted and harvested acreage tend to be very close for most crops. In view of the incentives to produce accurate estimates, this series does not appear a likely candidate for concern.

MONTHLY INDEX OF PRICES RECEIVED BY FARMERS FOR MEAT ANIMALS

This series, and the next one on vegetable prices, reflect the SRS decision in the fifties to concentrate its statistical resources on the crop and production surveys and use cheaper (it says) judgment samples to produce price indices. At the end of the year "cost to packer" data from federally inspected packing plants are used as a check, but how these are used was not described.

These price series are important in making aggregate estimates of the value of farm production and the construction of parity ratios. There does not seem to be much pressure for accurate farm price indices as evidenced by the fact that parity ratios are based on 1955 input weights.

SRS has made some tests of the difference between estimates of price *change* derived from a mailed judgment sample and estimates based on an enumerated probability sample. They made available the results of a comparison of estimates of beef price changes in Ohio over a more than two-year period.

---

12 See "A Program for the Development of of the Agricultural Estimating Service," February 1957, by the House Subcommittee on Agriculture Appropriations. This is usually referred to as the Whitton Report.

MONTHLY INDEX OF COMMERCIAL VEGETABLE FOR FRESH MARKET

This is another price series essentially based on a judgment sample. Prices are obtained from Marketing News Service Reports, mailed inquiries, and reports from auction managers. There were no estimates of error presented.

Availability of Error Studies

Apart from the question of how much the data producers in the federal statistical system know about error, there is the further question of how accessible this knowledge is to outside users. As noted, some of the documents submitted to the Commission were internal, usually the product of a quality control system. Some of the descriptions of survey design and estimates of sampling error also were not in a form that would be widely distributed. An effort was therefore made to find out whether these reports were made available in some convenient form or if a user could have at least obtained a copy if he made a general request about documentation on errors.

One study submitted to the Commission but not available to outside users is the Department of Agriculture study on the differences between a judgment mail survey and random enumeration in the estimation of beef prices. The restriction on the public use of this study was reported by SRS to be in accordance with a policy of not releasing data that may be subject to misinterpretation.

Bureau of the Census reports based on probability samples contain appendices describing the sampling design and giving sampling errors which are also frequently displayed in the text tables. Decisions on the release of internal memoranda on nonsampling errors such as the study of the coverage of housing starts by permits in permit issuing areas and list errors in retail sales are up to each division. There has not been much demand for these memoranda but it appears that they would be made available if requests were made. These studies are sometimes referred to in the published reports containing the data, as in the case of housing starts, but sometimes not, as in the case of retail sales. Periodically the Bureau of the Census publishes an annotated list of available papers and reports under the title *Census Bureau Methodological Research*. The 1969 list, for example, includes several reports on errors in constructing the retail trade sample which seem to include the material submitted to the Commission.

The IRS report on errors in manual data abstraction containing what might otherwise have been internal information was prepared for a quality control conference. This might indicate the usefulness of journals or conferences which would give statisticians professional incentives to make error studies available.

Some of the documents submitted which seemed to be in internal use form will eventually be published. For example, the description of the survey design and estimation of sampling errors of the 1964-66 natality study by NCHS will soon be published along with the results of the survey themselves.

In the many cases where the information on error is based on differences from independent benchmarks, the user could make the calculation himself from the same sources or by keeping track of successive revisions. In some cases these comparisons are presented in appendices to the statistical reports, as in the case of the establishment employment data in *Employment and Earnings* which gives, by major industrial categories, benchmark comparisons for the previous three years. A contrary example, which seems much more typical, is the monthly Census report giving manufacturers' inventories which does not give or refer to any evidence on error.

The timeliness of some of the error estimates might also be mentioned. As noted in the summaries, the analysis of errors in the BLS *1960 Consumer Expenditure Survey* was sent to the Commission in manuscript. Furthermore, the sampling errors that BLS publishes for the *Consumer Price Index* are averages for the previous calendar year, and while this may be a reasonable policy, it may have its dangers because of possible changes in sampling error over time.

CHAPTER 5

STATISTICS AND THE PROBLEM OF PRIVACY

By
Arthur L. Moore

STATISTICS AND THE PROBLEM OF PRIVACY

TABLE OF CONTENTS

INTRODUCTION

An enormously complex and sensitive cluster of attitudes and emotions has shouldered its way into the world of statistics.

Federal statistical programs, and private ones as well, are operating in a climate sharply different from that of a decade ago. The new climate is one of rising controversy, skepticism and deep concern, much of it centering around the problem of privacy.

Many social and physical scientists urge a more rational and efficient system of federal statistics based on new techniques of data storage and retrieval.[1] Opponents fear that such a system would be used to invade the privacy of individuals.

The debate over a federal data bank is part of a much wider controversy over the future of a society based largely on science and science-related technology. The climate in which statistical programs will operate in the future probably depends more on the

---

1   Social Science Research Council Committee on the Preservation and use of Economic Data, report submitted to the Bureau of the Budget, Richard Ruggles, Chairman; Review of Proposal for a National Data Center by Edgar S. Dunn, report to Bureau of the Budget, 1965; Task Force on the Storage of and Access to Government Statistics, Carl Kaysen, Chairman, report to the President, 1967.

outcome of this wider controversy than on the development of any particular hardware or any advance in methodology. In what follows, the wider controversy will therefore receive some attention.

Federal statistical programs have long recognized the importance of protecting privacy and confidentiality. Elaborate regulations and sturdy traditions have evolved to guard the interests of individuals and organizations. Yet there is a widespread feeling that these safeguards no longer suffice. This concern is not directed at statistics especially. It involves the discoveries of science as these have been applied to controlling, exploiting and sometimes perverting the forces of nature. Until recent years, most of this concern was for the physical manifestations of nature: forests, water, soil, air. But new techniques of psychological testing and conditioning, electronic surveillance, surgery, drugs and now computerized information focus attention on man as a self, an individual. This uneasiness cuts across ordinary lines of social contention. It is shared by radicals and reactionaries, liberals and conservatives, the poor and the rich, school drop-outs and holders of advanced degrees, student activists and hard hat activists. It may well be the common denominator of our restless times.

It is the purpose of this paper to survey literature bearing on the issue of statistics and privacy and to draw from this literature whatever seems to bear most directly on the future of federal statistical programs.

This survey suggests that statistics may be the flash point of the whole broad problem of man and technological society. Philosophers will debate the ancient question: What is man? Legal experts will debate whether there has been a right of privacy in existence all along or whether one is only now beginning to emerge. They will argue whether new law is needed or whether the established law of torts is sufficient. Some scientists will debate whether man is a machine at birth and becomes "human" by social conditioning, or whether he is a machine at birth and is never anything else. Other scientists will argue that man is neither a machine nor in any final sense capable of being conditioned to act like a machine. These are fascinating questions, some at a higher order of abstraction. Statistical programs, in contrast, touch in a direct way the life of the common man. It is the common man who is called upon to be the giver of statistics.

The common man fears now for his flesh and bone. Nuclear war, pollution of air and water, harmful side effects of new drugs, slums that breed physical violence, death and injury from unsafe mechanical devices, all these concern him. In recent years we have been witnessing how these fears affect social goals and expectations. Now it seems likely that the common man is coming to resent and fear intrusions of statistical programs into his innermost life.

In scores of ways, the citizen is expected to leave a statistical trail behind him. As long as such information existed in fragments, with no means of gathering it together, concern over privacy remained dormant. But now that the technology exists to bring the scattered bits together, the rules of the game have been altered. Questions that once were answered without a qualm may now seem threatening. The users of computerized information systems — government officials, corporation officials, scholars — are aware of how technology is changing. It is doubtful if many of them yet realize how the new situation may affect the giver of statistics. It is the likely effect on the giver that makes statistical programs and policies so explosively controversial in the current social climate.

Because of its peculiar characteristics, privacy may never achieve the sudden and dramatic recognition other problems attract. It is, after all, a matter of the inner man. Moreover, its protection is necessarily a most sensitive matter, requiring a deft touch to keep it from passing over into attitudes that could be harmful to science, social progress and efficiency in government. Yet the record does indicate that privacy and the importance of protecting it is emerging from its dormant, pre-computer state. Over the past decade, concern over privacy has been quietly getting a vocabulary, a grammar, a recognizable syntax of the kind that eventually expresses new social issues. Vaguely felt apprehensions are being put into words, ideas crystallized, possible solutions proposed. The matter seems to have reached the point where it is being drawn into the political process. Politics in the sense of partisan stance is not yet a factor and may never be; separate party positions on these issues are difficult to visualize. But the political process, in the broad sense, will almost certainly be used in defense of the private personality.

The procedure in this paper will be, first, to identify certain events in recent history which have contributed to the concern for privacy. The interpretation of these events by influential writers and scholars will be noted. Shortcomings of the basic science-technology view of man, as this view is applied to the problem of privacy, will be discussed. In conclusion, possible developments to protect privacy will be assessed.

INFLUENCE OF EVENTS ON THE PROBLEM OF PRIVACY

History offers few real turning points. But a scholar as careful as W. H. McNeill, in *The Rise of the West*, a survey of the human community from the earliest time, east as well as west, describes the year 1917 as a serviceable landmark from which to date a new phase in Western and world civilization. "A survey such as this," he writes, "is always liable to underestimate the enduring continuities and stabilities of the social scene and to overestimate the elements of novelty and disruption." Yet, ". . . it still seems correct to believe that Western civilization had come to an unusually critical pass in the first decade of the twentieth century, even before plunging into the operations of war and revolution."[2]

As McNeill notes, powerful forces of change had been building up well before 1917. Older traditions had been cast aside in painting, music and literature. The intellectual world was in ferment. Darwin had applied the theory of evolution to man explicitly in 1872. The certainties of Newtonian physics were crumbling; Einstein, for example, published his theory of relativity in 1905. Freud, by stressing the primitive in man's psyche, was changing man's views of himself. Marxism was being embraced as a new religion of certainty in an increasingly uncertain world. It appealed, as McNeill observes, "both to the self-righteousness of industrial workers and to the rebellious idealism of intellectuals who found the confusion of things as they were hard to bear."

---

2 *The Rise of the West*, Mentor edition. For Professor McNeill's treatment of the influences that contributed to this critical pass see "Artistic and Intellectual Aspects," pp. 821-833.

The particular events which McNeill believes makes 1917 a landmark year were the entry of the United States into World War I and the overthrow of the tsarist government of Russia by the Bolsheviks. In addition, 1917 was marked by a third development which, in present-day, modified forms, bears directly on the issue of privacy. This was the effort of the German general staff to achieve victory by means of total mobilization. All resources of German society were to be brought to bear: political, cultural, technological, scientific. This was an act of military necessity, directed by military men, but in its fundamental aspect, it was an act of politics. The concept of total war applied to a modern, industrialized state, with its technological and scientific resources, ushered in the possibilities of tyrannies more efficient, more intrusive and more cruel than those of the past. Total mobilization failed the Germans in 1918. But as a political idea it survived and still flourishes.

McNeill points out that what the German general staff contrived in 1917 as an emergency measure in the midst of war, "became in effect for Russian Communists a norm applicable indifferently to peace and to war."[3] Hitler later applied the concept to Nazi Germany; Mussolini to Fascist Italy. The idea also influenced the manner in which the liberal democracies of the West organized to conduct World War II. In extreme form as in Communist Russia, Nazi Germany and more recently in Communist China, the over-riding priorities are public and political as against private and personal. In such societies the very idea of privacy comes to be viewed as anti-social, anti-general welfare, anti-government and therefore dangerous.

The feeling that such tyrannies are novel because of their dependence on science and technology was expressed by Albert Speer, Hitler's minister of war production, at the Nuremberg war crimes trials after World War II. In his memoirs, *Inside the Third Reich*, Speer explained that he wanted to establish more than the bare record of judicial guilt. He felt that during the Nazi regime, "A factor in addition to human depravity had entered history, a factor that distinguished our tyranny from all historical prece-

---

3 *Ibid.*, p. 869.

448 -559 O - 71 - 23

dents, and a factor that would undoubtedly increase in importance in the future." Thus in his final speech before the tribunal, facing possible sentence of death, Speer declared:

> *Hitler's dictatorship was the first dictatorship of an industrial state in this age of modern technology, a dictatorship which employed to perfection the instruments of technology to dominate its own people . . . eighty million persons could be made subject to the will of one individual . . . The instruments of technology made it possible to maintain a close watch over all citizens . . . Dictatorships of the past needed assistants of high quality in the lower ranks . . .The authoritarian system in the age of technology can do without such men. The means of communication alone enable it to mechanize the work of the lower leadership. Thus the type of uncritical receiver of orders is created.*[4]

There is some over-statement here. A people's thoughts are not as easily manipulated through mass communication media as Speer's words would indicate. But the essence of Speer's warning has become firmly implanted as a factor in technological lore, as witness the continuing discussion of the effect of radio and TV on American political campaigns and the heated objections to subliminal TV messages when these were used for a time in 1957.

Other types of manipulation have also made deep impressions on the American mind. The treatment of our prisoners of war during the Korean conflict was deeply troubling, particularly because the communist effort at political indoctrination seemed to have more effect on Americans than on British and Turkish prisoners. Out of a total of 4490 surviving Americans, 21 decided to remain with their Chinese captors after the war, an unprecedented event in American military annals. One out of three Americans were judged later to have collaborated in some degree with their captors. About 75, after their return to American authorities, were

---

4   Macmillan, 1970; p. 520.

discovered to be espionage agents willingly working for the Chinese.[5] The Chinese method was to combine cruel treatment, including physical abuse, with heavy-handed but familiar teaching techniques. They used lectures and exposure to Marxist and Left-leaning books, some by Americans, to try to instill hatred of America and admiration for communism. The techniques were repetition (memorizing communist pamphlets), harassment (being aroused in the middle of the night to recite a passage forgotten during the day), and humiliation (to set a stubborn prisoner's comrades against him). Brutal punishment and fear of even greater brutality were always present.

A development with the same general effect on American thinking was the so-called brain-washing of selected intellectuals by the Chinese Communists. The purpose here was more ambitious than merely changing a person's political beliefs and loyalties. It was to destroy the victim's sense of personality. The techniques are those of psychological conditioning. The method starts with personal degradation. The prisoner is reduced to lapping food and water like an animal, urinating and defecating with hands chained behind his back, and subjected to psychological assaults by interrogators and cell mates on the single theme, "You are guilty, admit it." The prisoner seems finally to be overwhelmed by fear of annihilation as a person; he "confesses" as a touchstone with sanity, as a way to maintain a semblance of selfhood.[6]

The significance of such events is not that they settle anything in themselves about the ultimate impact of science and technology on the human condition. But they do help explain widespread concern over the possible use of such techniques to invade and perhaps destroy the psychological defenses of privacy. The bare events themselves have left a residue of uneasiness about these matters in American thought.

---

5 *Techniques of Persuasion,* J. A. C. Brown, Pelican, 1963, pp. 255-259. In contrast, out of 980 British prisoners, only one defected according to an official British study cited by Brown. The 229 Turkish prisoners remained a solid, well-disciplined group, impervious to indoctrination though unusual efforts were made in their direction.

6 *Ibid.,* p. 280. See also Dr. Robert J. Lifton's *Thought Reform: A Psychiatric Study of 'Brainwashing' in China.*

THE ROLE OF PROPHECY

This uneasiness has been dramatized and enhanced by novelists, poets, playwrights, painters, and other artists. A familiar theme in the arts is the seemingly dangerous affinity between political power and science. The two most widely read works in this field, and probably the most influential, continue to be Aldous Huxley's *Brave New World* and George Orwell's *1984*. Both are so strongly topical — Orwell in particular — that the books might have disappeared years ago from the paperback book shelves if their subject matter were not still a living concern. Each paints a grim picture of what society might become if government authorities were to make maximum use of behavioral control techniques.

Of the two, Huxley's is the more extraordinary as a work of prophetic imagination. It was written in 1931. He somehow missed the coming of nuclear fission but he did foresee the development of electronic communication systems and the direction of biological research. Since its first American edition in 1939, *Brave New World* has gone through 26 hardback printings and upwards of 44 paperback printings.

In a foreword added in 1947, Huxley made several points that help explain the continuing relevance of the issues he raised 40 years ago. The aim of those governing the brave new world, he observed, is not anarchy but social stability. The rulers might not be sane, but they are not madmen. "A really efficient totalitarian state," he continued, "would be one in which the all-powerful executive of political bosses and their army of managers control a population of slaves who do not have to be coerced because they love their servitude. To make them love it is the task assigned, in present-day totalitarian states, to ministries of propaganda, newspaper editors and school teachers. But their methods are still crude . . ." The more refined methods in *Brave New World* include psychological conditioning of infants, personality testing and thus proper assignment of each person to his place in society, universal use of euphoriant drugs and a system of eugenics designed to standardize the human product and so make the task of the managers all the easier.[7] In this 1947 foreword, Huxley observed that

---

7   Foreword to *Brave New World,* Bantam Modern Classic edition, pp. X-XIII.

346

"technically and ideologically we are still a long way from bottled babies." Yet biologist James D. Watson, co-discoverer of the shape of DNA, the heredity molecule, recently told a House of Representatives subcommittee that "within a year," a scientist will conceive a baby in a test tube and successfully place it in a woman who will bear the child.[8]

Orwell's *1984* has a more nightmarish quality than Huxley's novel, perhaps because he had a real-life model to work from: the Stalin dictatorship in the Soviet Union. It still sells readily in a paperback edition which had reached its 40th printing in 1970.

Novelists have not had prophecy to themselves. The public also is addressed on these issues by scholars writing from a wide range of specialties. Perry London, professor of psychology and psychiatry at the University of Southern California, in his book *Behavior Control,* writes that Orwell's views of the technology by which tyranny could impress its will upon men's minds were "much too modest." By 1984, London goes on, "the means at hand will be more sophisticated and efficient than Orwell ever dreamed and they will be in at least modest use, as they have already begun to be, not by the will of tyrants but by the invitation of all of us, for we have been schooled to readiness for all these things and will demand their benign use regardless of potential risk. The capacity for control will continuously grow, evolving from benevolence."[9]

This enlarged capacity for control will develop, in London's view, along lines pretty much laid down: psychotherapy, hypnosis, psychological conditioning, drugs, surgery (including remote control radio implants) and computer technology. Conditioning techniques may be combined with each other and ". . .with drugs, surgery and electronic communication and computing equipment . . . to teach virtually any attitude from authoritarianism to xenophobia, any skill or emotional disposition."[10] Burgeoning computer technology ". . . discovers better and better data processing methods, making it easier all the time to track and predict virtu-

---

8   Washington Post, January 29, 1971, p. 1; article by Victor Cohn.

9   Harper & Row, 1969; pp. 7-8. At the time this book was published, Professor London was a Research Science Development Fellow at the National Institute of Mental Health.

10   *Ibid.,* Part II: The Tools of Mastery.

ally any kind of mass behavior trend; this makes it easier, in turn, to forecast, then control, the individuals who make up the mass." London points out that all this will arouse political, ethical and philosophical opposition, much of it around the concept of free will and the role of choice in human affairs. He also believes there may be theoretical limits on how much human beings can be controlled. Even with such restricting factors, he believes "the development of a refined technology of behavior control in modern society is as inevitable as the maintenance of our other technologies." In summing up his opening chapter, London says there is "probably little point today, if there ever was one, in debating at length whether or not behavior control technology is feasible or should generally be attempted or avoided. In general, no such choice is any longer possible. What remains is to determine the characteristics of this technology, the rules for implementing control and the purposes which it should serve." [11]

Herman Kahn and Anthony Wiener in their widely quoted *The Year 2000* [12] also assure us that worlds such as those imagined by Huxley and Orwell can be extrapolated from existing trends in the sciences. Kahn and Wiener undertook their study at the request of the Commission on the Year 2000, a group appointed by the American Academy of Arts and Sciences. Kahn and Wiener put considerable emphasis on the dysfunctional effects of population pressure on individuals and society, and on steps that may be chosen to relieve stress. Their Chapter VII titled "Other Twenty-first Century Nightmares" has become something of a standard reference source for anyone seeking a catalogue of technological horrors. As society grows more complex, they point out, so will the apparent need for controls over individuals and organizations. "One need not assume the triumph of the policy mentality" to foresee an increase in social controls:

> "*Each restriction will have its valid and attractive rationale, which may even be libertarian. Federal safety regulations for automobile manufacturers and tests for*

---

11 *Ibid.*, Ch. I: The Advent of Behavior Control.

12 Macmillan, 1967; Introduction by Daniel Bell.

348

*drivers today increase the 'freedom' of the license-
holding driver to drive in safety. Coercive treatment of
the mentally ill raises the probability that they will be
able to lead freely constructive lives. Plastic hearts may
replace real ones and damaged brains may be linked to
computers. Therapeutic abortions, through the death
of the fetus, increase the freedom of the mother. And
the biological adaptation of man to his ecological niche
in a extremely complicated and overpopulated society
will increase his freedom to live a satisfying and useful
life."*

If that is the good news, they follow with the bad immediately:

*"It is still possible that the terminus of the process
may be inconsistent with anything we would regard as
freedom or dignity, or even human. The evolution of
society may produce the devolution of man ... Man
may, in the not-too-distant future, be adapted in a
specialized sense, while society through the control of
genetic science maintains its general adaptability by
fitting men to the varying tasks that time and environment provide. (Thus the survival of the fittest may be
replaced by the fitting of the survivors.)"* [13]

By way of illustration, the authors point out that if society
becomes dependent on a complex, interlocking computerized information system, and if miniaturized nuclear weapons become
available and fall into the hands of criminals or political black-
mailers, then "forms of surveillance and control far surpassing any
now in existence" may seem justified. The means to maintain
continuous checks on the entire population and to scan it automatically "for disturbing words and phrases will be available by
the year 2000." Kahn and Wiener suggest that if mass behavioral
controls are attempted it may be done under the rubric of mental
hygiene, something which they believe the American predeliction

---

13 *Ibid.*, p. 347.

for self-medication with tranquilizers may be preparing us for.[14]

Studies such as those of London or of Kahn and Wiener, can hardly be expected to allay the concerns of those who look to the future with apprehension. On the contrary, such studies raise new fears for the future of privacy and individual freedom and give credence to the prophetic insights of creative artists such as Huxley and Orwell.

SCIENCE AND THE FUTURE OF PRIVACY

If mass behavioral control were inevitable, then the future of privacy, though painful, would be simple. If we proceed as though a man were, literally, a machine, then he could presumably be controlled through the same iron laws of mechanics that are used to control clocks and computers. Not much to that. Things would appear a bit more complicated if man comes to be viewed as a creature that could be conditioned to act like a machine. The view is sometimes expressed that because a man gets up to answer the telephone, he has been conditioned to be part of the telephone. If he chooses at times to sit and ignore the ring, that is bothersome but he just needs more conditioning. In any case, man's role would be to accept a place as part of the vast technological linkage society would become. It would be a mistake to encourage privacy or try to protect it. Privacy would be seen as disruptive to the general linkage on the grounds that no part of a machine can have a useful life of its own away from its linked parts. Elementary engineering. The machine-conditioning of man in a free society would have to be gradual, perhaps under the rubric of mental health as Kahn and Wiener suggest, but more likely under some such rubric as efficiency, general welfare or national security. If their day comes, those who lean to the machinability of man would not lack for slogans or charismatic sloganeers. Journalism would produce the first; politics the second.

But there is an opposing view which sees privacy in quite a different light. It is grounded in science, though it is critical of the

---

14 *Ibid.,* pp. 348-349.

way science is presently organized and motivated.

Rene Dubos, professor at the Rockefeller University, a microbiologist and experimental pathologist, argues that the kind of life so widely foreseen for the twenty-first century is unbelievable to a biologist such as himself because "it is incompatible with the fundamental needs of man's nature." [15]

The needs of man's nature "have not changed significantly since the late stone age," Dubos continues, "and they will not change in the predictable future; they define the limits beyond which any prediction of the future becomes literally unbelievable." Man will continue to live by his senses and to perceive the world through them. "As a result he will eventually reject excessive abstractions and mechanization in order to reestablish direct contact with the natural forces from which he derives awareness of his own existence and to which he owes his very sense of being." Dubos sums up: "In my opinion the world in the year 2000 will reflect less the projections of technologists, sociologists and economists than the vital needs and urges of biological man."

In a series of lectures at the Museum of Natural History in New York, Dr. Jacob Bronowski — mathematician, statistican and philosopher of science — opened with the question: "A Machine or a Self?". These lectures, later published under the title *The Identity of Man*,[16] made the point that "the self derives from the way in which it turns experience into knowledge — that is, into readiness for action." The self "is not something fixed inside my head," Bronowski continued. "If it exists at all my self is a process by which I turn new experience into knowledge." "In order to see if there is a self in man which is not mechanical we have to look not inside the brain but into his acts of experience." A machine, he points out, is not a natural object but is a "human artifact which mimics and exploits our own understanding of nature." As that understanding changes new machines will be forthcoming. But we "cannot now conceive of any kind of law or machine which could formalize the total modes of human knowledge." This is because the total of man's sense perceptions plus his stored

---

15 *So Human An Animal,* Scribner's paperback edition, 1968; pp. 20-21.
16 The Natural History Press, 1965; Ch. 1.

memories and the interplay between the two "includes a mode of knowledge that cannot be written out in symbols as the new input for a machine."

Lewis Mumford in his latest book, *The Pentagon of Power*[17] makes a related point. The view of the brain which he believes still dominates much of science sees it as a separated, isolated member of the body, functioning without relationship to other parts and dedicated to the one specialized purpose of mathematical reasoning. Yet:

> *"Recent experiment shows that on the contrary, the human brain, so far from having the limitations of a computer, which can work only with definite symbols and exact images, has a marvelous capacity for coping with vague, indistinct, and confused data, making sense out of information so incomplete that it would paralyze a computer — as in translating a wide range of sounds, tones, different pronunciations into the same intelligible words. It is these unifying properties of the human mind, with its ability constantly to bring together symbolically relevant portions of the past, the present and the future, that has made it possible for man to react with some measure of success to a diversified environment and an open world, instead of retreating into a safe niche, with a limited range of opportunities and responses, like all the other species."*

Dubos and Mumford are critical of the way science is currently conducted, with its stress on the repeatable experiment. "The very nature of the experimental methods," Dubos points out, "leads scientists to focus their efforts on phenomena that are reproducible and therefore are largely independent of free will." Yet the ability to choose among ideas and courses of action "may be the most important of all human attributes; it has probably been and still is a crucial determinant of human evolution. The most damning statement that can be made about the sciences of life as presently practiced is that they deliberately ignore the most important phenomena of human life." On this same point, Dubos

17   Harcourt Brace Jovanovich, 1970, pp. 54-55.

later observes: "If scientists elect to study man only by physio-chemical methods, they will naturally discover only the physio-chemical determinants of his life and find that his body is a ma-chinery of atoms. But they will overlook other human character-istics . . . One of them is that man hardly ever reacts passively to external forces. The most characteristic aspect of his behavior is that he responds not only actively but often unexpectedly and creatively . . . The mechanical definition of man misses the point because what is human in man is precisely that which is not me-chanical." [18]

After reminding his readers of what the Harvard biologist, George Wald, calls the Harvard Law of Animal Behavior, ("Under precisely controlled conditions, an animal does as he damn pleases."), Dubos goes on in a later section to point up the result of this concentration on what is provable in the laboratory. Of some twenty papers read by scientists in celebration of the 50th anniversary of the National Academy of Sciences in 1963, not one "touched on the problems that the man of flesh and bone meets in the twentieth century world." One reason for this shortcoming is "the strange assumption that knowledge of complex systems will inevitably emerge from studies of much simpler ones;" [19] in short, the reductionist approach that has dominated modern science from its beginnings. The peculiarly human elements in human af-fairs do not reduce to simple and separable components. It is what Mumford has in mind when he refers to present-day science as underdimensioned.

Mumford emphasizes that the world view dominating most of science since the day of Galileo leaves out man's cultural inheri-tance. "When Galileo's successors pulverized this immense cultural heritage into what was measurable, public, 'objective,' repeatable, they not merely falsified or obliterated the basic facts of human existence, but curtailed the possibilities for human growth." The world view of Galileo has retained its hold because it succeeds as a labor-saving device; Mumford believes that ". . . by making mathe-matical description the test of truth, by utilizing only a part of the human self to explore only a part of its environment, the new

18   *So Human An Animal*, pp. 128-132.

19   *Ibid.*, p. 214.

science successfully turned the most significant attributes of life into purely secondary phenomena, ticketed for replacement by the machine." The "masters of the scientific guild, with their many imitators and disciples, now wield more influence than any older priesthood," Mumford continues. Later, shifting his criticism to the influence of Descartes, he argues: "Under a rational system of ideas, all minds would be forced to submit to scientific 'law' as the subject of an absolute ruler to his edicts . . . Thus the ultimate aim of science, the proof of both its truth and its efficacy, would be to make all behavior as predictable as the movements of the heavenly bodies. To many scientists, even today, this is not only an unchallengeable axiom but a moral imperative." He adds that this attitude assumed, as in any absolutism, that there were no unruly elements that "could not be rounded up and imprisoned indefinitely. . ." [20]

Hobbes appears to Mumford to be the first thinker to see the fully political implications of the mechanical world picture. In *The Leviathan*, Hobbes came to the conclusion that submission to absolute authority was the necessary condition for enjoying civilization, the only path for man away from the short, brutal and nasty way of life he equated with primitive man. [21] In a world of machines or of creatures that can be reduced to machines, "technocrats would indeed be gods," Mumford says. [22] Hobbes saw this. He also saw that as soon as science, through technology, affects man-to-man relationships or man-to-nature relationships, it becomes a factor in the political arrangements of society.

Dubos, Bronowski, Mumford, and a growing number of scientists and social critics, see man not as a largely "public" object in a vast technological linkage, but as a largely private entity, with a private view of the world, privately arrived at through biological inheritance, cultural imprints and responses to the varied experiences of living. In this view, a sense of privacy marks man as human.

---

20 *Pentagon of Power*, p. 82.

21 *Ibid.,* p. 98.

22 *Ibid.,* p. 72.

PRIVACY AS A POLITICAL MATTER

Dubos and Mumford call for a fundamental redirection of science and technology to encompass the whole existence of man. They seek a more humanistic science. They see grave perils if changes are not quickly made. Each in his own way is saying that the uneasiness of the broad public concerning science and technology is justified.

Ordinarily where there is a widespread uneasiness over some matter, a response from the political system can be expected. But the impact of science and technology generally, and the matter of privacy in particular, create unusual problems.

In the first place, there is the possibility that privacy, though greatly treasured by a few persons, is not something of prime importance to the mass of Americans. Thus Peter Drucker in his most recent book, though he recognizes the danger to privacy and the wisdom of protecting it, nevertheless is of the opinion that few people probably desire it.[23] A writer in *American Psychologist* has argued that the overriding moral imperative in our society is not to protect privacy but to share our thoughts freely. "As a matter of fact," the author states, "the average citizen has few secrets that are not recorded somewhere and more or less available to anyone with a serious interest in probing." What is more, ". . . there is reason to feel that the public welcomes as much as it resents the invasion of privacy."[24] This is a view shared by many who gather data professionally. The readiness with which individuals will answer questions about sex habits is often cited. For years, the public has been inundated with surveys and questionnaires, perhaps to the point of accepting them as a permanent fixture in American life, no matter what the subject matter.

There is also difficulty in stating the issue of privacy in traditional political terms. Normally the American system operates through pressures applied by contending groups. The contending groups in this case are not readily discernible; they may seem at first not even to exist. They do exist, though they are far from typical political groupings.

---

23 *The Age of Discontinuity,* by Peter F. Drucker, Harper & Row, New York, 1969.

24 *American Psychologist,* May 1967; v. 22 (s); Article by Chester C. Bennett.

The science-technology-statistics community has already considerable political experience. It is characterized by wide individual and professional diversity, high ideals of public service, a rapidly growing social consciousness and a low political profile. Yet it is a grouping that — in its way — wields effective power. Don K. Price, Dean of the Graduate School of Public Administration at Harvard University, has pointed out that, "Scientists and professionals in the United States, in their ability to compete for influence and jurisdiction within the constitutional system, are in a far stronger position than one would think by looking at their formal legal power. They have the fundamental advantage of commanding privileged sanctuaries over which they have absolute control, while invading at will the battlefields of administration and politics . . .Professionals . . .are aware of the potentialities of exerting public influence through private organizations, and of the tactical advantage of possessing special knowledge not subject to public disputation."[25] If it becomes necessary to defend statistical programs before the committees of Congress, strong and effective spokesmen will be forthcoming.

It is more difficult to see how spokesmen for privacy can bring equally effective power to bear. Kahn and Wiener, referring to the possibility of a centralized federal data bank, point out that there is no existing pressure group organized to sound warnings on the side of privacy. If, step by step, centralized data regarding individuals is made available to government officials (in the name of law enforcement, for example), and eventually even to private organizations (in the name of an efficient credit rating system, perhaps) then "the final consequence could be an enormous invasion of privacy." Yet the people who value privacy would not have had an effective chance to express themselves. Kahn and Wiener observe that often enough, "the appropriate pressure group does not exist to resist those who support an innovation."[26] The implication here is that those supporting a federal data bank, because their views can be crystallized at the policy-making level, may eventually outweigh a diffused, unorganized opposition.

25 *The Scientific Estate,* the Belknap Press of the Harvard University Press, 1965; p. 199.

26 *The Year 2000,* p. 390.

In discussions to date, the idea that privacy needs some kind of protection against computerized information systems has been expressed by a wide range of individuals and groups, with often competing political views on other matters. A conservative group, for example, might heatedly oppose certain aspects of behavioral research (fearing thought control), but might favor enhanced power for the police to use technological means of exposing the radical left. A liberal group might be quick to oppose additional surveillance technology for the police (fearing political repression), but might favor behavioral research if this promised more aid to the underprivileged. Privacy has had its spokesman but it has been treated as a side issue by organizations which exist primarily for some other purpose. There is no National Association for the Protection of Privacy, no American Privacy Union. Formal, recognizable lobbies sometimes appear rather late in the political process, however. Their appearance is preceded by a period during which a vaguely held idea or belief gradually gains clarity, concreteness and new adherents. This formative period is often participated in by people who do not think of themselves as taking part in politics at all. Some spokesmen and intellectual leaders in this phase may advise against seeking political solutions. Ethical and moral considerations are stressed instead. Thus it may not appear to be a political matter, or a matter suitable to political action. I would place the privacy problem as still in this formative period. As will be shown in what follows, a privacy constituency seems to have been forming for some time now; it seems close to the point where an effective lobby might emerge.

In 1959, Edward A. Shils of the University of Chicago, a political sociologist, in a paper titled "Social Inquiry and the Autonomy of the Individual"[27] viewed the issue of freedom and privacy as an ethical problem confronting the behavioral sciences.

"Modern liberal society," Professor Shils wrote, "is the parent of individuality. It could not develop in a society in which there is not freedom to explore, to experience and to judge, and in which

---

27   In *The Human Meaning of the Social Sciences,* Daniel Lerner, editor; Meridian Books, 1959. Shils' paper was reprinted in "The Use of Social Research in Federal Domestic Programs, Part IV.," a Staff Study for the Research and Technical Programs subcommittee of the House of Representatives, April, 1967; pp. 337-359. Other page references are also to the Staff Study.

357

the individual need not bear some of the responsibility for the consequences of his judgment." Respect for privacy, though relatively late in arriving, now "has a place in the constellation of values of modern liberalism." It rests on "the appreciation of human dignity, with its high evaluation of individual self-determination, free from the bonds of prejudice, passion and superstition. In this, the respect for human dignity and individuality share a historic comradeship with the freedom of scientific inquiry, which is equally precious to modern liberalism. The tension between these values, so essential to each other in so many profoundly important ways, is one of the antimonies of modern liberalism."

Shils goes on to deal with ethical problems raised by new research tools, pointing out that the right to use such tools does have certain limits raised by tradition and law. He goes to some lengths to explain to his fellow social scientists why the bugging of a jury room by sociological researchers in 1959 aroused such a furor in the press and among politicians. Judge and counsel had approved the bugging, but the jurors were not told that their deliberations would be listened to and recorded.

Shils observes that almost all sociological researchers "have been primarily concerned with the anomic, the irrational, and dissensual and the vulgar elements in our society ... With all due respect for the devotion to truth of American sociologists and social psychologists and their disciplined detachment, I think it is not unfair to say that much of their work shows a certain measure of distaste and repugnance for their own society." This attitude results in a "moral distance" from the society they spend their lives studying which, Shils adds, "is not without dangers for the ethical conduct of social research."

In a concluding section Shils further delineates the confrontation between science and personal privacy. There are reserve forces in Western culture "which would inhibit social scientists from seeking to establish a tyranny over their fellow men." But at the same time there is "the scientific attitude and the impatience with imperfection which are also part of our cultural inheritance ... and which envisage men of science ruling society, bringing it into order, overcoming man's imperfections by the application of scientific knowledge." Shils sees the same ambivalence within the intellectual classes: On the one hand, the humanist tradition; on the other, "a cranky, embittered alienation which accentuates the anti-authoritarianism innate to liberalism." This alienation is "exacerbated by a harebrained belief in the ease with which men can be improved and the unreflecting conviction that social science is the right means to that improvement."

The confrontation posed by Shils in terms of professional ethics was moved closer to a political formulation six years later in an article by Oscar M. Ruebhausen and Orville G. Brim in the Columbia Law Review. [28] Their first citation, incidentally, was to the Shils article referred to above. Ruebhausen and Brim approach the matter as a problem of law. They state the fundamental tension more explicitly than Shils. They describe it as "the conflict of science and scientific research with the right . . . of private personality." This right evolved slowly because "privacy is in conflict with other valued social interests such as informed and effective government, law enforcement, and free dissemination of the news. Whenever competing rights and values confront each other, it always is a slow and arduous process to evaluate the claim and counterclaim in real life situations. This process, however, is the classic function of the law."

The authors refer to the findings of behavioral scientists to support their view that human beings have both a need to communicate and a need to withhold: ". . . to protect ourselves, or our processes of creativity, or our minority views, or our self-respect, all of us seek to withhold at least certain things from certain people at certain times." They continue: "The essense·of privacy is no more, and certainly no less, than the freedom of the individual to pick and choose for himself the time and circumstances under which, and most importantly, the extent to which, his attitudes, beliefs, behavior and opinions are to be shared or withheld from others. The right to privacy is, therefore, a positive claim to a status of personal dignity — a claim to freedom, if you will, but freedom of a very special kind." The authors refer to accusations

28 *Columbia Law Review,* November, 1965; reprinted in "The Use of Social Research in Federal Domestic Programs, Part IV.," a Staff Study for the Research and Technical Programs subcommittee of the House of Representatives, April, 1967, pp. 367-394.

that science "now poses an unprecedented and grievous threat to the privacy or personality." Despite some exaggeration by popular spokesmen for this position, Ruebhausen and Brim go on to say that developments in such fields as accoustics, optics, medicine and electronics ". . . have made it clear that society must now work out some reasonable rules for the protection of private personality." The problem posed in this article is how the interests of the community — in scientific research, law enforcement, economic growth — can be accommodated to the right of privacy.

The line of development continues from the Ruebhausen-Brim article directly to Alan F. Westin's *Privacy and Freedom,* published in 1968.[29] Westin, professor of Public Law and Government at Columbia University, undertook the study at the request of the Special Committee on Science and Law of the Association of the Bar of the City of New York, which Ruebhausen served as chairman. Since its publication, and due largely to its influence, both the underlying social tensions and the arguments for positive action can be seen with increased clarity.

Westin describes the computer-born revolution in man's capacity to process data as an "enormous boon" but adds: "The issue of privacy raised by computerization is whether the increased collection and processing of information for diverse public and private purposes, if not carefully controlled, could lead to a sweeping power of surveillance by government over individual lives and organizational activity. As we are forced more and more each day to leave documentary fingerprints and footprints behind us, and as these are increasingly put into storage systems capable of computer retrieval, government may acquire a power-through-data position that armies of government investigators could not create in past eras." He identifies a number of factors that intensify the pressures of information technology on privacy. We are already "the greatest data generating society in human history." "To help himself, to help science, to help society run efficiently, the individual now pours a constantly flowing stream of information about himself into the record files — birth and marriage records, public school records, census data, military records, public health records, civil defense records, loyalty-security clearance records,

---

29   *Privacy and Freedom,* Atheneum; 1968.

income tax returns, social security returns, land and housing records, insurance records, bank records, business reporting forms to government, license applications, financial declarations required by law, charitable contributions, credit applications and records, automobile registration records, post office records, telephone records, psychological and psychiatric records, scholarship or research-grant records, church records – and on and on." [30]

Private and government investigators have already amassed personal dossiers on tens of millions of Americans. These are seen by Westin as a potential "record prison"; past mistakes, omissions or misunderstood events become permanent evidence; "out-of-date facts such as former political affiliations or nervous disorders may go unreviewed and haunt a person's life for decades." As this becomes known to more and more Americans," Westin continues, "psychological conflict with offical bureaucracies can grow deeper, and living one's life to make a good record can become a preoccupying concern." [31]

This matter of psychological conflict with bureaucracies is worth serious attention by the gatherers and users of statistical data. Traditionally, Americans have cooperated in the role of statistics-giver. But to be told that the managers of complex sociopolitical programs have good intentions, or that some business enterprise somewhere may be benefited, may no longer allay the doubts of the typical giver of statistics in light of what he now stands to lose. Formerly, he stood to lose little or nothing. Now he may wonder.

It is not unreasonable to assume that if statistics-givers are denied what seems to them to be adequate protection of their privacy, many will seek other methods of protection.

Consider the difficulty that the Census Bureau has had for years in getting an adequate count of single black males. Many such men, especially those living in urban slums, have very good reasons for not wanting to be counted or catalogued in any set of social statistics. Given the problems they face and the life pattern they adopt, it is simple self-protection to avoid the census taker.

---

30 *Ibid.*, pp. 158-159.
31 *Ibid.*, p. 160.

In their situation, even allowing themselves to be enumerated appears as a potentially harmful invasion of privacy.[32] Their motivations to cooperate in the census are weak or nonexistent; motivations to keep their heads down, to avoid being noticed, are to them overwhelmingly strong. So at this simplest data-gathering level, a straight head count of citizens, the givers may confound the users.

The Federal Housing Administration has private agencies investigate more than a million loan applicants a year, including their "marital stability." These investigations presumably are confidential yet they can be bought by private mortgage lenders for $1.50 each.[33] Applicants who learn this may decide it is better to lie than to give an honest answer.

Experimental psychologists have long been concerned about the validity of results obtained by testing college students, who realize before the tests are given that deception is often part of the procedure. Some students try to determine what the tester really is after in order to supply answers that will please the tester; others try to outwit the tester, using deception against deception, by giving responses deliberately chosen to confuse the results.[34]

Along with the spread of personality testing in the 1960's as a means of screening job applicants came a book titled *How to Beat Personality Tests.*[35] The advice was always to give heterosexual responses to sex questions, admit to no cultural interests, and if ink blots are used, always report seeing animals in motion, never mentioning sex organs. The user of such advice could plausibly claim to be acting in self-defense against efforts to extract from him, by trick questions, more than he wanted to reveal about himself to a personnel clerk or a machine.

---

32 See *Tally's Corner* by Elliott Liebow, Little Brown, 1966, for a sympathetic account of the life style of such men. He refers to census under-counting on p. 20.

33 Westin, pp. 159-160.

34 *The Human Use of Human Subjects: The Problem of Deception in Social-Psychological Experiments,* by Herbert C. Kelman; reprinted in "The Use of Social Research in Federal Domestic Program, Part IV.," a staff study for the Research and Technical Programs subcommittee of the House of Representatives, April, 1967; p. 410.

35 Westin, p. 267.

Scientific studies reported by Westin[36] show that it is possible for some well coached subjects to beat the lie detector. Some assumed an impersonal, detached attitude; others conjured up strong sexual phantasies; still others "jammed" the polygraph by flexing muscles vigorously while being questioned.

If statistical programs and data processing continue along present lines, without additional protection for privacy, doubts, suspicions and resentments will increase among the givers. Traditional appeals to civic responsibility as reasons for cooperating will decline in effectiveness. The motivational weight will shift toward avoidance, withholding, deceit. Individual counter-measures will increase and will not necessarily be limited to an underground existence; avoiding or misleading the gatherers of statistics might come to enjoy a certain vogue, with "how to" articles in the press. The tone of society could move from open to secret. Some lives would be lived on two tracks: One for the record, the other designed to protect the sense of privacy. Significant economic consequences could be expected. Social inventions which operate largely on trust — bank checking accounts, credit cards, the self-assessed income tax — would be subject to serious erosion. "Mom and Pop" type enterprises would rise in popularity as a means of maintaining a degree of privacy while the attractiveness of corporate and government employment would decline accordingly. Cash transactions might increase. Private mortgage lending might revive.

One theory about the future is that men in technological society will become accustomed to invasions of privacy, that they will adapt to computerized information networks, choosing to submit and survive quietly rather than insist on changes in the system. This view misunderstands the temper of the American people, underrates their resourcefulness, ignores their tradition of individualism.

Ruebhausen and Brim in their 1965 paper pointed out that if social needs (including the needs of science) cannot be successfully accommodated with the need for privacy, the consequences ". . . are predictable: They begin with the recoil and revulsion of the community, they conclude with arbitrary legislation." Trust be-

---

36 *Ibid.,* p. 213.

tween the statistic-giving public and the users has a pragmatic importance: "The quality and effectiveness of behavioral research will depend . . . on the confidence the public has in the behavioral scientists and in the way they pursue their science." Confidence is the key to dependable results; fear drives out confidence.

The cry of paranoia may be raised by some who feel that privacy is already adequately protected. But a strong response to protect privacy may also be viewed as normal and healthy. Perhaps the guiding principle for data gatherers and processors should be: The American people will attempt to maintain psychological privacy sufficient to their sense of well-being, if possible through the political process, if not, then by individual use of avoidance, evasion or deceit.

LINES OF RESPONSE

Developments relating to privacy will continue along several lines regardless of possible changes in official policy:

1. Automated data processing will continue to make rapid strides.
2. Its use will expand in government, business, finance and science.
3. Concern for privacy, already a lively topic in the news media, will increase.
4. Legal redress will be sought increasingly by individuals claiming invasion of privacy; a body of law as interpreted by judges will therefore develop at a swifter pace than in recent years.

In addition, suggestions will increase for a number of innovations.

Westin believes information systems should be required by law to include technological safeguards at three points: input, storage and output. These can be quite effective on behalf of privacy. But technical safeguards can either be corrupted from within or penetrated from without, Westin concludes. He therefore believes personal information should be defined as a property right and be surrounded with all the legal protections we have bestowed on the rights of property, including the due-process guarantees. The individual would be given the right to examine what goes into files concerning himself, to offer explanations of raw data that might be harmful to him, and to have a hearing (with right of judicial review) in cases of serious dispute with the managers of the information system. [37]

Westin recommends that review of automated information systems should be lodged in an independent regulatory agency with ombudsman-type authority. Senator Sam Ervin of North Carolina, one of the leading experts in Congress on privacy, also favors an agency that would keep a watchful eye on how the federal establishments use their powers of information.

It may be that an independent agency would be the best answer to rising fears about the effect of information lodged in government and private data banks. The very creation of the agency would tend to lessen concern. As the public became familiar with its functions, it could be a means of strengthening confidence in statistical programs. Congress would have to establish such an agency but it should be independent in the sense that the Federal Reserve Board, the Federal Trade Commission and the Food and Drug Administration are independent. A degree of risk must be recognized. In the wrong hands, an agency directed to protect privacy could become the very means of invading it. The concept of privacy and the rights of individuals concerning privacy, as against the right of the government to demand some types of information, is still an area marked by legal and moral uncertainties. A certain amount of confusion would be unavoidable in the early years. Lines of authority for the agency would be difficult to draw through the thicket of federal programs that gather and store data for purposes already approved by Congress.

These are formidable difficulties. They could be markedly reduced if, preceding serious consideration by Congress of legislation establishing an independent agency, a national conference were held on the subject of privacy and its protection. Congress should have important representation at such a conference, along with the executive department of government, the judiciary, attorneys with a background in the privacy issue, scholars, and persons from private life to speak for givers of statistics.

---

37 *Ibid.,* pp. 323-25.

Much good, or much harm, will come from information technology.

If we are to open the way to the good, democratically adopted safeguards to assure the private citizen that he is, indeed, a private person and can remain so while still meeting his public obligations, seem essential.

CHAPTER 6

USING CONTROLLED FIELD STUDIES TO IMPROVE PUBLIC POLICY

By

Richard J. Light
Frederick Mosteller
Herbert S. Winokur Jr.

USING CONTROLLED FIELD STUDIES TO IMPROVE PUBLIC POLICY

TABLE OF CONTENTS

369

Evaluation is a necessary foundation for effective implementation and judicious modification of our existing programs. At this point, evaluation is probably more important than the addition of new laws to an already extensive list of educational statutes. . . . Evaluation will provide the information we require to strengthen weak programs, fully support effective programs, and drop those which simply are not fulfilling the objectives intended by the Congress when the programs were originally enacted.

The Honorable Robert H. Finch (1969)

At a time when "consumerism" has become a major concern, programs using public funds encounter the demand that they should be carefully monitored to ensure that they are in the public interest. Competent evaluation makes an important contribution to answering that demand. By measuring the effectiveness of a program, an evaluation serves the needs of Congress, the program designers, and most important of all, the program's intended beneficiaries and the taxpayers. The virtues of program planning, devel-

371

opment, and evaluation have been argued extensively by D. T. Campbell, J. P. Gilbert and F. Mosteller, G. H. Orcutt, A. M. Rivlin and P. M. Timpane.

Although we have a substantial technology available for evaluating programs, this technology has not been used as frequently, or as effectively, as it might have been. In particular, we believe that the role of "controlled field studies" in program evaluation has been largely overlooked, despite the high payoffs that such studies could yield. Such studies have wide application, covering many disciplines, such as economics, medical trials, social and welfare programs, education, agriculture, and the area in which they were originally developed, physical or laboratory experiments. Furthermore, despite the obvious political character of many decisions concerning social policy, the public should be as concerned if a program goes unevaluated as it is if a well executed evaluation shows it to be ineffective. When a program is found to be ineffective, it can be modified and improved, or its funds may be diverted to more useful programs directed towards similar goals. If nothing is known about program effectiveness, an ineffective and perhaps even a *harmful* program may continue on its unfortunate way for years.

ASSESSING PROGRESS TOWARD GOALS

The procedures we discuss in this essay have been and can be applied to both large and small programs. For example, they have been used to evaluate an innovation introduced in an attempt to improve the quality of life and humanity of conditions in some nursing homes. They have also been used to evaluate the effectiveness of a poliomyelitis vaccine in a field trial on a national scale (Salk vaccine). In both situations, program goals had to be carefully stated.

Whatever the program of interest, it may have one of several types of goals. The first type is the "immutable" goal. This goal is usually specified in advance, and a program evaluation is directed entirely toward answering the question of whether this specific goal has been achieved. An example of this is the Salk vaccine field trial discussed later in this essay. Here, the clear goal was to determine the effectiveness of a new vaccine in reducing the occur-

372

rences of different kinds of poliomyelitis in young children.

Another type of program may allow for "adjustable" goals. As we shall illustrate below, a program may have unintended consequences which, after being observed, are incorporated into its goal structure. Trying to anticipate all possible indirect effects of any program is impossible, but spotting them when they arise may have important policy implications. It may spur us to rethink a program's original goals. If we monitor a wide variety of unintended consequences, then we may redirect a program which is failing to achieve its principal goals, but which is succeeding in other ways.

An example where favorable unintended consequences were incorporated into program goals is the Tennessee Study, conducted by R. A. Klaus and S. W. Gray (1968). That study indicated that younger siblings of children who received special tutorial help tended to outperform their peers whose older brothers and sisters had received no special help. Thus, indirect benefits to younger brothers and sisters were an unintended consequence of an educational program.

Finally, a program may have more than one major goal. A good example of such a program is Head Start, currently funded at the rate of nearly $400 million annually. Head Start is a preschool enrichment program specifically directed towards children from families with low incomes. [For a detailed discussion of the political aspects of Head Start's development, see S. H. White (1971).] This program for disadvantaged children lists as its goals:

a. the improvement of cognitive performance
b. the improvement of social awareness
c. the improvement of self-esteem
d. improved medical care.

When a program has multiple goals, such as the four above, some may actually conflict with others. For example, in Head Start, it may be that maximum cognitive improvement occurs in a relatively competitive setting. At the same time, however, an additional goal may be to increase cooperation, and reduce competition, among children. In this event, a program evaluator can profitably divide the several goals into subgroups, so that goals within a

373

subgroup are similar, while goals across subgroups may differ substantially. Frequently, if a program is successful in achieving one goal in a subgroup, it will also do quite well in achieving other goals in the same group.

A program's goals may take one of several forms. These forms, although related, may require slightly different evaluative techniques. One form can be described as "improving output," in the sense that agricultural programs work towards improving crop yields for given amounts of land. Programs such as Head Start, directed toward raising the output of most members of a group, fall into this category. A second form of program goals can be described as "preventing catastrophe." Programs directed specifically toward forestalling infrequent but catastrophic events, such as onset of poliomyelitis, or malnutrition of children, fall into this group. In any case, we need to find out whether the goals are being met.

ALTERNATIVE METHODS OF GATHERING INFORMATION

A variety of procedures are available for collecting data used to evaluate programs. Some are well-known and inexpensive, but also relatively inefficient. Others are more difficult to implement, but yield more informative results. For convenience, we can divide the sources of information into four groups.

1. Impressionistic or anecdotal observation.
2. Managerial or accounting records.
3. Surveys (including longitudinal studies).
4. Controlled field studies.

FIGURE 1

Summary of Strengths and Weaknesses
of Three Kinds of Information

	COST	INFERENCE
Anecdotal Evidence	S It can be cheaply and widely used, with little advance planning.	W Inference from "selected data" is the most questionable kind of inference. W Observations have not been obtained from a probability sample taken from a specific population, and the population to which these anecdotes and inferences apply is usually difficult to specify *post hoc*.
Managerial Records	S The cost of obtaining management data is usually low, as the data consists of standardized forms to be filled out, rather than careful measurements being taken on program participants.	W An evaluator is necessarily tied to the fairly narrow data already available in record form. No planned experiment has been conducted to throw some light on a question such as: "what would have happened if money were allocated differently?"
Sample Surveys	S Of all methods which allow us to control which questions we ask, the sample survey usually is cheapest. It is cheaper than a complete count of the target population, which is usually what managerial records involve.	S To the extent that variation in the field in different versions of any program already exists, a sample survey enables us to determine the relationship among input and output measures for the different versions of that program. This should help us to make programs more effective as well as helping us to decide which programs are currently effective. W While it is possible to relate sets of inputs and sets of outputs, it is usually difficult to get a complete picture of these relationships. It is especially difficult to project what might happen to these relationships if they were extended beyond existing ranges in the data collected. This is because of the non-experimental character of *post hoc* surveys.

KEY

S A strength of this type of evidence.

W A weakness of this type of evidence.

375

	QUALITY OF INFORMATION	OTHER COMMENTS
Anecdotal Evidence	S The first evidence of a new phenomenon, or change in existing conditions, may often appear in anecdotal evidence. Thus, field observers, or medical doctors studying individual cases, may develop initial insights from such evidence. W Anecdotal evidence is not subject to careful quality control in terms of quality of information and observations, scaling problems, control of extraneous conditions, unreliability among many observers, unstandardized tests, and reporters' particular biases. Thus, it is difficult to generalize from several reporters' anecdotal comments, and identify commonalities among anecdotes.	S Because the variety of observers and situations is broad, anecdotal data may not be bound up in preconceptions of the structure of a study. Thus, an observer may focus on aberrant or unusual cases as they attract his attention. To the extent that such aberrant cases are important, and extra attention paid to them yields valuable information, this is a virtue. W This form of evidence is most difficult to quantify to permit a thorough statistical analysis. W Although the evidence may have captured some valuable insights, our relatively unquantitative review of this evidence may not pick up these ideas.
Managerial Records	W Data may be unreliable or particularly biased, because people who keep records may wish to make themselves look good, or have an axe to grind. The lack of an outside or an "objective" evaluator may lead to great temptation to "fudge" data. W Sometimes records do not provide needed information. When people come in and out of a program, or change programs, we may not keep records across programs. Thus, we may not be able to maintain the accounting on a level precise enough to follow individuals.	S Studies which draw their information from ongoing management reports cast their conclusions in terms which are readily recognized by a funding agency. Thus, if a program is input oriented, such as a welfare program, which allocates money among eligible recipients, data on program recipients is easily kept. W Records may be kept sloppily because they are viewed as a bureaucratic requirement to be met, rather than as an important and integral part of a program. This seriously transgresses the idea of an evaluation being used to improve an ongoing program. W If anonymity is desirable, records cannot be kept on individuals.
Sample Surveys	S The quality of information is usually high, if the survey is well defined. However, the data is available only for existing programs.	W If a particular version or idea is not being tried out in the field currently, we cannot get any good estimate of how well it works or might work if implemented.

Figure 1 states some summary strengths and weaknesses of the first three kinds of evidence. On the three rows, it presents anecdotal evidence, managerial records, and sample surveys. The first three columns list factors of cost, inference, and the quality of information gathered for these three methods. The final column presents some additional comments for each technique. Next to each comment appears either an *S* or a *W*. An *S* indicates the feature to be a strength, a *W* a weakness, of a method of data collection. Not surprisingly, all three methods appearing in Figure 1 have some strengths and some weaknesses. We now mention briefly one situation where each kind of evidence is used.

Anecdotal evidence is often used in medical research for defining syndromes. Medical researchers put together sets of anecdotal evidence which appear in the literature, and attempt to develop lists or taxonomies of often-cited symptoms. For anecdotal evidence to be useful in a *cumulative* fashion, the procedure requires, first, that carefully documented cases appear in journals, and, second, that a plan be drawn to develop the evidence into taxonomies.

An example of a program that uses managerial records is Title I, authorized under the Elementary and Secondary Education Act (ESEA) passed by Congress in 1965. The purpose of the program is to provide monetary grants to school systems with enough children who, according to family income guidelines, are disadvantaged. The school systems then apply this money as they see fit within a general range of options provided by the ESEA guidelines. Further, the systems are required by law to keep detailed records of how they spent their Title I funds. Thus, Title I records from various school systems in each of the fifty states provide a vast amount of managerial data. By increasing the use of managerial records in Title I to improve future versions of the program, local personnel who keep these records might be encouraged and motivated to keep them more accurately.

Scientific sample surveys, which form our next topic, have been developed primarily in the past forty years. The U.S. Bureau of the Census has been a strong creative factor for sample surveys in this country, and the nation has become adept at using survey techniques. Organizations that conduct excellent sample surveys can be found in government, universities, and private corporations. [For a summary of some strengths and weaknesses of surveys in social policy work, see R. J. Light and P. V. Smith (1970).]

An example of problems that can occur with a survey is given by the Martin Company Study (1966). That survey dealt with the re-employment experiences of men who had been laid off after the closing of a Martin plant in Denver. The main survey finding was that the future employability of the men differed and depended upon their background characteristics. Some of these characteristics could be influenced by government policy intervention, and others could not. As the authors point out in their report, the effect of general background on the men's future employment opportunities was thoroughly entangled with the effect of having held particular jobs at the Martin plant, and it was therefore impossible to develop an effective strategy for government aid. This entanglement is often a feature of sample surveys, as opposed to experiments or controlled field studies, as we shall now explain.

An important difference between research conducted in a "field setting," as compared with that conducted in a laboratory, lies in the amount of "control" that can be exercised. In laboratory research, after a background variable of interest is identified, a carefully planned experiment can often be run to study the relationship between this variable and an outcome variable. The feature of planned experimentation that permits us to study such relationships is that all other background variables can be held fixed or nearly fixed, so that a two-variable relationship can be isolated. In field research, unfortunately, it is usually impossible to hold many background variables fixed, while we study one variable at a time. Although we have emphasized changing only one variable at a time, it is not the "oneness" that is important here. It is the control over all or practically all the relevant variables and variation that matters, and the fact that we can choose the values of all but the output variables in the idealized laboratory experiment.

How might we have worked out a controlled field study – or experiment – in the Martin case? Start with a large pool of laid-off men with similar backgrounds, and suppose that we wanted to study the effects of a particular retraining program on future job experiences. We would randomly divide the men into two groups; one group would receive the retraining, while the other would not. If the group exposed to the retraining had substantially better job experiences in the future than the non-exposed group, we would with reason believe that the program had had a positive effect. This example oversimplifies a bit, but captures the crucial idea that for a study to yield useful information about a program, it should involve some device that strengthens our understanding of causal linkages. An after-the-fact survey, such as the Martin Study, does not have such a device. It requires us to resurrect, by hindsight, our best guess of what happened to make a program work or not work. The authors of the Martin Study point out this shortcoming, and note that a randomized study would have been much more useful.

The fourth kind of evaluation listed above is the controlled field study, or experiment. The controlled field study uses the statistical technique of randomization; that is, the random assignment of subjects from a specified population among one or more treatment groups. For example, in the Martin case, different kinds of retraining might have formed the treatments. If this randomization is properly done, the distribution of each background variable should be similar over all of the treatment and control groups. Thus, for example, if socioeconomic status is a background variable, the distributions of socioeconomic status for all subjects in each treatment group and each control group should be similar. Note that while the importance of "controlling" background variables which we believe are related to an outcome variable is generally acknowledged, the advantage of randomization is that background variables whose importance has not occurred to us are also controlled for.

Lest it be supposed that it is only in the social and biological sciences that randomization is required for strong inferences to be made, let us look back at the opening section of Chapter 1, Volume I. This section of this report describes experimentation in the field of weather modification. Such controlled field studies require randomization because it is not possible for the experimenters to hold all background variables constant and change only the ones that they want to study. Consequently, experimenters must take special pains to randomize – decide by lot – which clouds to seed and which not. Otherwise, some personal quirks might influence their choices and bias the study's results.

ADVANTAGES AND PROBLEMS
WITH CONTROLLED FIELD STUDIES

A prime advantage of the controlled field study is the strong causal link it provides between the input variables and the output variables. This link comes from our ability to randomize. It enables us to explore the relative value of different inputs.

Although controlled field studies have this virtue, they also have disadvantages. One of these is cost. Since extensive preexperimental planning may be necessary, together with careful randomization procedures, costs may be greater than those of a sample survey or keeping of repetitive management records.

A second drawback of controlled field studies is that until recently they have rarely occurred in public policy programs. Thus, the developers of a controlled field study may have to explain carefully their reasons to funding groups or to participants. A considerable extra effort by the developers may be necessary. It may also be necessary to break down fears of new procedures among program managers. It is understandable that all but the most self-confident program directors will resist efforts at evaluation, and an unfamiliar procedure may offer superficial grounds for even stronger resistance. Such psychological and political problems are real and must be dealt with at the level of the sponsoring agencies. Developing a rationale for a controlled field study in the context of any particular program may therefore require money, study, effort, and time. Further, program managers are subject to conflict between roles of advocacy versus objectivity. Those responsible for a program may permit their enthusiasm to override their objectivity. One way to deal with this problem, recommended by D. T. Campbell (1969), is to reward program managers for evaluating programs carefully, rather than rewarding them for success and punishing them for failures of the program.

Third, because controlled field studies have been rare in evaluating large-scale social programs, few institutions have accumulated experience in carrying them out. Because many government agencies and private institutions have an extensive capability and experience with conducting sample surveys, it is not difficult today to commission a survey which will be done in a sophisticated manner. If field studies are to become more widely used as an integral part of social and medical programs, both government and private institutions must be encouraged to develop their capability for conducting controlled field studies.

Finally, we note that the yield of a controlled field study is very sensitive to the adequacy of both the methodology of the study and its theory.

An example of an extremely carefully designed and conducted field study was the essential part of the 1954 national trial of the Salk poliomyelitis vaccine. For a concise and readable summary of the study's design, see P. Meier (1971) and the introduction to Chapter 1 of Volume I. The purpose of the trial was to study the effectiveness of the Salk vaccine in preventing poliomyelitis. This field study involved hundreds of thousands of young children; it was so large because the event being investigated – the onset of poliomyelitis – was relatively rare. The part of the field study that we refer to used the techniques of randomization and placebo controls (children were given a simple salt solution instead of the vaccine) to eliminate observers' bias, and, of course, interference from other uncontrolled variables. Some children were given the Salk vaccine, some were given the placebo. These two groups were then subject to a double blind evaluation (neither a child, nor the administrator of the treatment, nor the child's doctor knew whether that particular child had received the vaccine or the placebo). The results of the study were clear: despite the rare occurrence of the disease being investigated, the Salk vaccine was effective in preventing the onset of poliomyelitis. Children who received the vaccine had much less than half the chance of contracting paralytic poliomyelitis than did the children receiving the placebo. As Meier indicates, "By carrying out this kind of study before introducing the vaccine, . . . we now have answers about Salk vaccine that we still lack after fifty years of use of vaccines in the case of typhoid, and after thirty years of use of vaccines against tuberculosis." The threat of polio has been greatly reduced in America today.

381

In conclusion, a major advantage of a controlled field study is that it yields firm information about the efficacy of a program, a drug, or other experimental treatment. This information is particularly valuable because in current discussions of social programs, federal control is often thought undesirable for political reasons. A controlled field study done by the federal government, however, perhaps in cooperation with state or local governments, can yield information that states or localities can use individually in developing and refining their own programs. Since there may be political difficulties in taking advantage of such findings, it is important that the program be prepared to cope with these problems. The Salk vaccine study is an example of how a centrally planned national experiment can yield results obviously beneficial and widely applied at a local level. In general, if a controlled field study forms even part of an evaluation of a new program, dissemination of the study's results should improve the operation of the program at all levels of government.

ESTIMATING EFFECTS
FROM CONTROLLED FIELD STUDIES

Let us review several possible results that a controlled field study may produce. The happiest result is a clear and simple "success." This occurs when a program's desired goals have been achieved, and when, in addition, we understand what features of the program influenced the successful attainment of goals. This latter idea is important because as times change, programs may have to be modified. Thus, if we understand clearly the effect which different features of the program have upon its recipients, we may be able to modify it when necessary and have reasonable confidence of achieving a continued successful outcome.

A second and perhaps second-best result might be that a program has no effect at all. This is important to know, and if we have confidence in this result, we can avoid wasting money on an ineffectual program. One example of a "no effect" field study which produced a valuable result is the nursing home study, mentioned above, conducted by H. R. Kelman (1962), and summarized by J. Elinson (1967). This study involved an effort to help nursing home patients develop their self-care capabilities through special training. More than two thousand patients took part in this study, which involved randomized assignment of patients into two training groups and a control group that received no special training. The self-care status of each patient was measured both before and after rehabilitation service efforts. The findings of the study were that rehabilitation efforts towards increased self-care had practically no effect on the functional status of the patients. In addition, the treatment programs failed to influence hospitalizations and mortality. Although the results were disappointing for those who developed the program, it was important that such findings be available, so as not to promote widely the program as it stood. Let us emphasize that in this example, a carefully planned rehabilitation program was well evaluated, and the program was not a success, an event which is not uncommon, as we discuss below.

A third possible result from a field study is the discovery that a program has a small positive effect. This is more troublesome than when a program is a clear success or has no effect at all. The ability of a controlled field study to detect a small positive effect is, however, a virtue, for such a finding may lead to modifications which improve a program's performance. Thus, as a result of data generated from a field study, we might wish to adjust the independent variables in directions which the evaluation suggests look promising.

A fourth possible outcome is that a controlled field study might show a program as not only a clear failure, but also as actually *harmful*. Such a result should spur us to look for input variables which seem to be particularly associated with harmful results on output variables. This knowledge may be useful in helping us to avoid undesirable outcomes in future programs.

To conclude, since the technology required is currently available, field studies should be built into evaluations of many programs. The technology of controlled field studies, especially when combined with a suitable theory about the relations among the variables in a social program, can lead to considerable efficiency in the search for an improved version of a program.

383

INPUT MEASURES IN CONTROLLED FIELD STUDIES

A controlled field study enables us to select a subset of input measures from a larger group of candidates. We thus are able to determine which variables from a large potential list seem to be especially important. For policy purposes, we can then examine each of these seemingly important input variables, and determine which of these are under our control. [A lengthier discussion of this idea of control appears in D. T. Campbell and J. Stanley (1963).] While we cannot control the characteristics of individuals as such, the value of a field study is that we can select particular groups of individuals to go into a program. This enables us to study different combinations of people's characteristics, together with other input variables, and determine their combined effect on the output variable. Finally, clusters or groups of input variables, which may work interactively in terms of affecting output, should be identified. Different clusters of input variables may be relatively more effective with different types of program participants. Therefore, we may decide after using a controlled field study selectively to direct different versions of a program to different potential participants.

ADVANTAGES OF FIELD STUDIES IN
PROGRAM DEVELOPMENT: TWO EXAMPLES

When designing a program evaluation, it is helpful to have a theory clearly in mind in advance, and then try to match a statistical methodology to it. We illustrate with two examples of controlled field studies.

The first example is the New Jersey Work Incentive Experiment currently being conducted under the sponsorship of the Office of Economic Opportunity (J. T. Allen, 1970). This is a carefully designed study, involving a large number of families under schedules of different minimum guaranteed incomes, and different "tax rates" based on additional earnings. An eligible family has at least one able-bodied male between the ages of 18 and 58. The head of the family ordinarily has steady work. The reason most of these families are poor is that the heads of the families' hourly earnings are low, and the number of children large; it is not so much because the family has no one working, though there are periods of unemployment. The primary questions are about the effects of the rates and sizes of guarantees on families' work incentives. The theory supposes that different basic amounts of support and different tax rates will be important in influencing the working behavior of the participating families. Four minimum income levels were selected, together with three different "tax rates" on additional earnings. Eight of these twelve combinations are being studied. Some combinations were omitted because they did so little for the family, they were not thought worth trying; others did so much as to be politically infeasible. Along with the various combinations is a control group that receives nothing.

This Work Incentive Experiment illustrates how the consequences of a social innovation can be considerably more complex than originally conceived. The investigators found that supported families worked less, but made about the same amount of money, an unexpected finding. We quote at length from *Further Preliminary Results: the New Jersey Graduated Work Incentive Experiment* (O.E.O., May, 1971), pages 20-23:

> In the full sample of husband-wife families, a statistically significant difference in the number of hours worked appears between the control and experimental groups. The differential between the hours worked by those in the experimental group and the hours worked by those in the control group is about 12 per cent, with the experimental group working about five hours less a week than the control group. This difference, which did not exist at the beginning of the experiment, is largely accounted for by a difference in the average number of workers per family in the experimental group. Like the difference in the number of hours worked, the differential in the number of family workers is statistically significant. Since there are no significant earnings differences between the experimental and control groups, these results imply that the experimental families have significantly increased their average hourly earnings. Indeed, this did occur: for the full sample in the first year, average family hourly earnings

385

increased by 20 per cent for experimental subjects, compared with 8 per cent for the controls.

It is important to note, however, that there was no significant differential in the number of hours worked per family among the various income maintenance plans. Again, these data are too tentative to permit generalizations, but this lack of a significant differential does indicate that the various combinations of tax rates and guarantee levels have not yet affected the number of hours a family works. The differentials in average hours, employment, and earnings between experimental and control groups are detailed in Table III-1 in Appendix III.

These results are recent. While the differential in work effort (as measured by number of hours worked) was certainly anticipated by everyone associated with the experiment, the differential effects on hourly earnings seems not to have been expected. Hence, substantial analysis must be undertaken to try to clarify the reasons for this effect. The bulk of this analysis has not yet been done; indeed, much of it cannot be done until further data are collected.

Some further indications of how this differential is arising can be gleaned, however, from an examination of the behavior of separate members of the family. This examination suggests that about 40 per cent of the differential in family hours is attributable to the heads of families in the experimental group working less than those in the control group. This differential is 6 per cent of the average hours worked by the heads of families in the control group at the end of one year in the experiment. There is no evidence that this is associated with a few family heads totally withdrawing from the labor force and living only on the assistance payments. Rather, the effect seems to arise from the small differences in the amount of overtime worked, the length of periods of unemployment, or the time worked on a second job.

The remaining 60 per cent of the hours differential is attributable to spouses and other adult workers. Here the effect seems to be related to the rate at which these secondary workers entered the labor force as the labor market softened over the course of the experiment. In other words, the effect observed appears not to be a reduction in work effort by secondary workers in the experimental group, but rather less of an increase in this effort than appears in the control group.

An important point to note is that the controlled field study has not only brought a totally new idea to the attention of the investigators, but also, in this instance, put them in a position to find out the reasons for the unexpected effect. We further note that the general fear that heads of supported families would drop out of the labor market altogether has, at least thus far, proved groundless.

The second example suggests how field studies may indicate which components of a program are successful and which are not. D. M. Wilner (1962) conducted a study in Baltimore to investigate the effects of an improved housing environment on the health and social development of families, and on their children's school performance. These would be extra benefits over and above the improved comfort, heat, light, and sanitary facilities. The population of families came from the Baltimore Housing Authority's file of applicants for a new public housing project. All families originally lived in deteriorated housing in slum neighborhoods. The study, as summarized by J. Elinson (1967), involved three hundred matched pairs of families, matched on thirteen demographic variables. All six hundred families wanted new and improved housing. For each matched pair, one family received new housing and one did not. Note that randomization was not used, and so full protection from extraneous interfering variables was not available. The control from matching is less firm than that from randomization.

Results were mixed. Persons under 35 in the improved environment generally showed improved health and social development, while gains were not evident for persons over 35. Children had substantially fewer accidents. Further, while children's school performance did not improve using scores on standardized tests as a criterion, their attendance level and promotion rate improved. The improved housing environment program could thus be considered partially "successful" in giving additional benefits for education and health. The field study, or evaluation, was also successful, in that it generated valuable information about the program's effects. The results are not as firm as they would have been, however, had randomization been used for choosing the groups who got and did not get the improved housing. This example illustrates the point that different degrees of control can exist in a field study. In an appendix to this paper, Dr. Paul Densen discusses the issue, and describes how managerial records can be used effectively in evaluation.

COMPLEX PROGRAMS AND CONTROLLED FIELD STUDIES

Consider the general problem of developing a complex new social program. We know that extensive planning is required, and that despite this planning, we should not be surprised if most early versions of the program do not work very well. We have already mentioned Head Start and ESEA Title I as examples of programs which have fairly complex sets of goals. Compounding the difficulty in evaluating programs such as these is that the hoped-for gains are modest, and therefore are not so easy to detect.

Under such conditions, a controlled field study can be particularly useful. Both Head Start and ESEA Title I have been operating for more than five years. They have each been evaluated several times. Yet, all of the evaluations have been *post hoc* surveys, and thus suffer from the defects discussed earlier.

The point of setting up a controlled field study as part of a complex social program is that it enables us to identify the characteristics of those program versions which seem to be working best. Thus, even if most existing versions of a new program are found to be unsuccessful on some predetermined criterion, we may be able, step by step, to set up centers with new features, extended in directions suggested by the controlled field study. This increases the probability of having success in future versions.

Few people realize how rarely social programs succeed in their basic mission. In an attempt to give some evidence on this, at the

388

Ross Pediatric Conference, Jack Elinson (with the assistance of Cyrille Gell) reviewed ten substantial social programs designed to improve welfare or health. The programs they chose to examine all had controlled field studies associated with them, and the programs were all well conceived. What seemed to be true was that seven out of the ten showed that the control group did about as well on the dependent variable as those receiving the new treatment. In their book (in press), J. P. Gilbert and F. Mosteller write:

> *"The most valuable lesson here is that we find this out only because we had controlled investigations. Had experiments not been done, we would have had little way of knowing that the programs were not improving the performance they were intended to advance. Instead, encouraged by the originality, progressiveness, and plausibility of the programs, we might have initiated them at great expense throughout the nation. Now, at least we know that the particular techniques do not work well and in some instances why not."*

This finding of frequent failure of innovative social programs should not surprise anyone, however much it may be a disappointment. Every businessman knows that new business ventures go under with great frequency — over half fail in their first five years — and that even within established businesses, well-thought-out innovations often fail for unexpected reasons. Why would we expect our experience to be very different for social programs? No reason! But all the more reason for careful evaluation of social programs.

CONSEQUENCES OF DOING A GOOD FIELD STUDY

Let us not give the impression that the results from a controlled field study will always be so clear that program managers will instantly know how to adjust their programs. Especially with complex programs, even a good evaluation will tend to suggest to reasonable men several different courses of action. After all, there will often be more than one combination or setting of program inputs which lead to a desirable output. Managers must then make

389

choices: which program features should be strengthened, which features left unchanged, and which should be discarded. The investigators who design a controlled field study will not be able to answer all of these trade-off questions. Some may need to be resolved in the political arena. What a well-designed controlled field study can provide is a strong and reliable data base upon which each advocate's argument can rest.

Contrast the consequences of using a good controlled field study with what might come from an inadequate evaluation. Inadequate evaluations usually cost less money and take less time than a comparable field study, but there is a steep price for doing inadequate work. First, little is learned which can help program managers to improve versions of their program over time. Second, a poorly designed study has the more general cost of discrediting the role of evaluation in general. A poor evaluation may, at its inception, give the impression that its results will be useful. After it is completed, however, it may well be discredited, and properly so if it was poorly conducted. Finally, the more frequently evaluations are discredited, even if deservedly so, the more difficult it becomes to convince either legislators or program managers that it is both possible and worthwhile to conduct a good program evaluation.

It is ironic that some evaluation reports submitted to government agencies based on methods other than controlled field studies include an excellent discussion of the need for a controlled field study if a first-class job were to be carried out.

ISSUES IN DECIDING WHEN TO USE
CONTROLLED FIELD STUDIES

Ethical Problems

When are controlled field studies "ethical"? We consider here two situations: First, the case where a new program is expensive, or involves scarce resources, and second, the case where a program is inexpensive to administer, or involves plentiful resources.

Suppose first that a resource is scarce. We can take advantage of the scarcity in the design of a field study by randomly choosing

390

from among candidates those who will get the scarce resource. This appears to be an ethical procedure, and has the consequence of increasing the probability that a new program will truly be beneficial if its use is to be extended.

An example of this situation is D. Wilner's (1962) housing study. More than twice as many families wanted new residences as were available. Had the investigators randomized the assignment of families to the scarce housing, stronger inferences about the effects of new housing could have been drawn. As construction of new housing is expensive, it would have been useful to have strong inferences about its impact on the health and welfare of program participants.

The second situation arises when a new treatment or program is inexpensive, or the resources used are plentiful. In this event, the argument is sometimes made that everyone eligible for or needing the program should immediately receive it. But it is worth recalling here the high failure rate of new social programs. Full and immediate distribution of a new "good" is not always wise.

Sometimes our sights are set unusually low on evidence, as when we neglect to consider the controlled field study as a data-gathering device. If we allow ourselves to be satisfied with cheap but not very strong data, or even expensive data from which inferences are hard to draw, as when we use sample surveys as substitutes for experiments, we may not find out what we need to know.

As an historical example, consider the problem of smoking and health. This was scarcely a new problem thrust upon society in the last half of the present century. It has been with us since before 1900. Generally, critics have complained about the evidence brought forward against smoking, and have dismissed the possibility of doing a field study to find out the facts. Today, of course, the preponderance of medical opinion seems to be that smoking is bad for health. Consequently, it is probably not now ethical to do a field study using people as subjects.

On the other hand, during the early part of the century, when the question was more or less open and the evidence rather unsystematic, a field study might have been profitably done. Adults could have been asked to volunteer as subjects in such an experi-

391

ment. Then we could have randomly assigned some to smoke and others not to smoke. Subjects might have been paid a regular weekly fee both for smoking and for not smoking. An interesting question in a study such as this, which would have to be monitored, is whether the increase in income due to participating in the study might have improved the overall health of the "smoking" part of the sample, so that they would ultimately be no worse off than they might have been, had they not participated in the experiment. This would not have spoiled the experiment, because their health would have been compared with the health of those subjects who did not smoke and who also got increased incomes.

Inevitably, there would be problems in such an investigation, but it seems likely that such a study would have moved us further, sooner, to an understanding of the facts, perhaps even a better understanding than we have now. Society is often too quick to decide "we can't do a controlled study." The issue may not be one of feasibility, but at least partly one of what compensation society is willing to pay subjects for participation, and what value the information would have. Thus, some cost-effectiveness approach to questions such as the smoking-health relationship might help us to decide what controlled field studies are worth carrying out.

Costs in Neglecting Field Studies

For many programs, the relation between input and output variables may appear to be clear, and a question may arise whether in this situation a controlled field study has any value. Consider, for example, a program of food distribution to a target population of recipients. If the goal of the program is to distribute food to eligible recipients, there may be no "control group" of similar recipients who do not receive food. What role can a controlled field study play here?

There is good reason to incorporate controlled field studies into programs where every participant receives a benefit. A carefully designed field study generates data about how a program is functioning. It permits us to examine systematically alternative mechanisms for administering the program. There may be several strategies for food distribution; which strategies are most efficient, and for what purpose? Different "food bundles" might be de-

392

livered, at comparable costs. How do recipients utilize the alternative bundles? Questions such as these suggest that controlled field studies may provide valuable information, even for the seemingly simple goal of directing a commodity or service to a target population.

Beyond the study of efficiency of distribution, usually some payoff variable needs to be measured. In the food example, it may be that the basic purpose is to make children healthier. If so, we need to measure that variable, not just the amount of food distributed. (This feature can be conveniently incorporated in an experiment, but it could also be part of a survey.)

Thus, we see that the issue of whether to conduct a field study is not a question of "all or none." As we have said, when a large-scale program is being broadly implemented, a small portion of its budget can be devoted to a carefully designed set of field trials. Then, as results become available from these trials, they can be "fed back" into the larger-scale program to make the general design more effective. This strategy has been called "evolutionary." It is discussed by G. P. Box and N. Draper (1969).

Field studies for evolutionary program development make a valuable contribution. It may not be sufficiently widely appreciated that when thousands of recipients participate in a new and unsystematically varied social or welfare program, they are really subjects in an experiment. But the experimentation is quite haphazard, so much so that it is extremely difficult to learn what features of the program are most valuable, are working well, and perhaps should be extended.

Physicians have decided for the medical field that once it has been decided to perform an experiment, ethical behavior requires that the study be carried out so that information permitting strong inferences is obtained. Perhaps social innovators could profitably adopt this attitude toward new programs.

SUMMARY

In conclusion, then, we see that the purpose of evaluation is to tell us whether a program is reaching its goals, and also how different features of the program influence its success or failure. Knowing which program features are related to its output enables us to improve programs which seem to be working reasonably well, and reject or modify programs which are clearly unsuccessful. Controlled field studies are a useful and efficient means for conducting many evaluations, and they should be used much more frequently in the future. If circumstances do not permit "advance testing" of a new program, then a controlled field experiment can be included as a small component of a large new program.

Most important of all, as citizens, we are naturally disappointed when a competent evaluation shows that a well-planned program simply isn't working. But we have learned something valuable. Possibly the program can be modified. The time for the practical-minded citizen to become especially concerned is when no program evaluation has been done, and time and money are being spent on an endeavor which may be fruitless. Essentially, in this last circumstance, people are being used as guinea pigs without the redeeming feature that something to their own and to society's advantage can be learned. Unsystematic variation makes it very hard to draw firm inference from experience.

RECOMMENDATIONS

We make two general recommendations with respect to controlled field studies, and give examples of some specific steps for their implementation.

1. **Increasing use of controlled field studies**

   Controlled field studies should be used more frequently to improve both new and continuing social, health, and welfare programs.

   The following actions exemplify steps that would help implement this recommendation.

   A. *Developing Organizational Capability*

   There do not now exist standing groups with a capability for carrying out controlled field studies; instead, each group is formed especially for each particular field study. Organizations need to be developed so that we can move quickly. One way to develop this capacity would be for existing organizations to create units that specialize in field studies. Government agencies could help to finance such organizations. A second option would be to place such a unit in the Bureau of the Census.

B. *Writing Field Studies into Legislation*

When social programs are instituted, they might well carry a controlled field study component in the enabling legislation. New programs should have money specifically earmarked for evaluation through controlled field studies. The government's budgetary process, perhaps through the Statistical Policy and Management Information Systems Division, should make sure that controlled field studies of high quality are carried out.

C. *Long-term Funding*

Some programs will, by their nature, require an advance commitment of long-term funding. This is especially important if controlled field studies are to be integrated into the program design. In the past, this has often been possible. The need for such long-term funding should continue to be recognized.

2. **Creating a suitable climate for field studies**

Steps in several areas should be taken to create a more suitable climate for doing controlled field studies. Specific examples of such steps follow.

A. *Education of Public*

The public needs to be better informed about the difficulties regularly encountered by new programs. It needs to realize that new programs often do not work in their earliest versions. Most social problems are extremely complex. Government agencies should explain to the public that programs designed to ameliorate social problems need to be gradually developed and improved, as more information is gathered about their effectiveness. Statisticians should explain to the public how controlled field studies can play an integral part in program development, providing information to improve program effectiveness. It will require considerable education if the public is to appreciate that an iterative procedure of program design, field studies, and program redesign may take a fair amount of time before satisfactory program operation is achieved.

B. *Political Issues in Controlled Field Studies*

Those who design and execute controlled field studies need to understand better than they have in the past the political requirements of running such studies: The need to work closely with government agencies in the initial design of programs; the need to convince program developers and managers that relatively complex designs may sometimes be required if we are to understand how and why a program functions; the need to consider the political problems associated with the participants in the program and the attitude of the general public toward systematic evaluations. To meet these and other needs, experts in political problems should frequently be called to join field study teams as key members.

C. *Legal Issues in Controlled Field Studies*

The legal community should work on problems that already exist, and will continue to exist, in program evaluation. One such problem is the issue of privacy and confidentiality in the collection and analysis of data. These problems may be especially acute in longitudinal studies, which follow persons over time. Another problem is the protection of managers of controlled field studies from legal entanglement while properly carrying out their missions. These problems need careful thought and attention.

REFERENCES

Allen, J. T. Department of Health, Education and Welfare Income Maintenance Experiments. Washington, D.C.: Government Printing Office, 1970.

Box, G.P., and Draper, N. *Evolutionary Operation.* New York: John Wiley and Sons, 1969.

Campbell, D. T. "Reforms as Experiments." *American Psychologist,* 24, April, 1969.

Campbell, D. T., and Stanley, J. "Experimental and Quasi-Experimental Designs for Research on Training." *Handbook of Research on Teaching,* Chicago: Rand McNally and Company, 1963.

Elinson, J. "The Effectiveness of Social Action Programs in Health and Welfare." Paper presented at the Ross Conference on Pediatric Research: Problems of Assessing the Effectiveness of Child Health Services. Airlie House, Warrenton, Virginia, March 1967.

Finch, R. H. *Hearings on the Extension of Elementary and Secondary Programs, Part IV,* Committee on Education and Labor, U.S. House of Representatives, Washington, D.C.: Government Printing Office, 1969.

Gilbert, J. P. and Mosteller, F. "The Urgent Need for Experimentation." *On Equality of Educational Opportunity,* (eds.) F. Mosteller and D. P. Moynihan. New York: Random House (forthcoming).

Kelman, H. R. "An Experiment in the Rehabilitation of Nursing Home Patients." *Public Health Reports,* April, 1962.

Klaus, R. A., and Gray, S. W. "The Early Training Project for Disadvantaged Children: A Report after Five Years." *Monographs of the Society for Research in Child Development,* 120, 1968.

Light, R. J., and Smith, P. V. "Choosing a Future: Strategies for Designing and Evaluating New Programs." *Harvard Educational Review,* 40, February, 1970.

Martin Company Employees: "Reemployment Experiences." The U.S. Arms Control and Disarmament Agency (publication 36). Washington, D.C.: Government Printing Office, December, 1966

397

Meier, P. "The Biggest Public Health Experiment Ever: the 1954 Field Trial of the Salk Poliomyelitis Vaccine," *Statistics: a Guide to the Unknown*, eds. Judith Tanner *et. al.*, San Francisco: Holden, Day Inc. (forthcoming).

"Preliminary Results of the New Jersey Graduated Work Incentive Experiment." Mimeograph from Office of Economic Opportunity, 1970.

Orcutt, G. H. "Research Strategy in Modelling Economic Systems." *The Future of Statistics.* Paper delivered at the University of Wisconsin, June, 1967.

Orcutt, G. H. "Data, Research, and Government." *American Economic Review,* May, 1970.

Rivlin, A. M. "Systematic Thinking and Social Action." Berkeley, California: H. Polan Gaither Lectures, January, 1970.

Timpane, P. M. "Educational Experimentation in National Social Policy." *Harvard Educational Review.* 40, November, 1970.

White, S. H. "The Political Impact of Head Start." *The Disadvantaged Child, Vol. III,* (ed.) Jerome Hellmuth. New York City: Bruner, Mazel Inc., 1971.

Wholey, J. S.,*et. al.* Federal Evaluation Policy. Washington, D.C.: The Urban Institute, June, 1970.

Wilner, D., *et. al.* Housing Environment and Family Life. New York: Johns Hopkins University Press, 1962.

APPENDIX

Paul M. Densen

There are circumstances when it is not possible to assign individuals to the comparison groups in random fashion. For instance, much interest has arisen in the impact of various methods of financing and delivering health care upon the utilization and costs of health services. It is difficult, however, to assign individuals to particular health care programs or impose patterns of financing. Yet the question is of considerable public interest, and the need is pressing for evaluation as a basis for the development of policy.

In such instances, every effort should be made to approximate as closely as possible the degree of control over background variables achieved through randomization. The first step in the process is to examine in detail the process by which individuals choose to enter the comparison groups, so that as far as possible one can attempt to assess the nature and degree of bias introduced by this selection process. The more detailed this scrutiny, the more likely that one will be able to choose pertinent variables on which to match the comparison groups. Because of the necessity for matching, the process will, in general, require considerably larger samples than if one were able randomly to make assignments to study and control groups.

The following study reported by P. M. Densen, *et al.* (1958) illustrates both the problems and the process described above. The study had "as its primary objective an attempt to determine the influence if any of a program of comprehensive insurance for medical care upon hospital utilization as measured by rates of admission to hospitals, the kinds of conditions for which hospitalization is sought, and the length of stay in hospitals. The essential comparison is between two population groups differing primarily in the extent of their insurance coverage for *medical* care, and in the organization of medical practice through which this medical care is received. Both population groups have the same *hospital* insurance coverage."

The two populations studied were the Health Insurance Plan of Greater New York (HIP) — 52,877 individuals in the sample — and the United Medical Service of New York (Blue Shield) — 52,578 individuals in the sample. The authors describe in detail the benefits to which each group of individuals is entitled and the method for paying for these benefits. They go on to state that "since the primary purpose of the study is to examine the influence of a difference in insurance coverage for medical care on hospital utilization, the comparability of the two samples is of primary importance." In examining the selective process involved for choosing one or the other of the two plans, it was found, for instance, that slightly over 72 per cent of the total HIP enrollment were employees of the City of New York. The Blue Cross/Blue Shield sample was therefore drawn from accounts containing a thousand

399

or more subscribers located in New York City and not exclusively manufacturing plants. In both cases, (HIP and Blue Cross/Blue Shield), only enrollees with Blue Cross coverage throughout the entire year were included.

It is stated that "the restriction of (the Blue Cross/Blue Shield) accounts to large employer groups was designed to parallel employment situations among city departments with respect to such matters as sick leave, vacations, and general personnel policies. Also these accounts have generally been covered by hospitalization and surgical insurance for a number of years . . . over 80 per cent of the enrollees in the final sample had been covered by Blue Shield for over 5 years. . ."

While all persons in the HIP sample were residents of New York City, it was not possible for technical reasons to limit the Blue Cross/Blue Shield sample to residents of the City. "The best that could be done was to restrict the accounts selected in the sample to those with subscribers working in New York City and their covered dependents. As a result, a much higher proportion of the admissions in the Blue Cross/Blue Shield sample were in hospitals outside New York City proper (37.4 per cent) than in the HIP sample (4.7 per cent)." The authors examined the possible effect of this difference in residence on hospital utilization. They concluded that "no differences are apparent which would support the hypothesis that there is a different pattern of hospital utilization among insured residents of various suburbs of New York City than among those who live in the City proper."

A detailed description is given in the appendix of the report of the methods of selecting the two samples, so that the reader may judge for himself whether, as the authors state, "they are reasonably similar, and that differences in the hospitalization pattern of the two groups are not likely to be due to differences in the nature of the two populations." The analysis itself attempts to exercise a degree of control over possible differences in the comparison groups by making the data specific for age, sex, and employment group. Differences in coverage in the two groups are also taken account of by calculating rates specific for class of coverage (medical or surgical).

In general, it was found that the hospital admission rate was

400

lower in the prepaid group practice situation (Blue Cross-HIP) than in the fee-for-service solo practice situation (Blue Cross/Blue Shield). The length of stay in the hospital was essentially the same in the two groups.

This initial study was followed by two other studies (1960, 1962), in which an additional element of control over background variables was introduced because of the opportunity to examine the hospital experience of members of two unions, each of which had a choice between a prepaid group practice program and an alternative fee-for-service solo practice program. Since the union membership were all engaged in essentially the same type of employment, the possible effect of differences in employment which might have been present in the first study was eliminated in the subsequent studies.

In the second of the three studies, the findings, in general, were similar to those in the first study. In the third, the admission rate in the prepaid group practice situation continued to be low, but the rate in the comparison group was also low, raising "the interesting possibility that a highly disciplined fee-for-service program administered by a union health and welfare fund may have an important influence on hospitalization."

These studies emphasize that while it may not be possible to achieve as tight a control over background variables as one would like to do, the obligation to carry out as careful a program as possible is still incumbent upon the managers of a program — particularly one which has broad national policy implications. The effort should be made whenever possible and reported in detail.

Because the tight control achieved through randomization is not always possible, an effort should be made to replicate the less well-controlled study in a variety of situations to see if there is consistency among the several studies. Each study should be as carefully controlled as possible, and the reader given an opportunity to judge for himself the comparability of the comparison groups.

The studies just discussed illustrate again the supportive relationship between managerial records and controlled field trials. In these studies, not only were the samples for the comparison groups drawn from the managerial records, but the information on hospital utilization was also obtained from the managerial records. Indeed, this latter fact resulted in a degree of accuracy of this information which would be difficult to achieve otherwise. In fact, in the HIP sample, because of the Blue Cross coverage, it was possible to obtain information on *all* hospitalizations, irrespective of whether they were hospitalized by a HIP doctor or not.

REFERENCES

1963 Densen, P.M. and Shapiro, S. "Methodological Problems in the Study of Special Population Groups, Health Insurance and Industrial Groups," *Annals of the New York Academy of Science, 107,* Article 2, pp. 490-505.

1958 Densen, P.M., Balamuth, E. and Shapiro, S. "Prepaid Medical Care and Hospital Utilization," *American Hospital Association, Hospital Monograph Series No. 3.* Chicago, Illinois.

1960 Densen, P.M., Jones, E. W., Balamuth, E., and Shapiro, S. "Prepaid Medical Care and Hospital Utilization in a Dual Choice Situation," *American Journal of Public Health 50,* ll, 1710-1726.

1962 Densen, P.M., Shapiro, S., Jones, E.W., and Baldinger, I. "Prepaid Medical Care and Hospital Utilization: Comparison of a Group Practice and a Self-Insurance Situation," *Hospitals, Journal of the American Hospital Association.* November 16, 1962.

CHAPTER 7

SOCIAL REPORTING FOR THE 1970's

By
Eleanor Bernert Sheldon

SOCIAL REPORTING FOR THE 1970's

TABLE OF CONTENTS

405

ACKNOWLEDGMENTS

This statement, prepared by Kenneth C. Land, Raymond A. Bauer and me is based on discussions with and written memoranda from many social scientists engaged in work on social indicators. Represented are persons from both the private and public sectors — primarily researchers who have contributed significantly to the recent thrust of interest and study of social change and its measurement. Many of these contributors, who are listed here, will find that most of their suggestions are included — and often in their own words. However, I assume full responsibility for the basic approach, the organization and the selection of contributed materials.

Eleanor Bernert Sheldon
Russell Sage Foundation

Contributors

Raymond A. Bauer, Harvard University
Albert D. Biderman, Bureau of Social Science Research

407

Angus Campbell, University of Michigan
James Davis, Dartmouth College
Otis Dudley Duncan, University of Michigan
Abbott L. Ferriss, Emory University
Peter Henriot, Seattle University
Robert L. Kahn, University of Michigan
Kenneth C. Land, Russell Sage Foundation
Stanley Lebergott, Wesleyan University
Herman P. Miller, U.S. Bureau of the Census
I. M. Moriyama, National Center for Health Statistics
Eleanor Bernert Sheldon, Russell Sage Foundation
Donald Shoup, Social Science Research Council

INTRODUCTION

This statement has been prepared in response to a request made by the President's Commission on Federal Statistics. The primary charge from the Commission was to propose a long-term program for the development of social indicators. It is clearly understood by Commission members and by contributors to this statement that the proposals suggested represent but one approach to developing social indicators. Consequently, the recommendations are made in general terms, together with a set of illustrative steps suggesting ways that the proposed program can be carried out.

Though several factors help account for the resurgence of interest in social measurement, perhaps the most apparent and overriding is the commonplace observation that far-reaching social change is taking place in the structure of American society. The obviousness of the change brought questions from both the policy-maker, lawmaker, and academicians — creating a new demand for social information.

The public policy demands continue to be couched in terms of the limitations of purely economic considerations in dealing with modern American social problems. Policies and programs aimed at alleviation of problems seek data for planning, for implementation — and eventually for evaluation. Common objectives for these demands for social information have been stated in the following terms: Quantitative social information (indicators) is required for: (1) the establishment of social goals and priorities; (2) the

408

evaluation of public programs; and (3) the development of a system of social accounts that could provide guidance among alternative interventions. An additional demand seeks data that: (4) would further our knowledge of the functioning of society and enhance our capability in social prediction.[1]

Emerging from these demands for social data is a recognition of three types of indicators designed for different uses:

1. problem-oriented or direct policy-oriented indicators which are intended for direct use in policy and program decisions;
2. descriptive indicators intended primarily to describe the state of society and the changes taking place within it;
3. analytic indicators that serve as components of explicit conceptual and causal models of the social system or some particular segment of it.

Both (2) and (3) might be viewed as indirectly policy-oriented, for in the long run it will be these measurements and models that could provide guidance for social intervention.

Particularly with respect to problem or direct policy-oriented indicators, the following three considerations might be viewed as possible criteria for adding or dropping substantive areas of particular measures.

1. *Acknowledged social goals.* Each national goal may well be represented by one or more social indicators. For example,

---

1 These different claims for the potential utilization of social indicators provided a focus for debate. During its course it was pointed out to those seeking social information for policy and program purposes that their promises far exceeded any possibility for realistic attainment. It was noted that: 1) priorities and goals are more dependent on national values than on assembled data; 2) that program evaluation necessitates the demonstration that the programs determine the outcomes (measured by indicators) rather than uncontrolled extraneous variables, and, 3) that the essential theoretical prerequisite for the development of a system of social accounts — defining the variables and the interrelationship between them — was particularly deficient, if not completely lacking.

The social science research community was reminded that data are useful for planning and development of policies and programs; that such data could be improved without awaiting the methodological and theoretical advances of the social sciences.

This early debate has since simmered down to a mutual recognition of different types of indicators designed for different uses.

all seven of the areas described in the 1969 Health, Education and Welfare publication, *Toward a Social Report,* probably meets this criterion, and certainly the first five do so. (Those five are described as follows: Health and Illness: Are We Becoming Healthier?; Social Mobility: How Much Opportunity is There?; Our Physical Environment: Are Conditions Improving?; Income and Property: Are We Better Off?; Public Order and Safety: What is the Impact of Crime on Our Lives?; Learning, Science and Arts: How Much Are They Enriching Society?; Participation and Alienation: What Do We Need to Learn?)

2. *Emerging social goals.* Beyond measures for acknowledged goals, policy decision should also attend to emerging goals. For example, in the area of work, the protection of the worker from undue exposure to noxious materials is an acknowledged goal and already a matter of considerable legislation. However, the protection of the worker from stultifying and monotonous tasks, or, to put it positively, providing some measurable level of intrinsic job satisfaction is not yet an acknowledged goal. It may be an emergent one. Conceiving measures for such future goals can contribute to their realization.

3. *Potentiality for change.* A major purpose of social indicators is social improvement, not only explanation. Priority should go to those indicators likely to aid in achieving intended change. For example, counting homicides does little or nothing in itself to reduce the likelihood of murder; we can change the homicide rate only by changing something else. The level of intergroup and interpersonal tensions, however, might be an indicator more directly amenable to change. The example is valid, of course, only if the level of tensions is a causal factor in the homicide rate.

WHAT HAS BEEN DONE AND
PROPOSED DEVELOPMENTS

1. **Public Safety and Legal Justice.** The problem-oriented approach to social indicators of public safety as well-exemplified in

410

the Health, Education and Welfare volume *Toward a Social Report*:

> To assess the quality of American life, we must consider *the impact of crime on our society.* People neither want to be the victims of crime nor to live in fear of crime. Moreover, crime challenges the basic assumptions of civilized society. A society cannot claim to be minimally civilized if greed and aggression are regularly permitted to override respect for other people.
>
> An increase in crime has a variety of implications for the well-being of a society. It is reflected in (1) the workload of the police, (2) the amount of harm to victims, and (3) the prevalence of criminal behavior and attitudes. The impact of crime needs to be appraised from each of these perspectives to determine how crime can best be prevented and controlled. (Emphasis and numbering are added.)

In contrast, the traditional descriptive-analytic approach of social scientists to crime has tended to be more concerned with (1) the causes of crime and (2) the social characteristics of criminals and their proper treatment.

Both of the above approaches to public safety, however, have had to rely on data which primarily indicated the "objective" dimensions of criminality, indicators which moreover were extremely crude at best. For example, the major source of information on the incidence of serious crimes in the United States has been the Federal Bureau of Investigation Crime Index. The Crime Index gives rates per 100,000 population for reported crimes in the following categories: (1) homicide, (2) rape, (3) aggravated assault, (4) robbery, (5) burglary, (6) larceny, (7) auto theft. From such statistics, criminologists know, for example, that reported major crimes increased at an average rate of 8.7 percent per year between 1958 and 1967, and that there is considerable variation in the rate of increase in major crimes with categories (1) through (3) tending to increase at a lower rate than (4) through (7). On the other hand, the deficiencies of the Crime Index are numerous.

411

Indeed, Albert Biderman, in discussing social indicators, came to the following conclusions regarding the Crime Index:

1. The errors and biasing factors affecting the Crime Index operate to show spurious increases, rather than decreases, in the rate.
2. The Crime Index does not provide a sound basis for deter mining whether criminal behavior is increasing, or decreasing, in the United States.
3. The Crime Index is highly sensitive to social developments that are almost universally regarded as improvements in the society. Thus, it is altogether possible that year-to-year increases in crime rates may be more indicative of social progress than of social decay.

In response to the inadequacies of the Crime Index as a measure of the incidence of crime in the society, the President's Crime Commission initiated in 1965 the practice of taking sample surveys to assess the rate of criminal activity. Such "victimization surveys" generally show that at least twice as much victimization occurs within a period of time as is officially recorded by the police. These surveys also show a decline in victimization rate as one moves from central cities to the suburban periphery, though the decline varies by type of crime. Despite methodological and other weaknesses, victimization surveys have the potential of providing valid and reliable indicators of trends in the incidence of certain types of criminality in American society.[2]

Apart from "objective" questions pertaining to rates of criminal behavior, there are a variety of issues pertaining to the "subjective" perception of public order, police behavior and service, and the behavior of the criminal justice system. (We know from earlier surveys, for example, that crime victims and witnesses are no more apt to take precautionary measures against crime than are those who have not been victimized.) Very little exists in the way of established empirical trend measures or, much less, models of social processes regarding these aspects of criminality. Recently,

---

2 Among the more apparent weaknesses of victimization surveys are: victim surveys require very large sample sizes because crime is a very rare and heterogeneous class of events. Further, some types of crime, such as homicide, are not amenable to victim reports. "Victimless" crimes would require self-reporting rather than victim reports in the use of surveys.

Albert J. Reiss, Jr. has suggested that our efforts to study the qualitative aspects of criminal justice systems should be concentrated on (1) the behavioral and attitudinal consequences of victimization by crime, (2) the quality of discretionary authority and service for citizens, and (3) the accountability of public servants.

On the basis of these recent developments in social indicators of public safety and legal justice, three proposals for further developments seem obvious.

First of all, *for the immediate future we recommend the continuation and expansion of victimization surveys and their analysis.* The Crime Commission's idea has already been adopted by the Census Bureau (commissioned by the Department of Justice). However, we feel that development of such surveys is so crucial that it deserves emphasis here. Furthermore, we are fully in accord with the use of the Census Bureau as the data-gathering facility for this set of indicators. These surveys can be expanded to cover additional aspects of crime. In addition, certain analytical techniques could be brought to bear on victimization data. In particular, it seems clear that comparisons between police records and rates computed from victimization data could lead to an improved understanding of the nature and extent of underreporting and of its variation by type of crime, by community, by police organization characteristics, and by season of the year. Other analytical challenges arise from the problem of relating victimization to social variables. Certainly, there is need for the development of rigorous analytical models of the distribution of victimization by social variables. Such models could also help us analyze the relation of victimization to subsequent behavior and attitudes.

Second, *we recommend as a possible short-term development the expansion of victimization surveys into more general surveys of the criminal justice system.* In particular the inclusion of data on the "qualitative" aspects of criminal justice system such as those cited above from Reiss. For example, attitudinal items on the relative satisfaction of citizens with their police and judicial services might be included.

Finally, we should emphasize that both of the above recommendations refer to indicators of the extent and the effects of various types of crime and criminal justice in our society. To get a

413

more complete picture of the impact of crime on our society, we believe that considerably more data is needed on the causes of crime, or, put differently, on the motivation for a criminal act. Continued study of the social and psychological causes of criminal behavior would aid in clarifying and interpreting our indicators. In particular, we need considerably more knowledge of the reasons which lead to criminal behavior as the most desirable alternative and of the possible ways in which the situation may be changed. This recommendation impinges on the more general study of crime as much as on social indicators. However, we feel that continued work on these problems is necessary to the more complete understanding of spatial and temporal variations in indicators of criminality as well as to the eventual use of public policy to effect changes in such indicators.

2. **Health.** Again, the policy-oriented approach to health and illness was clearly stated in *Toward a Social Report:*

> . . .the first half of the twentieth century saw extraordinary advances in health and life expectancy, but . . . the rate of advance has been slower in the fifties and sixties. In large part this slower rate of advance has been due to the fact that many of the most serious health problems of infants, children, and young adults, have been solved by mid-century, and to the fact that it has not been possible to make many significant scientific breakthroughs in the treatment and prevention of degenerative diseases associated with the process of aging.
>
> Nonetheless, the considerably longer life expectancy in some other countries, and the differences in health status among the different groups in our own country suggest that we could have better health and longer life, even without any new breakthroughs in medical science. There can be little doubt that appropriate public policy decisions can help to alleviate some of the factors adversely affecting the health status of our population. Public policy can aim to redress the imbalance in health resources, prevent and

control harmful environmental factors, and even influence our thinking about those personal habits and forms of behavior which may prove detrimental to our health.

Although this statement indicates a belief that public policy can affect health status, it does not at all point to procedures for effecting such changes. The fact is that there is an immense lack of knowledge regarding our system of health care. Recent work has been devoted to improving our indicators of health status. Indeed, a large part of the section on health in *Toward a Social Report* was devoted to the exposition of the "expectancy of *healthy* life" (i.e., life expectancy free of bed-disability and institutionalization). As I. M. Moriyama has noted, however, this index has certain conceptual problems. For example, the major component of the measure is the expectation of life at specified ages. Thus, there is some question as to the sensitivity of the measure. Also, the expectation of life and the duration of disability may vary independently. Therefore, it would be necessary to analyze the two parts separately in the assessment of the disability problem. As an alternative index of health of a population, C. L. Chiang has developed a mathematical model of the mean duration of health or the average fraction of the year in which an individual is healthy.

In addition to indicators of health status of persons and populations in a given area, the United Nations Study Group on the Measurement of Levels of Health has pointed out that we need two additional groups of indicators: (1) those related to physical environmental conditions having a more or less direct bearing on the health status of the area under review, and (2) those concerned with health services and activities directed to the improvement of health conditions (availability and use of hospitals, physicians and other health personnel). Such indicators should not be neglected in order to develop indicators of health status. Indeed, the latter indicators are meaningful in the context of the former.

On the basis of this brief review, we arrive at the following two recommendations. First, *for the immediate future we recommend the continued development and improvement of indicators of (1) health status, (2) environmental conditions relevant to health, and (3) health services and activities.* Second, and complementarily to

415

the first, *we recommend as a long-term development the construction of analytical models of the relations of various elements of
the health care system.* In particular, we encourage the development of models of the distribution (economic and social) of health
care and of its consequences for health status.

3. **Social Mobility.** In *Toward a Social Report,* the relevance of
indicators of social mobility was explained as follows:

> The belief that no individual should be denied the
> opportunity to better his condition because of the cir-
> cumstances of his birth continues to be one of the
> foundation stones in the structure of American values.
> But is the actual degree of opportunity and social
> mobility as great now as it has been?

In brief, any inventory of the state of American society must ask
how much equality of opportunity we have, and whether there is
more or less than there used to be. Complete equality of opportunity exists when the social, economic, and political status a
person has is determined by his own abilities and efforts rather
than by the circumstances of his birth. If a person's family background, for example, affect his ability to achieve socially desirable
values, then the idea of equality of opportunity has not been
realized. On the other hand, an improvement throughout the society in the prospects for high income, an advanced education, or a
professional job does not necessarily mean greater equality of
opportunity. Such improvements in "life chances" for the population as a whole are, of course, important. Here, we focus instead
on the extent to which a person's status, relative to that of others
in his society, is determined by his ability and effort, rather than
by his social origins.

In order to assess the degree of opportunity and measure its
changes over time, we must be able to determine a man's relative
"position" in society, so that we can say whether he has risen or
fallen in status relative to someone else or relative to his own
status at a previous point in time. Although there is no single ideal
measure of social and economic position, a man's occupation is
probably the best single indicator of his socioeconomic level. Such
additional characteristics as high income, education, social stand-

ing, community influence, and membership in professional organizations, can also bring high socioeconomic status. In brief, occupational mobility is not a perfect indicator of social mobility, and we cannot be sure that there is more or less equality of opportunity just because a man's occupational position is more or less dependent on his family background than at some earlier point in our history. On the other hand, changes in occupational mobility probably tell us as much about changes in social mobility as any other single measure we could use. It has been found that all of the dimensions of a high status usually vary with occupation and are roughly measured by it.

Fortunately, the policy-makers' interest in equality of opportunity has also been matched by a solid theoretical and empirical interest of sociologists in social mobility and social stratification as one of the major components of social structure. On the empirical side, the most important study to date is based upon a survey of "Occupational Changes in a Generation" conducted in 1962 by the Bureau of the Census. This survey asked a sample of American men not only about their own first occupation, income, education, and the like, but also about their father's usual occupation. A separate survey asked a sample of the American public what degree of status they thought attached to each occupation, and these responses were used to derive a numerical status "score" (ranging from 0 to 96) for each of 446 detailed Census occupations. On the basis of these two surveys, it is possible to compare the occupational score of each man surveyed in 1962 with the score his father had, and thus see how much influence the father's relative socioeconomic position had on the ranking of his son. Since the men surveyed were of different ages, it is also possible to get some impression about whether equality of opportunity has been increasing or decreasing by comparing the father-son status relationship of the older men with that of the younger.

An analysis of the survey results undertaken by Otis Dudley Duncan and Peter Blau, published in 1967, shows that the occupational achievements of the sons were not in any large degree explained by the socioeconomic levels of their fathers. Furthermore, estimates based on these data suggest that opportunity to rise to an occupation with a higher relative status has not been declining

417

in recent years, and might even have increased slightly. They also show that by far the largest part of variation in occupational status was explained by factors other than the occupation of the father. There is one dramatic exception to the finding that opportunity is generally available. That is, the opportunity of Negroes appears to be restricted to a very great extent by current race discrimination and other factors specifically related to race — with other minorities being distributed between whites and Negroes and with respect to opportunity.

Several observations on the analysis of the Occupational Changes in a Generation survey are in order. First of all, the survey was conducted in 1962 which makes the data nearly a decade old. Second, this has been a decade of broadened governmental activities to influence the distribution of opportunities throughout the society, particularly with respect to racial and ethnic minorities. Therefore, it is a matter of considerable urgency to ascertain the effects, if any, of such activities on social mobility. Finally, excellent though the survey was by comparative standards, it could certainly be improved in both its execution and analysis if repeated today. Therefore, on the basis of these considerations, *we recommend for the immediate future the replication of the Occupational Changes in a Generation survey in 1972 and the repetition of the survey on at least a decennial basis.* This will provide the means for a continual analysis of trends in social mobility.

Although national surveys of intergenerational mobility have contributed substantially to our understanding of the mobility process and to our knowledge of the extent of opportunity in our society, the causes and consequences of various rates and patterns of movement remains a relatively unexplored area. It appears that we need considerably more experience at observing relative mobility rates under different economic and social circumstances before we possess knowledge sufficient to predict the changes resulting from various policy changes. Therefore, *as a long-term development* in the area of social mobility, *we recommend the construction of indicators relating rates and patterns of intergenerational occupational movement to other social and economic variables.*

4. **Youth.** In addition to the necessity of indicators for general

418

trends in social mobility, recent research has emphasized the importance of the educational and early occupational aspects of the status attainment process. Apart from these basic theoretical concerns, the broader differential socialization of successive cohorts of children into American society has long been considered a basic "social issue." However, here we are, well into the 1970's, not knowing what to expect because we do not know what has happened already. It is virtually a truism that cultural change is largely initiated – or, if not initiated, effectuated – by the young. Everyone has his favorite speculation about how America has been altered by the "youth culture," about how the "mood of youth" has changed since the "silent 50's" and so on. But there is a dearth of reliable observations. We assume, moreover, that experiences in youth are portentous for the orientations that will be fairly firm in later phases of the life cycle; but we have little or no documentation of what these experiences may be.

Two alternatives exist. One, of course, is to continue to exist with no systematic research – then everyone can continue to expound his favorite explanation of what is happening. The other is to do the job properly, making use of the techniques of modern social science.

Taking the latter alternative requires a study design that gives simultaneous attention to life cycle, cohort, and historical change. Therefore, *we recommend as a short-term development the establishment of a National Youth Panel covering the ages 10 to 28 to be surveyed periodically over these years with respect to their achievements and participation in the major institutions of the society. The panel would be augmented with a new sample from the youngest cohort each survey period.*

Preconceived ideas about panel or "follow-up" studies should not inhibit the imagination when considering the possibilities of a National Youth Panel. We want to involve these youth not in a regimen that treats them as passive objects of technological surveillance, but as themselves observers and reporters of the youth scene. Of course, we shall want to ask them some direct questions and request them to take some "tests." What we are after is the degree and quality of involvement of youth in each of the major

419

institutions of the society — family, school, church, polity, economy, and culture — comparing the responses of each cohort with those of preceding cohorts at the same age, noting associations between reaction patterns in evidence at one age with those evinced at a later age, and changes between cohorts in such associations.

ORGANIZATIONAL ARRANGEMENTS

An organizational framework for doing the work required for the development of sets of social indicators and inquiring into their interrelationships must take cognizance of the different uses of such measurements as well as of different institutional sponsors of the work. We have found it useful to approach the organizational structure in accordance with the following paradigm:

Institutional Sponsorship

TYPE OF INDICATOR	GOVERNMENT	OTHER
Problem-Oriented	(1)	(2)
Descriptive-Analytical	(3)	(4)

1. To a large extent government agencies are concerned with problem (or direct policy) oriented indicators. Collecting, compiling and utilizing social information for policy and program purposes are the primary responsibility of the federal agencies. The data are addressed mainly to the description of the objective conditions of life and generally exclude those considered to be politically sensitive (such as religious affiliation). Government agencies usually will not be responsible for experimenting with and developing subjective measures, though it is conceivable that once the reliability, validity and utility of such measurements have been established by the private sector, (2) government agencies would be responsible for their periodic collection, thereby incorporating these indicators within the federal statistical system. Some analytical work will be done by many of the agency staff members (particularly those at the Census Bureau), though this appears to be of secondary importance.[3]

---

3 The establishment of a Council of Social Advisors as a "social monitoring, data gathering and program evaluation agency," set forth by Senator Walter Mondale in the proposed Senate S.5, *Introduction of the Full Opportunity and National Goals and Priority Act,* 92nd Congress, 1st Session, provides a possible alternative. A reading of the bill suggests that some analytical responsibility may rest with the staff of the proposed Council.

2. The development of time-series information covering the subjective dimension, as well as topics presumed to be politically sensitive, will continue to be the *primary* responsibility of non-governmental research and university centers, such as the Survey Research Center and the National Opinion Research Center. This work requires considerable conceptual innovation and field experimentation, activities particularly appropriate to institutions independent of governmental agencies. Developing subjective indicators, which are somewhat more elusive to reliable and valid measurement than objective conditions, necessitates experimentation, refinement and persistent long-term commitment on the part of scholars and researchers.

Cells (3) and (4) differ from (1) and (2) in that the work to be accomplished is not aimed at immediate policy or program usefulness. Rather, the intent is the development of social information and analytical schemes and models that would provide an understanding of the social system and its component sub-systems. From these eventual policy relevance may emerge.

3. It is unlikely that government agencies would or should be encouraged to engage in "basic" social indicators research, the findings of which are not geared to obvious program application. On the other hand, it should be recognized that the expertise of federal data collection agencies such as the Census Bureau can be utilized to provide the basic empirical observations on nationally-based samples for analysis by non-governmental social scientists. As a particular example, the resources of the Current Population Survey should be increasingly used to provide social scientists with empirical observations in such areas as education, social mobility, criminal justice, and alienation, presuming, of course, that the basic measurement instruments have been developed and proven by professional social scientists working in each area, regardless of whether they are in government, in universities, or in research institutes.

4. Even though government agencies should be involved in the process of data collection for descriptive-analytical social indicators at some point, most of the actual analysis of such data should probably be carried on in non-governmental research and university centers. The analogy with the analysis of economic indi-

cators works well here. That is, most of the work on the major econometric models of the United States such as the Federal Reserve Board-Massachusetts Institute of Technology Model and the Brookings—Social Science Research Council Quarterly Model were developed by private or university-based research centers either working alone or in conjunction with governmental agencies. In either case, the models were used to analyze and explain patterns in the economic time-series collected by the government. What we advocate is the development of a similar symbiotic relationship for the analysis of social indicators. We believe that research social scientists working in conjunction with governmental data-collection agencies are best-equipped in terms of conceptual, mathematical, and statistical skills for the development of social indicator models.

With the suggested institutional arrangements for developing different types of social indicators and their models of interrelationships, there is a need for a mechanism that will monitor and coordinate the various activities, both within and outside government.

1. Within the government structure there should be some entity whose primary function is the development of social indicators; it should be manned by social scientists and statisticians; it should have authority to influence what is done in the various federal statistical agencies; and it should have continuity of top personnel (See our recommendation below concerning the Statistical Policy Staff of the Office of Management and Budget). It would have available adequate funding for both developmental work and operating social statistical series; to publish regularly an appropriate package of social indicators from data available at a given point in time; monitor, encourage, and facilitate developmental work both in the government and outside; identify newly developed measures that should be included in regular series, and see to it that these series come into being; and stop old series when it is appropriate.

2. A parallel function should exist outside the government — perhaps in the form of an advisory committee. It would serve as a liaison between government and non-government activities. It

could be responsible for trial social reports – partially to offset an official social report which is apt to be more political in nature and partially to serve as a device for stock-taking on current and potential data series.

RECOMMENDATIONS

Below, we describe an approach to the development of social indicators, as well as the organizational arrangements and suggestions for launching a continuing effort. We recognize that it represents only one of many possible alternatives. It is presented, however, as a point of departure from which we could exploit the momentum gained from work already completed and underway.

Federal Agencies

We recommend a review of existing series of social data produced by governmental agencies (including the Census returns, the Current Population Survey, the health surveys and the vast array of administrative statistics) to identify what we have.[4] Such an examination would provide an inventory of available measures and facilitate recommendations concerning their retention and elimination, revisions, modifications, additions and substitutes.

To implement this recommendation we suggest that subject-area panels be organized – each comprised of government and non-government experts. The following content areas might be considered as a point of departure:

1. Socio-economic Welfare

   a. Population
   b. Labor force and employment
   c. Income
   d. Knowledge and technology
   e. Education
   f. Health
   g. Leisure
   h. Public safety and legal justice
   i. Housing

---

4   This is not an untrodden field for much has already been done by Abbott L. Ferriss, Eleanor Bernert Sheldon and Wilbert E. Moore and currently the Statistical Policy Staff work on social trends.

423

> j. Transportation
> k. Physical environment
> l. Social mobility and stratification

2. Social participation and alienation

> a. Family
> b. Religion
> c. Politics
> d. Voluntary associations
> e. Alienation

3. Use of time

4. Consumption behavior

5. Aspiration, satisfaction, acceptance, morale, etc.

Although there is need for review of existing social statistics as suggested above, a quinquennial census would facilitate the development and refinement of social measurements as well as a more adequate monitoring of changes over time — particularly for sub-groups of the population and for smaller areas. Though smaller, more focused studies might well satisfy the particular needs of population sub-groups and local areas, the analysis of national data would require comparative measures for constituent groups and areas.

As a further step in implementation, the Bureau of the Census should be encouraged to continue its current and developmental work in exploiting the use of the Current Population Survey. The current and proposed periodic series on the social and economic conditions of whites and Negroes, Spanish Americans, fertility trends, population concentration, crime victimization, occupational mobility, family growth, the burdens or benefits of government expenditures, retirement, housing, migration and consumer expenditures provide core data for the development and utilization of social indicators.

Similarly, the National Center for Health Statistics should be encouraged in its current and developmental work in the measurement of health conditions and health status.

The Department of Housing and Urban Development is currently sponsoring work on the development of social indicators for local urban areas. Appropriate federal agencies should support corresponding work in developing state and rural social indicators.

A large portion of social data is gathered routinely as a by-product of administering government programs. We suggest the imposition of statistical standards and analytical requirements on the data collection operations of nonstatistical government agencies (*e.g.*, Immigration Bureau, Armed Forces, Social Security Administration, law enforcement agencies).

The Statistical Policy Staff, which presumably coordinates social data from the various governmental surveys and a wide variety of administrative data, should be encouraged in publishing their periodic compendium of these data as rapidly as possible. This, too, will aid in the implementation of our first recommendation.

Private Sector

The above recommendation and suggested steps for implementation refer essentially to the ongoing and developmental work of federal agencies. A large role remains to be played in the private sector, requiring federal and other funding.

Our second recommendation is that federal agencies, especially the National Science Foundation and the Department of Health, Education and Welfare, encourage and fund developmental work on new statistical series. This developmental work would probably include some statistics of the traditional objective type (*e.g.*, measures of levels of knowledge and skill, improved measures of housing quality, measures of participation in voluntary associations) but should concentrate especially on subjective measures which presently do not exist in systematic time-series.

Measures should be developed pertaining to the subjective dimensions of the social welfare areas listed in our first recommendation. For example, in the area of employment we might measure job satisfaction, occupational aspirations, and perception of career opportunities. In the area of education similar measures could be developed.

In addition we should be developing subjective measures of perception, aspirations, satisfactions, and attitudes that do not relate to these specific categories, such as the quality and style of

425

interpersonal relations. (Here the reference is to such differences in the quality and style as the desired anonymity of urban life and the intimacy of communal life.)

Measures transcending any given area of life experience — *i.e.,* those pertaining to a person's more generalized life experience, such as alienation, happiness and values, should also be developed. Some work has been done in each of these areas. Now it is necessary to expand the range of measures being developed to explore their validity and reliability and to continue them long enough to establish their usefulness and practicality.

Although some proposals for new social indicators no doubt will be developed by the subject-area panels recommended above, there are a few that can be specified at this time. We present them here as steps that can be taken toward the implementation of our recommendations.

On the basis of our discussion of "youth" above, we recommend the establishment of a National Youth Panel to be administered by a private survey research center, covering the ages 10 to 28, to be surveyed periodically over these years with respect to their achievements and participation in the major institutions of the society, and to be augmented with a new sample from the youngest cohort each survey period.

On a regular periodic schedule (of, say, five years), we recommend the investigation of some set of related social issues (*e.g.,* college education, leisure activities, working conditions, or hospital care). These would be in-depth investigations every five years with time and funds for various kinds of research on the topic. After five years, the next topic would be launched. Some of these intensive studies could spin off permanent social indicators of their own. The primary product would be a regular sequence of large-scale studies of topics of major importance to the nation which could be thought of as a series. Some topics might be proposed for study again if they were important, but no topic would likely be repeated in a 25-year period. Some federal panel would undoubtedly need to be established to coordinate these activities although most of the actual research would be done by scholars working individually or in teams and housed in research centers or universities.

There seems to be little doubt that the regular production of social indicators would lead to large infusions of new information into the political system on a periodic basis. Moreover, there are inevitable policy implications of social indicators work, whether that work is done for explicit policy-oriented purposes or for more general analytic purposes. We recommend study of the relationship between social indicators and public policy. In particular, both on national and local levels, the impact of social indicators work on policy decision-making and the impact of policy on social indicator development should be studied.

As we discussed earlier, there is an acute need for better understanding of the causal relations among the phenomena of the society. This is required for two reasons; (1) so that we can better understand the policy implications of such data, and (2) to better understand social change. *Accordingly, we recommend the development of testable explanatory models, particularly at the subsystem levels.*

This work is perhaps best accomplished by researchers outside government agencies, though funding would be required from federal sources.

Institutional Arrangements

We recommend that the Statistical Policy Staff, on behalf of the government sector, and the Social Science Research Council, on behalf of the private sector, monitor, coordinate, encourage and facilitate developmental work on social indicators.

The Statistical Policy Staff should be encouraged in its efforts to coordinate and guide federal agencies in developing series of social indicators, including the improvement and standardization of administrative statistics. The Staff should also be responsible in conjunction with the non-governmental advisory committee (see below) for appointing and staffing the subject-matter panels discussed in our first recommendation.

The Social Science Research Council should appoint and staff an Advisory Committee on Social Indicators.[5] This committee,

---

5   A joint committee, appointed and staffed by both the Social Science Research Council and the Behavioral Science Division of the National Academy of Science — National Research Council might also be considered. However, to the extent that the two agencies might address different constituencies and

with its office in Washington, D.C., would participate in the coordination of the activities of the governmental and private sectors; it would initiate and in some limited instances fund developmental work in the private sector which might otherwise be neglected.

Currently there are three university-based research centers that have demonstrated both a commitment and capability for the development of social indicators. The Survey Research Center at the University of Michigan, the National Opinion Research Center at the University of Chicago and the Survey Research Center at the University of California, Berkeley, have already contributed substantially to this effort. These institutional capabilities should be developed and strengthened, and others should be identified and supported. Thus, as a further step in implementing our first three recommendations, we urge that each of these institutions be granted for a period of five years, funding to develop concepts, instruments, experimental surveys and training covering both the objective and subjective dimensions of social change. It is anticipated that model building would be an inherent part of this work.

There is a decided lack of available skilled manpower competent in the social indicators area. While the large number of social scientists in the country might lead to the inference that these skills and interests are in good supply, the fact is that they are not. As evidence, a number of key positions in the field have been long vacant because of the absence of qualified candidates. Accordingly, again as a means of implementation, *we recommend the support of various training programs to develop social science manpower skilled in the measurement and analysis of social indicators.* This could take the form of university training centers, as well as internships and mid-career fellowship programs in federal government agencies for social scientists. What we have in mind here is not general social science training. Rather, we are concerned that social scientists with traditional training be given the conceptual and methodological skills necessary to contribute to the development of social indicators and their analysis. To encour-

operate with different organizational procedures, a joint arrangement might prove to be cumbersome. Insofar as the agencies tap the skills of an overlapping social science community of directors and consultants, placing the administration of this endeavor in one may outweigh the other advantages of a joint effort. The Council's prior work in social indicators is enhanced by this proposed committee.

age this effort, we suggest that National Science Foundation and Department of Health, Education and Welfare consider such programs for the training of at least 15-20 social scientists each year for a period of five years.

We recognize that our recommendations and the suggested steps for implementing them present essentially the beginnings of a five-year plan. We have limited ourselves to a five-year perspective because of the marked uncertainties associated with many of the aspects that we have proposed. There are many practical difficulties involved in social indicators work. While we have no doubt that much of what we have proposed should be practical and useful, it is impossible to predict the extent of success across the board, the extent to which the product will find acceptance, the success of many of the institutional arrangements we have proposed, and the like. To a considerable degree, the success of the endeavor will depend upon the extent to which varying parts of the plan can be coordinated. The success of the work of the panels and the two committees are crucial for balanced development of the effort.

Accordingly, we recommend that the two committees take stock at the end of the third year and make recommendations for longer-term development.

SUMMARY AND CONCLUSIONS

Otis Dudley Duncan has provided a succinct statement covering many aspects of this paper. We append it here, with a few modifications, as a concluding summary on the basic social and political issues raised in the discussion of social indicators. We begin by posing a not uncommon question:

WHO reports WHAT to WHOM, HOW and HOW OFTEN, with WHAT INTENT and to WHAT EFFECTS?

WHO. The issues of auspices, support, public relations, invasion of privacy, credibility are all relevant here. It may be argued that social indicators could become a "third force" in regard to many issues wherein various sectors of the public are proffering competing claims to public resources. Thus, if the issue is how well are women (labor, blacks, Chicanos, college professors, the poor, sectarian religious groups, etc.) doing when compared to men

429

(management, whites, Anglos, other professionals, the middle classes, the religious establishment, etc.), then it may be expected that the claimants will make their own studies and issue their own social reports; but we assume that the general public and the intellectual community will take special interest in data and analysis not preordained to serve immediate axe-grinding purposes. What we may need (as the BASS reports and others have suggested) is some kind of cooperative endeavor with core private support and a high priority claim on large-scale government effort and funds with long-term commitments, and clear and meaningful autonomy with respect to research procedures, drawing of conclusions, and presentation.

WHAT. Here the reference is to arguments about what are or should be social "indicators," "social accounts," or social statistics. What we must have, minimally, are quantitative statements about social conditions and social processes, repeatedly available through time, the reliability and validity of which are competently assessed and meet minimal standards. If such statements — "social measurements" — can be organized into accounts and respondents motivated by their contribution to filling out an accounting scheme, so much the better. If some combination of measurements or quantities derived from elementary magnitudes can be shown to serve a clear interpretive purpose as "indicators," so much the better. As accounting schemes, models of social processes, and indicators are developed and tested, our ideas of what to measure will, of course, change. But that does not alter the principle that the basic ingredients are the measurements themselves. We are talking about information, the processing of information, and the reporting of processed information.

TO WHOM. To the public; to the Congress; to the President; and to the fraternity of social scientists, administrators and technicians engaged in social reporting. Different kinds of reports for different audiences involving different sorts of analysis may be considered. Ideally the pool of information should be equally available to all interested parties, inviting analysis and commentary from as many points of view as there are distinguishable interests.

HOW. Here the reference is to issues of method — not only how reports are presented, but more basically how they are developed in the first place. We have the opportunity to impose statistical standards upon the production of "administrative statistics" by the several levels of government. A great many social conditions and processes that we want described have to do with distributions and characteristics of persons, families, organizations, and the like over the population of such units. Thus, census, or more typically, the sample survey is likely to be the method of choice.

Numerous discussions over the past several years have featured remarks on the advantages – indeed, necessity – of much more ambitious kinds of analysis than we have been accustomed to accept in the past: cohort comparisons, longitudinal studies, controlled field studies, access to unit records (preserving confidentiality), and broadening of subject matter content are topics often featured in such discussions. We know, for example, that the Current Population Survey is a very powerful tool for generating social indicators. It remains to be more fully exploited.

HOW OFTEN. This question tends to have a more or less "natural" answer once you think about the phenomenon being measured and the time scale on which it moves. We report the weather several times daily because it changes and its prospects change that often (at least in some localities). Of course, our ideas on this issue are not immutable. If at one time a decennial census seemed enough, there is cause now to want quinquennial counts for relatively small localities. The rhythm of observation and the rhythm of reporting need not be exactly in phase – *i.e.*, not the same for all measures. One can certainly think of subjects like crime, health, and education for which annual reports are needed, while five- or even ten-year cycles of observation may be adequate for other subjects.

WHAT INTENT. With the intent to enlighten and inform in some broad sense, rather than in some narrow operational sense to provide specific criteria for decision and evaluation of public programs. This view is, of course, controversial. But the "social system" may not really be as "systematic" as the economic system, and we may for a long time yet have to proceed on the basis of wisdom rather than models. The idea is that it should be informed

431

wisdom rather than speculative wisdom. That is what social indicators are for — to reduce somewhat the number of erroneous premises on which policies are based or political arguments conducted.

WHAT EFFECTS. A fixed result is not anticipated — for the infusion of information into a system seems to have unpredictable consequences, as Karl Popper has argued so persuasively in his polemic against historical determinism. The better we know our collective selves, hopefully, the more rationally we may hope to select means to common goals and the more circumspectly we may endeavor to define those disagreements that really have to do with values rather than facts.

The argument to be anticipated is that social indicators are additions to the armory of centralized control or manipulation. There is, of course, that danger. Thus both the importance of indicators catering to a wide spectrum of political and social interests and the importance of the sponsoring auspices of indicator production re-emerge. We bring the circle back to the "Who?"

In closing, we emphasize again that the approach we have presented provides a point of departure for furthering the work on social indicators. We recognize that there are alternative perspectives on social indicators, on their usefulness and on their conceptualization. We offer our comments in the spirit of getting on with the job.

SELECTED BIBLIOGRAPHY ON SOCIAL INDICATORS

Programmatic Statements

Raymond A. Bauer (ed.), *Social Indicators*. Cambridge, Massachusetts, The Massachusetts Institute of Technology Press, 1966a.

Raymond A. Bauer (ed.), "Detection and Anticipation of Impact: The Nature of the Task," Chapter 1 in Raymond A. Bauer (ed.), *Social Indicators*. Cambridge, Massachusetts, The Massachusetts Institute of Technology Press, 1966b.

Albert D. Biderman, "Social Indicators and Goals," Chapter 2 in Raymond A. Bauer (ed.), *Social Indicators* Cambridge, Massachusetts, The Massachusetts Institute of Technology Press, 1966.

Otis Dudley Duncan, *Mobility of the American Negro.* Prospects for a program of Studies, Paper drafted for the Ford Foundation, New York (mimeo), 1964.

Otis Dudley Duncan, *Toward Social Reporting: Next Steps.* Paper No. 2 in Social Science Frontiers Series, 1969.

Bertram M. Gross, "The State of the Nation: Social Systems Accounting," Chapter 3 in Raymond A. Bauer (ed.), *Social Indicators.* Cambridge, Massachusetts, The Massachusetts Institute of Technology Press, 1966.

Wilbert E. Moore, and Eleanor Bernert Sheldon, "Monitoring Social Change: A Conceptual and Programmatic Statement," Social Statistics Proceedings of the American Statistical Association: 144-149, 1965.

National Commission on Technology, Automation, and Economic Progress. *Technology and the American Economy,* Washington, D.C.: U.S. Government Printing Office, 1966.

Concepts and Measurements and Models

Albert D. Biderman, "Social Indicators and Goals," Chapter 2 in Raymond A. Bauer (ed.), *Social Indicators,* Cambridge, Massachusetts, The Massachusetts Institute of Technology Press, 1966.

Peter Blau, and Otis Dudley Duncan, *The American Occupational Structure,* New York, John Wiley and Sons, 1967.

Angus Campbell, and Philip Converse, *The Human Meaning of Change,* New York, Russell Sage Foundation (forthcoming).

C. L. Chiang, "An Index of Health Mathematical Models," Public Health Publications No. 1000, Series 2, No. 5, National Center for Health Statistics, Public Health Service, Washington, D.C., 1965.

James S. Coleman, *Resources for Social Change,* Interscience, New York. John Wiley and Sons, 1971.

Otis Dudley Duncan, *Mobility of the American Negro,* Prospects for a Program of Studies, Paper drafted for the Ford Foundation, New York (mimeo), 1964.

Otis Dudley Duncan, "Discrimination Against Negroes," *The Annals,* 371 (May): 85-103, 1967.

Otis Dudley Duncan, "Social Stratification and Mobility: Problems in the Measurement of Trend," Chapter 13 in Eleanor Bernert Sheldon and Wilbert E. Moore (eds.), *Indicators of Social Change: Concepts and Measurements,* New York, Russell Sage Foundation, 1968.

Otis Dudley Duncan, *Toward Social Reporting: Next Steps,* Paper No. 2 in Social Science Frontiers Series, New York, Russell Sage Foundation, 1969.

Bertram M. Gross (ed.), "Social Goals and Indicators for American Society: I," *The Annals,* 371 (May), 1967a.

Bertram M. Gross (ed.), "Social Goals and Indicators for American Society: II," *The Annals,* 373 (September), 1967b.

Abbott L. Ferriss, *Indicators of Trends in American Education,* New York, Russell Sage Foundation, 1969.

Abbott L. Ferriss, *Indicators of Change in the American Family,* New York, Russell Sage Foundation, 1970.

Abbott L. Ferriss, *Indicators of Trends in the Status of American Women,* New York, Russell Sage Foundation, 1971.

Kenneth C. Land, "Social Indicators," *Social Science Methods,* New York, Free Press, 1971.

Iwao M. Moriyama, "Problems in the Measurement of Health Status," Chapter 4 in Eleanor Bernert Sheldon and Wilbert E. Moore (eds.), *Indicators of Social Change,* New York, Russell Sage Foundation, 1968.

Albert J. Reiss, Jr., "Monitoring the Quality of Criminal Justice Systems," Angus Campbell and Philip Converse (eds.), *The Human Meaning of Social Change,* New York, Russell Sage Foundation (forthcoming).

William H. Sewell *et al.,* "The Educational and Early Occupational Status Attainment Process: Replication and Revision," *American Sociological Review,* 35 (December), 1014-1027, 1970.

434

Eleanor Bernert Sheldon, and Wilbert E. Moore (eds.), *Indicators of Social Change: Concepts and Measurements,* New York, Russell Sage Foundation, 1968.

U.S. Department of Health, Education and Welfare, *Toward a Social Report,* Washington, D.C., U.S. Government Printing Office, 1969.

Commentaries

Daniel Bell, "The Idea of a Social Report," *The Public Interest,* 15 (Spring): 72-84, 1969.

Mancur Olson, Jr., "The Plan and Purpose of the Social Report," *The Public Interest,* 15 (Spring): 85-97, 1969.

Eleanor Bernert Sheldon and Howard E. Freeman, "Notes on Social Indicators: Promises and Potential," *Policy Sciences,* 1 (April): 97-111, 1970.

CHAPTER 8

MANAGEMENT INFORMATION SYSTEMS

By
Leon G. Hunt

MANAGEMENT INFORMATION SYSTEMS

TABLE OF CONTENTS

439

INTRODUCTION

Statement of the Problem

The term Management Information System (MIS) is very ambiguous, embracing engineering and scientific uses of computers on one hand and administrative and information retrieval systems on the other. MIS is therefore nearly synonymous with computer applications, except for the strong presumption that such systems should be decision-making aids and that they are able to integrate dissimilar and formerly unconnected types of information.

Rapid growth of computer capacity in the federal government and in the associated development of MIS, has raised various social and political issues: libertarians have wondered whether easy access and manipulation of personal data would lead to invasions of privacy. Similarly, would real executive power fall progressively into the hands of the "keepers of the computer?"

We are not concerned with these broad social issues here, but rather with narrower, more operational questions: Has MIS been "successful," in the sense that it has enabled federal executives to manage more efficiently, or to do things which could not before be done at all? Has increased control attended the installation of MIS? What, if any, real changes in operations have accompanied the installation of MIS?

To address these questions, we first identify the different species of MIS; trace the history of these variants in industry – a history considerably different from what MIS had in government; then draw general conclusions.

The Meaning of "Management Information Systems"

Three distinct views of MIS are found in the current literature:

1. *The "Applications" view:*

   Here MIS are classified according to their specific uses. There are financial, personnel, logistics, marketing, research and development and strategic planning "management information systems." In this view, MIS is virtually equivalent to computer applications. Most textbooks on MIS, and most business writers adopt this view.

2. *The "Systems" view:*

   Held by programmers and computer specialists, the systems view regards MIS as equivalent to "generalized data base management systems" (GDBMS) or automated file management systems. Usage of the term, while entirely free from imputations of purposes, is much more specific than 1. It refers to software which is capable of manipulating one or more data files and generating specific reports from the files. It is the internal technician's view, rather than the external user's view in 1, and carries technical connotations of computer language types and programming problems. Some of the computer applications listed under 1 would not be classed as GDBMS at all because they lack the essential feature of a data file.

3. *The "Sales" view:*

   Least specific and most deceptive of all, the sales view is based on the imaginative power of the software salesman and the looseness of the words "management," "information," and "systems," none of which is definable in precise terms, and which, together, are practically meaningless.

Thus, MIS here is anything a manager may think he needs and which a salesman can talk about. While such a discussion may be meaningless, it has power to evoke visions of precision and control: the incantatory power of "management" wedded to the mystique of the computer has proved irresistible.

The preceding terminological foray is necessary if we are to talk about MIS, since it is so many things to so many different people. One hears statements like "MIS is bad" or "MIS is the answer." Such observations are uninformative unless one knows both the vocabulary and something of the psychology of the speaker. To a hard-pressed manager, MIS may be hope. To a technician, an absorbing problem, or at least a job. To a salesman, a sale.

CLASSIFICATION OF MIS

Classification by Application.

Earlier writers undertook direct descriptive classifications of MIS. Typical of this group are John Dearden and F. Warren McFarlin.[1] They distinguish between the major and minor applications (depending upon *how much* of the parent organization is affected):

MAJOR	MINOR
Routine	Marketing
Financial	Research and Development
Personnel	Strategic Planning
Logistics	

The major categories are obvious:

1. *Routine Data Processing:*

   Payroll, billing, routine accounting, stockholder records. These data provide little input to "management" decision-making.

2. *Financial:*

   Traditional "dollar flow" information. Major accounting,

---

1   Dearden, J. and McFarlin, F. W., *MIS: Texts and Cases,* Irwin, 1966.

budgeting, controller activities. Provides for financial control of a company.

3. *Personnel Information Systems:*
   All personnel record keeping.

4. *Logistic Information Systems:*
   Physical flow of goods within a company. Procurement, production, distribution. Involves inventory control, production planning, scheduling, transportation.

The minor classes are defined:

1. *Marketing Information Systems:*
   Processing all marketing data.

2. *Research & Development Systems:*
   Mainly information retrieval and update of research results.

3. *Strategic Planning:*
   Examining competitive alternatives through simulation, mathematical programming, etc.

This appears to be a classification of computer applications rather than management information systems as such. In fact, this lack of a distinction between simply using a computer and having an MIS persists. It is almost as if "management information systems" are any uses to which companies put computers which help management – in other words, all uses.

A more recent classification[2] follows general systems theory in looking at the information sources. This leads to:

1. *Traditional Information Systems:* which are *closed* with respect to the environment; that is, they process all data *within* the organization.

2. *Production and Operations Information Systems:* are *partially open* with respect to the environment, i.e., they respond to both internal information and external data such as price changes, raw material supply, etc.

3. *Marketing Information Systems:* are *open* systems, and depend mainly on *external data.*

---

2 Prince, T. R., *Information Systems for Management, Planning and Control,* Irwin, 1970.

Here again, the "systems" are merely the implementation (usually by computers) of data handling processes, and represent, as before, the automation of traditional functions. The idea of the "system" being open or closed with respect to the information source tends to classify *data* rather than the system itself.

Classification by Function

Other studies admit that MIS is really an abstraction, and consider computer applications directly.[3] With increasing computer capacities, applications fall into two categorically different groups:

1. *Replacement of Clerical Functions:* payroll, inventory reporting, accounts, etc. These functions already existed in companies before computers and had established procedures and administration.

2. *Unique Functions:* Communication switching, production control, passenger reservations, information retrieval. These are *operationally-oriented* functions which cannot be done in the same way without computers (mainly because of speed).

This "classification" exposes the ambiguity of the term "management information system." The first group contains most of what are generally called MIS, and there is little new about them. Furthermore, they contribute little to management.

The second group, on the other hand, represents principally scientific uses of computers, which have only gradually been applied to operational problems and are not part of most existing MIS.

Other authors pursue the functional classification in terms of a "managerial taxonomy."[4] Activities of management are broadly subdivided into the functions of planning and control. They occur in environments which are either structured or unstructured, "structured" being roughly equivalent to "programmable" in the

3   Blumenthal, S. C., *MIS: A Framework for Planning and Development,* Prentice-Hall, 1969.

4   Churchill, N. C., Kempsten, J. H. and Uretsky, M., *Computer-Basic Information Systems for Management: A Survey,* National Association of Accountants, 1969.

sense of a task being reducible to a set of specific instructions. This two-fold classification yields the tableau:

		ENVIRONMENT	
		Unstructured	Structured
	Planning	a	b
ACTIVITY	Control	c	d

Computer applications which support each of the four classes of management responsibility are each a different type of MIS. For example, class (d) includes routine accounting, billing, and labor distribution systems.

Classification by Software

Here we are concerned not with applications or function — the "purpose" of the system — but with intrinsic technical properties of software.

GDBMS languages have been classified[5] as *host* and *self-contained*.

> Host language systems are basically enhancements of a procedural language, usually COBOL. The enhancements are always oriented toward transferring data between one level of memory and another. "A self-contained system (sometimes called an information retrieval system) provides its own language, which claims to be more user oriented and which is designed for use by persons ... who do not necessarily understand procedural programming."[6]

While applications cannot be classified according to the kind of language they require, it is true that self-contained systems are chiefly restricted to uses involving a single master data file, while multiple-file applications usually demand a host language system. A distinction is also made between information needs of the user definable in advance (often true in lower echelons of an organization), and unpredictable needs of higher management.

---

5   Olle, T. W., "MIS: Data Bases," *Datamation,* November 15, 1970.

6   Olle, *op.cit.*, pp. 47-48.

MIS IN INDUSTRY: THE HISTORY
OF COMPUTER APPLICATIONS

Typical Growth Stages of MIS in a Company

Computers were introduced into business in 1953 and have progressively influenced corporate operations since then. A study of 12 companies, chiefly manufacturers, revealed a typical growth pattern of computer applications.[7]

> *Type 1 applications:* Computers were first used in 9 of the 12 companies in basic accounting, in sales analysis in 2 of the 12, and in material control in the remaining company. All applications consisted of the automation of routine clerical tasks; output of earlier reports was essentially unchanged in format and each application was treated as a separate subsystem, separately programmed and processed.

> *Type 2 applications:* In companies in which Type 1 applications were successful, separate subsystems and data bases were gradually integrated. Sometimes groups of files were redesigned for efficiency, sometimes to produce new types of reports. Motivation at this stage was not primarily clerical replacement, but to provide data on management of resources. However, information was still related to *routine control of the organization.* Few automatic decision-making rules were built into the the data handling systems.

The growth of computer applications in many companies has levelled off at this stage. This "plateau" in development has been quite striking:

> "Though it has transformed the administrative and accounting operations of U. S. business, the computer has had little impact on most companies' key operating and management problems."[8]

Similarly, a 1967 survey[9] of 100 top managers with access to 120

---

7   Churchill, *et al, op.cit.,* pp. 6-13.

8   "Unlocking the Computer's Profit Potential," McKinsey and Co., Inc., New York, 1968, pp. 6-7.

9   Brady, R. H., "Computers in Top-Level Decision-Making," *Harvard Bus. Review,* July-August, 1967, p. 8, (Quoted in Blumenthal, *op.cit.,* p. 14).

computers revealed that *not one of them* used computers directly in making decisions.

Type 3 applications: Here the individual systems of Type 1 and the partially integrated systems of Type 2 are replaced by a single integrated system which extends and coordinates management's control of operations. At the same time, decision-making programs are built directly into the integrated information system, so that the overall system depends upon an accurate representation of both routine operations *and* management processes (i.e., algorithms to represent the decisions made by managers).

Type 3 applications include the most sophisticated uses of computers in management. Inventory control and production scheduling belong here. Formal optimization techniques, such as sequential linear programming solutions to product mix, material utilization, scheduling, operate on outputs from the integrated data files. Only in rare cases has this level of integration and control been achieved, even in experienced companies.

Type 4 applications: These uses of the computer include all aids to "unstructured management planning." They may depend upon information external to corporate data files and involve poorly defined variables and little-understood relationships. Two areas have received some attention: the first is simulations of corporate strategy; studies of budgeting alternatives, plant location, etc. Such simulations attempt to define the consequences of alternative courses of action and are direct aids to management decisions. The second is information systems for unspecified management queries. These systems are still experimental.

Parallel Non-Routine Computer Applications

The stages described above are not necessarily sequential, except between Type 1 and Type 2. In fact, most of the decision algorithms, the "optimizing" routines in Type 3, are the products of quite early "scientific" uses of computers. Large linear and non-linear programming problems are practically insolvable except by computers, and related Lagrange multiplier and game-theoretic

448

methods require similar implementation. Various other engineering and scientific computer uses have also been adapted to management problems (e.g., decision models, network analysis, etc.).

In organizations where successful Type 3 applications have occured, there has usually been a tradition of prior "scientific" computer use. That is, engineering departments, operations research groups, etc., existed before the advent of the Type 3 application and had developed the mathematical (as opposed to the data handling) parts of these integrated systems for other, non-routine, purposes.

Interrelationship of Routine and Non-Routine Users

It is useful to distinguish between the data handling part and the control or decision part of a Type 3 system. Data handling software is essentially a GDBMS defined above, while a control or decision program embodies some mathematical devices (such as a linear programming algorithm) which operate on the data supplied by the GDBMS. These two parts have clearly grown from different corporate sources. The information on data systems came from the original automation of administrative functions, while the decision-aiding programs are the results of operations research or scientific activities. Their successful merging into a Type 3 system (the first real "management decision-aiding information system") is the product of special corporate structure and growth which permitted the parallel developments.

The importance of the control or decisional function is growing in industry. As far back as 1966, Booz Allen and Hamilton, Inc., surveyed 33 large companies and found that they estimated 70 percent of their computer capacity would go to activities other than financial and administrative use in the next few years.[10] We conclude that many companies are moving from the Type 2 plateau into genuine Type 3 applications which utilize the unique computational capability of computers, and are, perhaps for the first time, true MIS applications in the sense of influencing or aiding management decisions.

---

10   Blumenthal, *op.cit.*, p. 7.

MIS IN GOVERNMENT

Non-Administrative Computer Applications

Some of the oldest users of computers are agencies of the federal government. Parts of the Department of Defense (DOD), which pioneered both digital and analog computer development, have depended upon computers for the solution to research and development problems connected with weapons development. The old U. S. Weather Bureau was an early computer user, as was the Bureau of the Census. Uses varied, depending on organizational problems. DOD applications were mainly computational while Census uses were related to data handling.

Administrative Applications

Later, many parts of the federal government acquired their own computer facilities. Early uses were for routine clerical and administrative tasks: payroll, accounting, personnel record keeping. Then, the typical, non-technical federal agency experimented with computer use in the same way as the typical business organization (see Type 2 application).

Many routine operations have been automated in federal agencies and some have reached the post-Type 2 plateau. However, few have gone beyond it to the true management applications of Type 3. In a study of computerized information systems as decision-making aids, Westin[11] found that:

> "...during 1969 there was still hardly anything in operation in any of these systems that was affecting strategic or tactical decision-making by executive officials. Some of the 'most advanced' (and most publicized) systems were already out of business, the victims of factors such as post-1968 economic condition, poor performance on promised benefits, and a growing skepticism among government administrators about blue-sky information systems."

---

11 Westin, Alan F., "Information Technology and Public Decision-Making," 6th Annual Report, Harvard University Program on Technology and Society, pp. 58-67.

450

Interrelationship of Administrative and Non-Administrative Uses

There can be no doubt that MIS in federal government has been a failure in the sense that it has not provided significant decision-making assistance to executives. Westin[12] also states that:

> "...one is led to ask whether the shimmering visions painted by computer manufacturers, software firms, and allied consultants in the early 1960's, and the black record of accomplishment as of 1970, suggests a case of civic fraud."

A comparison of the histories of computer applications in federal agencies and business indicated some likely reason for this failure. First, we must note that not all business applications of decision-making MIS (Types 3 and 4) have been successful, and, conversely, many routine data systems in the federal government have paid their way. Beyond this, though, there exist real differences:

a. Businesses which have successfully developed Type 3 and 4 (non-routine) MIS have been those with an extended history of computer use. The development of the Type 3 system has been progressive and organic and represents a fusion of administrative data systems with scientific decision-aiding and control algorithms. Such companies have had experience with engineering, operations research, or other scientific applications of computers. They are used to considering normative problems in terms of clear measures of effectiveness, such as profit.

In contrast, unsuccessful federal agencies often have shorter histories of computer use, and few if any scientific applications in their experience. They often do not have a tradition of quantitative problem solving, and their operational goals are more diffuse and less susceptible to normative characterization.

b. Successful Type 3 systems may be largely the product of internal development. Companies have had years to understand their data needs, their decisional problems and the

---

12   Westin, *op.cit.,* p. 65.

relationship between the two. By contrast, federal agencies have been told by outside consultants what their data needs should be and how their decisional problems depend upon these data. In some cases, consultants may even have *prescribed* measures of effectiveness for operational goals. Lacking a tradition and familiarity with quantitative problem-solving (in addition to the basic intractability of their problems), many agencies, especially socially-oriented ones, have been easy marks for 'expert' advisers.

What can be done?

If, as we may optimistically hope, MIS systems in the federal government can develop to effective provision of higher capabilities, it may not be the best economy to strip present systems all the way down to the capabilities required by the Type 2 uses that are already paying for themselves. It is likely to be wise, if major economies are possible, to reduce either hardware or software to a point where only experimental Type 3 service can be supplied. During such an experimental interim, two sorts of actions can be taken to speed up progress toward generally effective Type 3 operation, namely:

> study of and experimentation with "scientific" methods of management guidance, whether or not highly computerized.
> introduction of both statistical techniques and statistical insights into the experimental production of higher-type information.

The case for the first of these has already been made above.

To the statistician, the siren song of MIS sounds much like the apocryphal: "The truth will make you free, no matter how disorganized or unanalyzed it be." Many MIS systems in the federal government are extremely large, involving many, many entities, individuals or firms. Sometimes there are needs for summary data covering all entities in the files, but many questions can be more efficiently answered in terms of samples. The samples may need to be structured with some care. Personnel files, for example, may well call for separate samples from two or more strata. (Perhaps one each for higher grades, for minorities, for women, and for all others.) Not only will samples allow more rapid and more economical responses to questions, but the mental effort involved in answering the questions that good sample designers will ask will help the agency move more rapidly toward an ability to make effective use of Type 3 MIS. A good job of sampling can do much to structure the problem and a considerable amount to suggest how it is analyzed.

In an opposite direction, there will often be useful economies and increased insights to be had by supplementing detailed files with smaller files containing aggregate information on groups of cases of intermediate size. While statisticians have not yet done as much development work on such techniques increasing the effectiveness of access to large administrative files for policy purposes is an ideal opportunity to develop such techniques further.

CONCLUSION AND SUMMARY

MIS come in many forms, including most computer applications that involve the handling of data. To date, few actually aid directly in the decision of higher managers. Those that do consist of two distinct parts — a data handling or information system; and decision-making or control programs.

Businesses which have achieved true *decision-aiding systems* have done so as a result of significant experience with both administrative data handling and "scientific" decision-making problems. Many federal agencies lack the latter experience, and also suffer from not having clearly measurable indices of their own performance, against which a control algorithm can operate.

At the same time, *routine data systems* are usually successfully employed in most federal agencies. They represent chiefly the automation of clerical functions and contain neither decision algorithms nor the capacity to retrieve or manipulate previously unspecified data items.

Where MIS systems are not producing useful aids to decision-making, they should be cut down to the scope required for routine operations, and steps should be taken to include sample-design and group-aggregation techniques, guided by statistically knowledgeable advice, in the continuing exploratory operation of their new decision-aiding functions.

Before going all out for decision-aiding computer systems, federal agencies should both study and practice the use of "scientific" decision aids, many of which need not be computerized.

CHAPTER 9

THE BUREAUCRATIC PATHOLOGY

By

Jacob A. Stockfisch

448-559 O - 71 - 30

THE
BUREAUCRATIC
PATHOLOGY

TABLE OF CONTENTS

INTRODUCTION

Implicit in modern government is the idea of a sharp distinction between policy makers, on the one hand, and the specialists who carry out policy, on the other hand. The specialists may also be described as "operators," or those who literally carry out specialized tasks that require a high degree of expertise. Operators may also be described as "bureaucrats," in the sense that formal institutions or sub-organizations emerge with their necessary trappings of formal procedures, record keeping, and special personnel selection and indoctrination. These trappings might be regarded as the institutionalization of the special brand of expertise that a bureau is created to practice.

It is a credo in modern government that policy makers make policy, and that operators (or bureaucrats) carry out and implement policy. However, for a variety of reasons unique to governmental and bureaucratic processes, bureaucrats consciously or unconsciously make policy; and policy makers frequently seek to operate. There is seldom a clear division of labor. The lack of clarity regarding functions creates tensions, the tensions generate suspicion, and the suspicion promotes struggle.

459

An important aspect of the struggle centers on budgets. Bureaucrats, as dedicated specialists, must also struggle to get dollars, and the resources dollars can buy, from reluctant taxpayers. They must also compete with rival bureaucrats in the budgetary process. From this complex struggle, a peculiar "secrecy" syndrome emerges. Through their specialization and expertise, senior bureaucrats are able to maintain an element of secrecy about their operations or production processes. This quality is the source of a bureau's power relative to both its executive and legislative branch superiors, and is the key to the "bureaucracy problem." In its broadest sense, the bureaucracy problem has three dimensions. They are: (1) The secrecy that is a by-product of bureaucratic or operational expertise can lead to an abuse of authority; (2) the abuse of authority poses special problems for the "sovereign" who must control subordinate officials; and (3) those individuals and groups who are affected by the decision-making of officials (bureaucrats) operating to influence administrative procedure and decision-making.[1]

Because of the critical role of "secrecy," the subject of bureaucratic behavior necessarily has a very high information or "intelligence" content. It would be astonishing, therefore, if the statistical information programs of bureaus were not greatly affected by bureaucratic motivations. The purpose of this paper is to focus explicitly on these information consequences of bureaucratic behavior.

THE NATURE OF BUREAUS

Bureaus consist of operators who perform complex jobs. Performance of any specialized function requires the development of a high degree of expertise. If the bureau itself is large and if the function is highly complex, it also develops fairly rigorous procedures and promotes a high degree of specialization between individuals and sub-agencies. Large elements of the job, therefore, become routinized and standardized. A further characteristic of creating such an organization, to the extent that it involves a number of specialized functional areas and divisions, is that the

---

1 Reinhard Bendix, "Bureaucracy," *International Encyclopedia of the Social Sciences* (New York: Macmillian, 1968) Volume 2, p. 214.

leadership attempts to impart esprit and create a sense of dedication on the part of its diverse members. It is important that people have pride in the work that they do. A specialization inherent in a given task will often become the focal point for generating that pride. Thus Air Force people, and particularly air crewmen, take great pride in the fact that they fly airplanes. They become "dedicated" to the airplane and more broadly to an abstraction called "strategic air power." This kind of pride and dedication is vital, if not necessary, if the job is to be done well. It is dangerous business at best even if the instrument is never used; when and if it is used, there is a very good chance that many of the people who operate it will be killed. Thus aviators truly have to have faith in airplanes, submariners in submarines, and so forth. Pride and esprit, both in one's self and in the organization with which one is associated, are therefore necessary ingredients to create and sustain an organization that performs any function. The intensity of these qualities may be particularly extreme in military organizations, but they are necessary qualities for all organizations.

A part of developing this kind of feeling is that each agency evolves its own image and style, which in any given time are a product of its past history. It simultaneously espouses its role and mission in such a way as to fortify and enhance its institutional status. At a minimum, a bureau will seek stability (it does not like to see its mission or function degraded or reduced in importance). For this reason it will resist any broader policy change which it judges, either rightly or wrongly, may contain the possibility that its function will become less important. At a maximum, a bureau will seek to expand its mission and function. Every man likes to see his organization grow in size and prestige. If its size grows, the probability of personal advancement is better; if it grows in prestige, the individual enjoys an enhanced feeling of personal self-esteem.

Because bureaus normally perform complex tasks and must employ ordinary people, and because they seek stability, they also develop their own procedures and doctrine, or "decision rules." These decision rules, usually in large organizations, often become "institutionalized." It should be pointed out, however, that the evolution of decision rules often reflects a compromise between

461

the power blocs within the organization itself. Organizations like the Army, the Coast Guard, or the Internal Revenue Service in themselves are by no means monolithic. They consist of subgroups who struggle among themselves. There is (and has been) a perennial struggle in an army among infantrymen and artillerymen and cavalrymen. Within a tax collecting agency there are struggles among auditors, lawyers, and enforcement specialists. The implications of this kind of struggle are that the organization's image of itself, as well as of its procedures and decision rules, is the product of a compromise among internal power blocs. Such a compromise is almost necessary if the larger organization, with which everyone identifies, is not to be shaken with divisiveness. The compromise maintains organizational stability and individual security, and hence esprit. But a frequent consequence of this kind compromise is that an organization tends to resist change in their way of doing things, because change involves the uncertainty that some segments of a bureau might experience a decline in their relative importance. Hence decision rules and procedures may not be modified promptly and expeditiously so as to implement whatever new policies the executive office may announce, or in response to technological change.[2]

For these reasons the bureau develops a special posture toward the executive office, and, indeed, toward outsiders generally. That posture is one of autonomy seeking, obfuscation, and suspicion. Let us discuss each of these qualities.

Autonomy

The bureau prefers to be left alone in its day-to-day operations, to perform them efficiently in terms of its own decision rules and effectiveness criteria. Operating demands in themselves are usually capable of consuming all of the energy an organization's members possess. The relationship between the bureau and the executive office which the bureau seeks to promote is that of assuring the executive that the job it is performing is vitally important, and that it is being done "efficiently." To the extent that it succeeds

---

2 For an account of one such case, see Edward L. Katzenbach, Jr., "Twentieth Century Horse Cavalry," in *Public Policy*, Carl J. Friedrich and Seymour E. Harris, (eds.), (Cambridge: Harvard University Press, 1958), pp. 120-50.

in creating this image, it may also create a powerful advocate for its own advancement, particularly in the form of larger appropriations and hence the means to foster the organization's growth. This outcome would be the best of all worlds.

The second best and most prevalent world is one where the executive is passive toward the bureau. In this case the bureau is likely to build up its own independent constituency. It establishes contact with Congressmen, particularly key committee chairmen and members who have cognizance over the particular bureau's authorization and appropriations legislation. Simultaneously, the bureau, either through the specialized services it provides private groups, or its spending for procurement of products and services, impacts upon constituents of Congressmen and simultaneously acquires advocates in the "body politic" for its endeavors. Thus a "triangle" consisting of senior bureau officials, special private sector interest groups, and Congressmen supported by those interest groups who in turn support the bureaus — conduct much of the day-to-day business that gets done in the capital.[3]

Obfuscation

This is a tool that enables a bureau to maintain its autonomy. It will indicate to the executive, in broad general terms, that its mission is to "fight the ground battle" or "to administer the tax system efficiently," or to "maintain law and order." Most bureaus also endeavor to convey a similar impression to citizens. If pushed on particular matters, assuming that the executive has the energy or ability to raise questions, the bureau is capable of coming up with many reasons why it is doing things its way. At this point the executive (or any other influential outside critic) is apt to be confronted with a mass of detail linked together with reasoning that reflects the bureau's own brand of logic, which can at best only be rationalized in terms of its self-image. Under the worst circumstances, it may employ biased samples or downright erron-

---

3   For a treatment of some of these ingredients, see Richard E. Neustadt, "Politicians and Bureaucrats," in *The Congress and America's Future,* ed. by David B. Truman, (Englewood Cliffs, N.J.: Prentice Hall, 1965), pp. 102-120; for a well-documented case study, see Vincent Davis, *The Admiral's Lobby* (Chapel Hill: University of North Carolina Press, 1967).

eous numbers to justify its case. Great powers of persuasion are employed to assure the executive or other skeptical outsiders that it is doing its job efficiently and effectively, and that its behavior is in harmony with the executive's own policy objectives or the "public interest." Unless the executive has the staff capability to analyze these offerings in great detail, the dialogue ends. The bureau is therefore left alone and it can get on with doing its job without interference, and with the task of building and enhancing the future stability and growth of its budget.

Suspicion

These problems are intensified by the nature of the executive branch or office where the main orientation is toward policy formulation. Executive offices experience much personnel turnover, particularly at the upper levels. This turnover is necessary and even desirable as administrations and policies change. But as a result there is apt to be a lack of operations or technical expertise in the policy organization. The latter kind of knowledge necessitates concern with minute detail. Top policy officials find it difficult to take time to learn this detail. Moreover, as they acquire it with lengthening tenure, the probability that they will leave increases. Personnel turnover, therefore, exacts a toll. For this reason the executive is usually forced to rely upon the offerings of the leaders of the bureau.

Another quality of the executive office is that it is the source of changing policy. But policy changes often create trouble for the bureau. They may cause a downgrading of its role or mission. At a minimum, a bureau may have to reexamine its function, and perhaps undertake changes that upset the internal balance of power. The executive office is thus a source of annoyance. At best, it epitomizes to the bureau the fact that here are some people they must "educate." At worst, the people "up there" will be the source of trouble which will necessitate going on the defensive (or the offensive) in order to preserve the status quo.

BUREAUCRATS AS BUDGET MAXIMIZERS

Although the behavior described above may seem to have a pathological quality, it nevertheless has understandable motivation. First, it is characteristic of most human beings to resent extensive probing by "outsiders" about their specialized activity, particularly if it is not done with great patience, tact, and skill. Many husbands have experienced this reaction on the part of their wives on matters related to managing the household budget. Second, and much more important in the case of the senior governmental bureaucrat, is the motivation to maximize his budget. Like all experts, he takes pride in his expertise and he is secretive about it. Because he comprises and strongly identifies with a subculture within a larger society, he strives to maximize the role his subculture plays in the social system. He can only do this, however, by getting resources from the society of which he is a part. His operations — and in some cases technical expertise — enable him to perform this maximizing function by virtue of the monopoly of knowledge his expertise endows him with.

Conventional economic theory can demonstrate that a monopolist operating in the business sector of the economy, if he operates under the constraints of linear cost and demand functions, will produce one-half the output that a competitive industry will produce. Essentially, the private monopolist sets a price that maximizes his profits. He enjoys excessive profits — i.e., a larger return from his activity that exceeds the opportunity cost of producing the product. Society gets less output of the particular product, and in the process pays more per unit than would be the case if it were produced competitively.

A bureaucrat/monopolist who is an instrument of the state cannot exploit a monopoly position to reap personal profits. However, it has been observed that the bureaucrat/monopolist is motivated to maximize the size of his agency or bureau, and in this fashion to derive personal fulfillment. By presenting to his superior a joint budget-output package, he can manage to obtain from the society the value equivalent that a business monopolist could mulct from consumers. What would be "excess profits" to a private monopolist are used by the bureaucratic monopolist to enlarge the size of his agency or service. By means of the calculus (or model) with which it can be demonstrated that a private business monopolist would produce only half the output as would an industry composed of competitors, it can be demonstrated that a bureaucrat monopolist would produce up to twice the output as would be called for by equating the relevant demand and cost functions.[4]

Now no bureaucrat literally offers the sovereign a strict budget-output package on a take-it-or-leave-it basis. Such behavior would be impudent if not downright insubordinate. Rather, a variety of techniques are employed, which in most instances are utilized in good faith and sincerity, but which are also self-serving. First is the assertion of the "requirement." The argument runs that failure to program adequate resources to cope with the need bodes ill for the country's safety. There is a tendency to exaggerate the threat or the problem that must be coped with. This exaggeration can be advanced in perfectly good faith on the part of military professionals since they are indoctrinated to be winners rather than losers in war, and numbers or size of force are the major determinant of the outcome. Moreover, in the judgment of historians and politicians, it is the generals who lose the battles if not the wars, not the political decision-makers who determine the budgets.

There are techniques employed with regard to the relation between "inputs" and "outputs" that serve the objective of maximizing the budget. The insider tends to be conservative about the capabilities of existing systems, if only because he knows something about their shortcomings. When budgetary cuts are suggested, they are countered with the query as to which outputs should be reduced, rather than with an effort to cut back overhead or to energetically seek more efficient ways of doing things. In military affairs, the insider also tends to be conservative about doctrine and organization, especially if they were successful in winning a past war. To be sure, one would like new, higher performance equipment that can be substituted for the old, but nevertheless one continues old doctrine. Thus innovations (as contrasted with technological inventions) are not apt to be forthcoming in a manner commensurate with our self-image of being progressive. There is also a tendency, when advocating new equip-

---

4   See William A. Niskanen, "Nonmarket Decision Making: The Peculiar Economics of Bureaucracy," *The American Economic Review;* May, 1968, pp. 293-305 for a rigorous demonstration and extension of this view.

ment systems, to underestimate their costs. This, too, is under-standable, both for natural human and bureaucratic reasons. We are all bargain-hunters at heart, and hope is eternal that cost (which is unpleasant to contemplate) will be low. Moreover, the assertion that cost will be low serves to sell the program; once the program is underway there is hope (and not a little pressure) that additional money will be found to complete the development.

IMPLICATIONS OF BUREAUCRATIC BEHAVIOR FOR BUREAUCRATIC INFORMATION SYSTEMS

The pathological aspects of the bureaucratic behavior pattern should not be regarded solely as a result (or the "fault") of bu-reaucrats themselves. Rather, they are a product of, and simultan-eously a vital contributing ingredient to, the perennial struggle between the executive and legislative branches, on the one hand, and between the varied private interest groups that comprise a pluralistic society, on the other hand. Given the nature of the "game," pervaded as it is with self-serving on the part of all con-cerned parties, it is amazing that the Republic is served as well as it is by the professional civil servants and the uniformed officer corps that constitute "the" bureaucracy. But whatever the roots or causes of the behavior pattern, whether it be inherent in the human or political condition, prime casualties of the process are the information and statistical systems internal to the bureaus themselves. Another casualty is the ability of bureaus to engage in critical program evaluation and, especially, experimentation.

A bureau's information system, including its generation of sta-tistics that are a by-product of its operations, tends to reflect its self-serving motivation to survive and to maximize its budget. Its internal statistics program, which can extend to the reporting re-quirements it places upon whatever private groups over which it exerts a controlling or regulating function, will mirror an inertia that characterizes the inherently conservative nature of an estab-lished organization. The self-serving motive means that seldom will information be gathered that can be used to show that a bureau's programs or operations might not be going well, or that they may

467

be creating unpleasant by-products. The conservative trait means that statistics and information are often gathered, at a cost to those required to keep records to report it, which have limited or no usefulness. An important cost of this latter effect is that an opportunity is foregone, or lost, to elicit information which may be of much greater use to policy makers and the general public, including scholars who need data. Finally, bureaus are frequently adroit at passing off numbers that may in large part be fabricated or the products of various manipulations when those data can be used to support the political - budgeting case a bureau seeks to make. We thus have the "avoidance," "inertia," and "fabrication" problems that afflict the statistical programs of bureaus. These elements interact and mutually reinforce each other so as to affect the government's overall statistical program.

Avoidance is responsible for a failure to gather data on program effects which may reflect unfavorably on a bureau's programs, either by way of showing that particular programs may not be achieving their objectives or that a program may be creating unfavorable side effects. Thus the Department of Agriculture — over many years of administrating agricultural price support programs — did not vigorously pursue gathering data on the attributes of farmers benefiting from these programs. The Urban Renewal Agency seldom followed through to determine what happened to low income individuals uprooted by the renewal programs. Highway commissions and port authorities do not pursue the matter of the possible traffic congestion their projects deliver to central urban areas. Although such agencies are often in the best position to gather these kinds of data, the information that is available is usually obtained piecemeal from diverse other sources, combined with whatever can be ferreted out or inferred from the agency's operating data.

For similar reasons, bureaus are reluctant to pursue program experimentation or field testing. It is perhaps the military departments that have the greatest opportunity to do field experimentation. Yet very little is done, and what little that is done is done poorly or in such a way as to yield ambiguous findings.

This problem seems to spring from inherent qualities of the experimentation process itself. An experiment may show or suggest that a doctrine or weapon favored by one or more powerful people may not be as good as touted. If prior decisions were made, involving either large amounts of resources and/or the personal prestige of decision-makers or staff advocates, the results of the experiment can be embarassing or personally damaging to powerful individuals. Such individuals may be either professional military officers, or civilian policy makers, or prominent scientists who have "staked" their professional reputation on a particular technical approach to an equipment or tactical issue.

This attitude toward field experimentation has its roots in the budgeting process. Budgets of military departments, for research and development and procurement, are aggregations consisting of individual items and are advocated at low levels of the hierarchy. Each department is motivated to maximize its share of a given total defense budget. New weapon concepts became a means of getting dollars. As long as this incentive prevails, it is difficult for military users to take a critical view of individual systems. Indeed, an opposite view is taken, and exaggerated claims of system effectiveness and optimistic cost estimates pervade the "data base" of a military service. Field experimentation, which is critical in its nature, is not a welcome activity in this kind of setting.[5]

Inertia is often responsible for not exploiting existing statistical sources or collection mechanisms where either relatively small modifications in the statistical program or extra effort would yield very large information payoffs. For example, by modifying business tax forms (through eliminating requests for certain kinds of information – like advertising expenditure) and requesting other kinds of information (e.g., total wages paid, as contrasted with executive salaries) it would be possible to obtain value added data, by industry and identified by major factor payments, for the entire economy. Such information could serve greatly to improve the quality of the National Income and Product Accounts, which are currently very laboriously built up piecemeal (and by a rather large staff) by the Office of Business Economics. But the Internal Revenue Service is reluctant to make what seems to it a "drastic"

---

5 For a further discussion of the status of field experimentation in the U.S. Defense Establishment see J. A. Stockfisch "Operational Testing," *Military Review* (May, 1971), pp. 66-82.

change of business tax forms, the design of which is determined by a committee on which is represented the various internal power blocs that comprise the Service.

A badly needed type of information necessary to understand the workings of the tax system is how taxpayers' income and taxable income behave through time. Existing data records show how the system behaves each year. Inferences from these data are apt to exaggerate, therefore, the proportion of individuals who are *consistently* in very low and very high income brackets. Information could be gathered that would portray behavior through time of a sample of individuals, and by means of such data the economic effects of the tax system and many of its complex features could be better understood. But it is laborious and costly to produce this kind of data — as contrasted with annual cross-section treatment — within the framework of a statistical program that is viewed by the Service to cost $10 million or so a year. The Service has no internal incentive to produce this information since its primary use would be for tax policy formulation as contrasted with administration of the existing system. Only if a higher authority, like the Office of the Secretary of the Treasury, directed it to be done would results be achieved. However, that higher Office has not pursued this matter, mainly due to other demands upon its energy.

Fabrication of data is widespread and achievable by a variety of subtle techniques. Military organizations have been known to exaggerate the capability of possible opponents and to understate friendly capability. One way to do this is to count only the equipment (e.g., tanks or aircraft) in friendly *combat organizations* and to compare that number with the other side's total equipment procurement, which also includes items in repair depots, those used for training, and stocks procured for combat consumption allowances.[6] Recently, the Senate Armed Services Committee noted that the U.S. Army's statements of rifle assets and requirements behaved in strange ways whereby the amount required was decreasing as the size of the Army increased during the early per-

---

6   For an account of one such example relating to the Royal Air Force's estimates of the German air order of battle, after the Battle of Britain, see R. F. Harrod, *The Prof* (London: Macmillan, 1959), pp. 3-5.

iod of the Vietnam buildup.[7]   One explanation of this behavior is that the Army might have been seeking to minimize its purchase of M16 rifles which the Army did not conceive and design, while it was trying to develop on a crash basis a newer and more exotic weapon of its own conception. Finally, modern cost-effectiveness studies spew out vast amounts of "numbers" by employing the technique of computer simulations. Frequently, the numerical inputs for these activities are either the "fudged" numbers generated by the bureaucratic process, or are derived *a priori* from engineering equations, many of which might be irrelevant to system effectiveness or, at best, related to effectiveness in an unknown way.

One of the discouraging implications of these points is that mere "analysis" of systems and programs is not adequate to assist rational decision-making. Policy-makers (and bureaus) may acquire analytical staffs, as was done extensively in the federal government during the 1960's as a result of adopting the Planning, Programming, and Budgeting System (PPBS). But the bureaus, by virtue of their "control" over the data available as "inputs" to the analytical studies, can greatly influence the "outputs" of the study process. Thus the managerial innovations instituted in the Defense Department were frustrated if not soundly defeated by the military departments they were imposed upon.

The process by which a bureau fabricates data, or avoids collecting it, can occur unconsciously and spontaneously. It is a consequence or by-product of trying, on a day-to-day basis, to counter the penetration of a bureau's affairs by "outsiders." One of the results of these poor information systems is that the senior officials of the bureaus themselves may not have adequate information to run their own organizations effectively, even though they may have a deep and sincere desire to do so.

Senior bureau officials are not happy about the situation. Bureau heads do want their organizations to be effective. To achieve this end, the workings of an organization must be visible to its leaders. But any workable auditing and inspection procedure that

---

7   U. S. Senate, Committee on Armed Services, "The Army's Rifle Procurement and Distribution Program" (Washington: Government Printing Office, May 31, 1967).

serves the bureau head can also serve the energetic staff of a superior headquarters, which in this case is a civilian secretariat and (in some instances) Congressional committees. To stave off penetration and possible detailed control by such outsiders, bureau heads must therefore pay a price. That price is the creation of information systems that generate information for advocacy and political purposes. There has been a great surge in cost-effectiveness studies and the development of computerized headquarters information systems, which, not incidentally, have greatly benefited the research and data processing communities.

The social value of much of this activity, however, is not clear. Its worth is particularly suspect as long as bureaus seek to avoid and prevent penetration by superior headquarters, because the basic data fed into the analytical models and information systems can be generated, doctored, and "fudged" to serve political and advocacy objectives.

Bureaus might thus be compelled to try to maintain two sets of information and communications systems: one system to deal with the external world as it is with regard to operations; the other system to serve its functioning in the budgeting/political process, which includes providing information that policy-makers like to hear. However, it is a rare organization that can pull off such a feat for an extended period of time. Usually, the outputs of dual information systems become mixed. Much relevant and real information is ignored; much propaganda and folklore come to be accepted as reality. Such duality provides the ingredients for occasional massive "intelligence failures." [8]

THE PROBLEM AND WHAT CAN
BE DONE ABOUT IT

It might be observed that bureaucratic behavior as we have described it afflicts the internal workings of all organizations, including private business firms. The point is correct. But there is a vital difference between the public, government bureaucracy on the one hand, and its private counterpart on the other hand. This

8   For a number of case studies of such intelligence failures, see Harold L. Wilensky, *Organizational Intelligence: Knowledge and Policy in Government and Industry* (New York: Basic Books, 1965).

difference centers around the way in which the two major classes of organizations are "financed."

The private business organization generally is financed by selling its output in the marketplace. In this setting, the consumer is free to take as little or as much as he wants at a per unit price that tends to converge toward production costs. Consumer demand thus places a constraint on the total "budget" available to the private business organization, or to entire industries comprising the private sector. If competition among producers prevails in the market, the consumer also has the option of choice. In this context, the internal bureaucratic pathology of a particular firm is of no concern to the general consumer. The firm's budget is constrained. Price and quality of the firm's output can be the consumer's sole focus.

With the government bureaucracy, however, financing is carried out through taxation or inflationary monetary techniques. Both financial devices are intimately dependent on the coercive power of the state. The "consumer-taxpayer" is caught up in the workings of a complex political-budgeting process, in which his preferences are only indirectly and imperfectly made felt and where they must compete with the preferences and aspirations of powerful producer groups, elected officials, and — finally — those of career bureaucrats. This difference in financing between the private and public bureaucracy, therefore, is sufficiently great so as to render the private one a "special" but not too interesting case.

It can be properly argued that the problem of the public bureaucracy is actually the problem of the democratic political process, including policy evaluation and policy making, public administration, and social conflict in its broadest sense. The point would be correct. But it should also be forcibly emphasized that this broader problem and the conflict it entails have a very high information content. And for many purposes, they can be fruitfully approached as information and statistical production problems.

Regardless of one's taste on how the subjects of politics, bureaucratic behavior, and related subjects are to be approached, the main force of this offering is to emphasize that the subject of government information systems, including the production and use of statistics, cannot be intelligently dealt with, let alone understood, if treated abstractly and hence devoid of an awareness of the complex interactions between producers and users of government statistics. These parties are also political "actors." An abstract approach to government statistics leads to platitudes or generalities that take the form of urging that "more" and "better" statistics be provided. Or it may be suggested that some "centralized" agency undertake the task of better "integrating" existing statistical programs, and laying down quality control standards. Yet if the bureaucratic animal is as hardy as it appears to be, and if the various self-serving private interest groups are as vigorous as they always have been, a centralized agency is unlikely to improve things much, and it is even possible that it might worsen them. The latter possibility is suggested by some of the consequences of the advent of the Programming, Planning, Budgeting System (PPBS) in the Defense Department during the 1960's.

This pessimistic picture suggests that the problems associated with statistical programs might not be coped with unless there is simultaneously more rationality, candor, openness, and skepticism in the political process itself. In their way, all parties — users and producers — are contributors to the present unhappy state of things. Indeed, a case can be made that the "bureaucrats," whom it is tempting to label as the "heavies" in the scenario, are products if not victims of the deeper and broader system. Society gets, in effect, the kind of bureaucratic behavior (and bureaucratic information systems) it demands and deserves.

Yet the information system, including the integrity and validity of the statistical system, is a good point upon which to focus critical (and constructive) scrutiny. And in this regard all users can play a key role. But not many do. For example, academic economists are extensive users of government produced statistics, particularly in the contemporary setting which places an emphasis upon mathematical economics and econometric techniques. The professional journals are full of papers presenting econometric findings. But few members of the profession probe behind the numbers for the purpose of gauging their quality, let alone to offer suggestions on how quality might be improved or to expose shoddy production.

Legislators and executive branch policy makers (and their

474

staffs) could and should devote energy to developing and voicing skepticism regarding any statistics that are presented to them. They should also insist, whenever it is feasible, upon purposeful program experimentation. In the process, all parties should give special attention to designing new institutional and, especially, associated incentives impacting on bureaucrats that operate in a healthy way. For example, in military affairs, there might be a hard requirement that claims of a need for high technical performance of new weapon systems be backed up by field trials that generate hard evidence, that validate the claim. Steps would also have to be taken, by way of establishing independent review boards, to monitor (not direct) such testing processes so as to be able to certify that the test was done in accordance with well-established standards governing the conduct of experiments.

Visiting boards could also be set up and encouraged to review critically, and in depth, the statistical production processes of other operating agencies, like the Internal Revenue Service, the Public Health Service, and so on. Some agencies do have "advisory boards" on statistical matters. But more often than not the individual members of these boards either represent special groups in a self-serving way, or give little time or energy to the effort, or both. Consequently, they are little more than a "rubber stamp" apparatus — a role generally pleasing to their bureau mentors.

These and other techniques for generating skepticism can go a long way toward improving the present situation. Another major source of improvement may spring from a recognition on the part of all parties that the present system's behavior is a creature of mutual self-serving on the part of the diverse interest groups and a large dose of "gamesmanship." To the extent that everyone comes to realize that this is the likely condition, then the parties who try to bluff and fabricate will know that others know the nature of their game. Such a mutual understanding might be both refreshing and healthful. And with the different attitudes, the process of ventilation could proceed expeditiously and fruitfully.

Chapter 10

COMMISSIONS ON STATISTICS: STATISTICS ON COMMISSIONS

By
Paul Feldman

COMMISSIONS ON STATISTICS: STATISTICS ON COMMISSIONS

TABLE OF CONTENTS

PRIOR COMMISSIONS AND
THEIR FINDINGS

General Summary

High level commissions on statistics established in the past have been of two general types:

1. "Technical" commissions or committees dealing with user interests.
2. "System overview" commissions dealing with producer interests.

"Technical" committees appear to have been more influential, i.e., what they have recommended be done has often come to pass. The recommendations of "system overview" commissions have varied widely but recommendations for organizational change have usually not been followed.

"System overview" commissions have inquired into many issues but they have all directed their attention to questions of:

1. Centralization (the concentration of resources into "best" agencies).
2. Allocation of specific subject coverage among agencies.
3. Duplication as a major indicator of inefficiency and excessive burden. (Generally, commissions have concluded that duplications *which should be eliminated* are almost nonexistent.)

Commission reports usually conceded the integral relations between data gathering, public recognition of problems, and governmental attempts to solve the problems, but they never discussed the normative issue of what government *should* do in its programs and, therefore did not derive proposals for what statistical support should be provided.

CHRONOLOGICAL REVIEW OF
COMMISSIONS ON STATISTICS

January 1844

The House of Representatives appointed a select committee (under Zadock Pratt) to "inquire into the expediency of establishing a Bureau of Statistics and Commerce in connection with the Secretary of the Treasury."

Pratt produced three reports between March 1844 and February 1845, all recommending establishment of such an agency as a subsidiary of an operating department. Congress responded only to the first report by authorizing the Secretary of the Treasury to hire three clerks. The Secretary did so but complained of the inadequacy of the authorization and, after several years, the department stopped doing the authorized work.

1866

An act was passed creating a Bureau of Statistics (BoS) in the Treasury; whether Congress was finally responding to Pratt's recommendations or to new post-war problems isn't clear — probably the latter.

1877

Because of criticism of the methods employed by the Bureau of Statistics and of the reported results of its surveys, Treasury Secretary John Sherman appointed a commission to investigate the BoS system of collecting, preparing, collating, and publishing statistics and to ascertain whether any duplications existed.

The commission concluded:

1. The BoS was doing its job as well as it could be done.
2. Its duties could not be enlarged in a satisfactory way without great and perhaps revolutionary changes in legislation respecting the duties of the executive departments.
3. Further centralization would not help.

1903

The BoS was transferred to the newly created Department of Commerce and Labor. The Secretary immediately appointed a commission to consider reorganization of statistical work of the department.

The commission recommended:

1. Consolidation of the BoS and the recently created Bureau

of Manufactures.

2. Organization of the consolidated agency in three divisions.

The recommendations were not carried out.

1907

The new Secretary of Commerce and Labor set up another commission to study the organization of the statistical activities of the department.

In 1908 they recommended:

1. The Bureau of Statistics and the Bureau of the Census *should not* be consolidated.
2. The Bureau of Statistics and the Bureau of Manufactures *should* be consolidated, i.e., they repeated the recommendations of the 1903 Commission.
3. Organization of the consolidated Bureau into divisions.
4. Establishment of an interdepartmental committee with a representative from each executive department and independent government agency.

Recommendations (1) and (4) were followed, although the interdepartmental committee never did anything.

1918

In 1918 the Central Bureau of Planning and Statistics was established. It evolved from work done by the War Industries Board and it performed, among other tasks, all work now handled by the Statistical Policy and Management Information Systems Division (SPMISD) in the Office of Management and Budget (OMB). In particular, it reviewed and consolidated forms, built up an index of all data collections by the government, promoted standardized classification, published the "Weekly Statistical News," and, after the war, examined the functions of the war agencies to determine which should be permanently continued. The functions of the Central Bureau were taken over by the Bureau of Efficiency in 1919 when that agency was directed by Congress to investigate:

1. duplication of statistical work
2. the scope and character of statistics needed by government, and

3. methods of collecting, compiling, and presenting statistical information employed by departments and independent agencies.

1922

In 1922 the Bureau of Efficiency issued a report which described the operation of the statistical system. The report did *not* discuss what is needed by government nor methods employed, but it did conclude that operations should be reorganized to concentrate, as far as possible, collection, compilation, and dissemination of all nonadministrative statistics in a central bureau because:

1. user access was difficult,
2. uncoordinated surveys were burdensome to respondents, and
3. cost was excessive.

Among the 33 recommendations offered were two recommendations to terminate publications of the Department of Commerce because they duplicated work done elsewhere. The report noted in small print at the bottom of the page that both of those publications had already been *temporarily* suspended, and recommended simply to make the suspension permanent. The organizational recommendations were very detailed (to the point of being trivial), but they were not apparently based on an explicit model of the relation between organization and system output, and they were not followed even in major outline. With no action on the report, the coordinating activity died.

1931

In 1931, acting "by direction of the President," the Director of the Bureau of the Budget set up the Federal Statistics Board in the Budget Bureau. Members of the Board were drawn from other departments but Board work was incidental to their regular duties. The Board gathered material for preparation of a subject index of primary statistical activities and for a study of methods, costs, and personnel. It also investigated several duplications and "studied" problems of several agencies. Apparently, however, the Board actually *did* nothing and passed out of existence with creation of the Central Statistical Board in 1933.

1933

In 1933 the American Statistical Association and the Social Science Research Council combined to form two committees:

1. The Committee on Government Statistics and Information Services (COGSIS) to advise government on organizational matters.
2. The Advisory Committee to the Secretary of Labor (ACSL) to advise on methods, adequacy, and usefulness of the Bureau of Labor Statistics.

The stated reasons for the establishment of COGSIS were:

1. A desire for improvement in the statistical program, and
2. funding of the government's statistical program appeared to be threatened under the economy program.

Although COGSIS was not organized until mid-June 1933, it was able to recommend establishment of a Central Statistical Board by early July 1933, and in late July, the Board was established by Executive Order. The report notes that COGSIS sought to evaluate: "statistical services as it found them without evaluating in any way the appropriateness of government activities, *per se* in the various fields under observation."

The final recommendations of COGSIS were to maintain decentralization, and to expand the Central Statistical Board as a coordinator with only the power to advise, not to command agencies to act. The report also notes that attainment of the ends (of coordination): "will require watchfulness by the friends of the Board both without and within the government."

Although the Central Statistical Board was converted in 1940 into the Division of Statistical Standards (now SPMISD) in the Budget Bureau (now OMB), the conversion involved no major change in function or powers.

COGSIS and the Advisory Committee to the Secretary of Labor operated as working advisory groups with regard to technical matters of production, and as representatives of user desires for data. The committee members and their staff became closely involved with agencies, studied their programs and produced interim working papers which forwarded recommendations on staffing, methodology, and expansion. These appeared long before the COGSIS final report which dealt only with organization. Many detailed technical recommendations were implemented immediately, under the watchful eyes of cognizant committee members, and, in several cases, COGSIS staff were hired directly by the agencies involved to follow through on their recommendations.

1942

The Federal Reports Act of 1942, passed without an antecedent commission, apparently reflected concern over the respondent burden which had increased with the advent of war. It gave to the Division of Statistical Standards four powers:

1. to forbid use of forms,
2. to designate a single agency to perform specific work,
3. to forbid agencies to collect "unnecessary" information (the definition of unnecessary was left to the BoB), and
4. to force agencies to divulge information they had gathered to other agencies.

1948

As part of the overall work of the first Hoover Commission, the National Bureau of Economic Research was asked to produce a report on the statistical system of the federal government. In the report, written by F. C. Mills and Clarence Long, no indication is given of the existence of any major concern deserving a special study. The authors surveyed the organization of government activities, found some problems, and proposed remedies. In describing the problems, the report noted their existence but did not suggest that they were particularly severe, that they represented a crisis in any way, or indeed that anyone should ever expect perfection. Problems noted were:

1. Overlapping jurisdictions of *agencies—not statistics.*
2. Lack of balance in resource allocation.
3. Lack of comparability of data from different sources.
4. Variation in quality.
5. Poor means of access by users (no catalog was maintained).

486

6. Gaps in coverage of some areas.
7. Inadequate staff quality and/or level.
8. Methodological blunders.
9. "Excessive" burdens imposed on respondents.
10. Publication, timing, and adequacy shortcomings.

In other words, as outsiders looking in, Mills and Long found that "the system" could be improved.

Apart from the above, the authors noted two major concerns:

1. The difficulty of expanding interagency transfers prevented the most efficient use of quality personnel and processing facilities.
2. Budgeting practices in the executive agencies, the BoB, and the Congress were uncoordinated and prevented the rational allocation of resources to statistical programs. (Nine appropriation subcommittees in each House of Congress passed on various items in the statistical budget — and still do. Presently, 26 different examiners in OMB review 25 major statistical programs.)

Among other Mills-Long *recommendations* were:

1. Centralize public use statistics in a single agency.
2. Make the Division of Statistical Standards an independent office in the Executive Office and expand its responsibilities to cover:
   a. efficiency of operations,
   b. coordination of focal agency activities, and
   c. assignment of priorities among statistical activities in the budget.
3. Create a catalog.
4. Expand interagency service for reimbursement.
5. Improved budgeting procedures in BoB and have BoB testify in Congress.

Minor recommendations dealt with other problems cited and included these:

1. Census should maintain a central mailing list for all agencies.
2. Respondents should be consulted more intensively to reduce the reporting burden.

487

3. Civil Service rules should be changed to allow for better quality staff.

An internal Bureau of the Budget (BoB) discussion of the Mills-Long Report appeared in 1955 detailing a number of real difficulties which would be encountered if centralization were attempted. The paper pointed out some inconsistency in the recommendations, noted that some recommended practices had been in operation since before the report, and noted cases in which the actions finally taken were opposite to the recommendations.

Generally, the Mills-Long Report was ineffective. It was written before the Hoover Commission made its recommendations on executive organization, and it didn't dovetail completely with those recommendations.

Notable *non*-actions were:

1. Centralization of public use statistics in a single agency.
2. Revision of budget procedures.

Notable actions (*not* necessarily a direct result of the report) were:

1. Special analyses of the statistical budget were started.

2. The Division of Statistical Standards was given greater authority in the Budget and Accounting Procedures Act of 1950 to develop programs and issue orders for improving statistical activities in the executive branch.

Despite its greater authority, the division staff was cut from 60 in 1948 to fewer than 40 immediately after the Korean War, and has continued at about that level up to the present. With unchanged responsibilities and reduced manpower, the staff has simply been spread thinner in performing its assigned tasks.

1966

In 1966 the Task Force on the Storage of and Access to Government Statistics (Kaysen Committee) was established by the Director of the Bureau of the Budget. This task force was asked to consider measures to improve storage of and access to U.S. government statistics. The task force concluded that it could only address the question in the context of the organization of the federal statistical system.

The task force concluded that the system was too decentralized. These are some of the consequences (which continue today):

1. Excessive time lags exist between collection and publication.
2. Micro-data are suppressed.
3. Confidentiality rules vary.
4. Duplications exist.
5. Data are not used as fully as they might be.
6. Production is inefficient.

To remedy these problems, the task force recommended that centralization of non-administrative statistics be set as a long-term goal, and that a National Data Center be established as a first step toward that goal to store and make available data collected by the government.

The report dealt also with the organizational relationship of the Data Center and existing agencies, recommending that the Data Center be placed in a newly created office in the Executive Office of the President (outside of the Budget Bureau). The director of the office should be known as Director of the Federal Statistical System, and also under his control would be the statistical standards group from the Budget Bureau, and the Bureau of the Census.

As an annex to the report, the task force noted that considerable anxiety had developed over invasions of privacy which might result from establishment of a large-scale, centralized data bank storing micro-data. While not proposing any guidelines to allay the anxiety, the report stated: "The question of the proper or improper use of information by different agencies is indeed a ticklish one, and procedures should be developed by both the executive branch and the legislative branch which will protect confidentiality and insure the privacy of the individual."

None of the recommendations of the task force have been implemented to date.

Four other commissions worthy of note were established in the late 1950's and early 1960's. They were concerned with technical aspects of statistics covering:

1. National Accounts (Goldsmith Committee, 1956)
2. Prices (Stigler Committee, 1959)
3. Employment and Unemployment (Gordon Committee, 1961)
4. Balance of Payments (Bernstein Committee, 1963)

These four committees made highly detailed recommendations for changes in definitions and sample characteristics, coverage of new subjects, and publication timing. They eschewed all questions of the organization of statistical agencies and of the allocation of effort between agencies. The general method of procedure was for the committee to solicit suggestions for improvement from producing agencies and to support those recommendations which appeared important and feasible of implementation.

Judged in relation to the "organization" commissions, these technical committees were resoundingly successful. The recommendations that were not followed apparently were viewed as being excessively "risky" by the agencies involved — they called for substituting an untried method for one which was well understood — or depended on a major increase in funding which was not forthcoming. At a much cruder level of generalization, it appears that when recommendations were made for widespread methodological applications, such as "make greater use of probability sampling," they received less attention than when specific applications were suggested.

INTERPRETATION OF THE HISTORY OF PRIOR COMMISSIONS

Observation No. I

Something about statistics is bothersome. Says Julius Parmelee: "To grumble is one of the inalienable rights of a free people; and the American people have exercised their right to the full. To grumble over government statistics has been a favorite occupation since the First Census, and one indulged in by all classes of people."[1]

---

1 Julius Parmelee, "The Statistical Work of the Federal Government — II," *Yale Review,* February 1911, p. 384.

490

Since Parmelee, commission after commission has worried over statistics and tried to improve them by changing the way producers are organized.

Two sources of the grumbling and worry can be distinguished:

a. Poor technical performance, i.e., the quality of measurement is less than what could be achieved for the same expenditure.
b. Lack of usefulness of statistics produced, i.e., data collected are irrelevant to the problem under consideration so that the most precise measurement imaginable can give little help in solving the problem.

HYPOTHESIS

It is the second item which is the greatest source of anguish.

EVIDENCE

a. Despite the fact that potential improvements in statistics can always be identified, it is commonly acknowledged that the quality of American government statistics is the highest to be found anywhere in the world. Innovations in methodology and processing are adopted without unreasonable lags, and are occasionally developed by government statistical services.
b. A complaint commonly heard, but heard particularly frequently when analysts attempt to evaluate government programs, is that "the data needed for evaluation don't exist." Evaluation of government programs is a constant activity but the emphasis placed upon it is increased greatly in periods of budget stringency. The establishment of commissions on statistics in this century — in 1919, 1933, 1948, 1970 — coincides with periods of budget *reduction*. At such a time the problem perceived by men in government is to cut out undesirable programs, and naturally they desire proof of undesirability. "Proof" requires specification of a welfare model which has always been lacking. Although the model we lack is one which indicates what measurements are to be made, analysts often thrust off that problem by claiming

491

that it is the data which are lacking, and the fault is thereby laid at the door of the government's statistical system.

c. Current pressure for creation of large-scale data banks and for construction of social indicators is a source of some interest in this commission. Both are expressions of interest in having data available to solve *unspecified* problems. Data are everywhere but available data are unusable. Data bankers apparently think that the problem is one of availability but when forced to it, they cannot say what data should be considered "currency" to be stored in the "bank." Those who advocate construction of a set of social indicators seem to think that the problem is mostly a matter of presentation of already available data. In any event, they are unable to say what should be presented.

Observation No. 2.

Organization has fascinated every commission in the past. Recommendations have ranged from shifting to extreme centralization to maintenance of the status quo. Maintainers have been "successful" in that their recommendations have been followed. Reorganizers have been remarkably unsuccessful. Despite the fact that it has been the subject of recommendations, there have been precious few attempts to establish a relation between organization and either the utility of output or the efficiency of production.

HYPOTHESIS

Concentration on organization arises more from aesthetic reasons than from identifiable system failure. Order is a natural goal of the human intellect and a decentralized system is "disorderly" to the casual observer. The poor quality output of some agencies offends the individual who feels he could improve quality at little or no increase in cost.

EVIDENCE

Complaints about the statistical output of offending agencies usually come from statisticians rather than from users. Examples most frequently offered of the "bad" outputs of the decentralized system are the statistics produced by regulatory agencies and the nonspecialized statistical agencies. Potential cost savings are minuscule in the overall picture and in reality have never been identified. The relation between statistics produced by the agencies involved and the "quality of life," or the relation of the quality of those statistics and the quality of decisions of government is undemonstrated and perhaps undemonstrable.

Observation No. 3

Commissions tend to sub-optimize. They refuse (for understandable reasons, perhaps) to deal with the hard problem of defining what government should or should not be doing — without which it is impossible to determine what data are "needed," how much expenditure for statistical support is warranted, and/or which user desires should be satisfied.

HYPOTHESIS

Concern over the statistical operations of the government relates to problems which are greater in import than technical shortcomings of the data themselves.

EVIDENCE

a. Collection of data is a precursor of programs involving control of the described activity. For example, in 1839 the Patent Office was directed to collect seeds and statistics, and that activity eventually was separated out to become the Department of Agriculture. Similarly, the Forest Service began as a statistical collection service, as did the Interstate Commerce Commission and a number of other agencies now functioning as governmental units. In discussions with individuals in and out of government, we encountered many who acknowledged that opponents of greater government expansion often use limitation of statistical collection to limit expansion of the government itself. Thus, statistical operations cannot be judged as a purely technical matter; the problems of statistics are a reflection of the problem of determining what government should do.

b. Very few recommendations are ever made to eliminate

493

series — to do so would require "proof" that they are *not* in the national interest. Proof requires understanding of *what is* the national interest — a hard question as yet not addressed by commissions on statistics.

Observation No. 4

Organizational actions taken by Congress or the Executive Branch are not related to commission findings. Political decision makers respond to problems of the moment on an *ad hoc* basis.

HYPOTHESIS

If there is a problem calling for creation of a commission, the solution is recognized when the commission begins rather than when it presents its findings. If there is a commission without a problem, no action will be taken.

EVIDENCE

"System overview" commissions and the actions taken on their reports are listed below.

COMMISSION

1844-45	Pratt Commission	No Action
1877	Sherman Commission	No Change Proposed
1903	Commerce and Labor Commission	NoAction
1907-08	Commerce and Labor Commission	No Action
1919-22	Bureau of Efficiency	No Action
1933-35	COGSIS	July 27, 1933
	(Set up in June: recommendation July 5, 1933)	CSB established
1948	Mills-Long	No Action
1970	Wallis Commission	

494

Notable actions taken are listed below.

Year	Cause	Action
1866	Post-war	Bureau of Statistics
1918	Post-war	Central Bureau of Planning and Statistics
1921	Depression	Budget and Accounting Act of 1921
1931	Depression	Federal Statistics Board
1933	Depression (COGSIS)	Central Statistical Board
1942	War	Federal Reports Act
1950	Depression-War (Hoover Commission)	Budget and Accounting Procedures Act

Of the actions taken, two may have been in response to commission recommendations (1933 and 1950). If the establishment of the Central Statistical Board was in response to the COGSIS recommendation, it would set speed records for "analysis" by a commission, and response by the government. It seems more likely that the action was prepared well before COGSIS was formally under way. The Budget and Accounting Procedures Act of 1950 may have been taken up in response to Hoover Commission recommendations, but the act certainly bore no resemblance to the Mills-Long report. The other actions listed may have drawn on the work of prior commissions, but clearly some "crisis" was necessary to provide the impetus for action.

CHAPTER 11

STATISTICS IN LEGAL SETTINGS IN FEDERAL AGENCIES

By

Herbert Solomon

STATISTICS IN
LEGAL
SETTINGS
IN
FEDERAL
AGENCIES

TABLE OF CONTENTS

INTRODUCTION

The community in which our federal government operates is the product of a modern and rich technology, and it is becoming more varied in its life styles. The growing impact of science and technology on society has been recognized in many recent papers and books. Two government sponsored studies [1] discuss some of these changes and urge increasing use of the social and the behavioral sciences in professional activities such as the law.

Our society is becoming attuned to more sophisticated ways of looking at issues that arise in the relations between the federal government, state and local governments, corporations, and individuals. This imposes fresh responsibility on attorneys in federal government agencies. Moreover, the increasing diversity and complexity of public issues yield new controversies for attorneys in government, and the swift pace of our daily life brings them before federal lawyers more quickly.

Most attorneys, whether in government or not, have had a

---

1 *Knowledge into Action: Improving the Nation's Use of the Social Sciences.* National Science Foundation, Special Committee on the Social Sciences, Washington, D.C.: U.S. Government Printing Office, 1969.
The Behavioral and Social Sciences: Outlook and Needs, Chapter 11, A report by the Behavioral and Social Sciences Survey Committee under the auspices

traditional education that emphasized legal doctrine and in no way prepared lawyers to understand or handle the methodology of other disciplines. The flexibility that did exist was within a framework of classical subjects in law. Most law schools in this country do not differ much in their requirements, and they tend to yield slowly to new disciplines or interdisciplinary work in their curricula. Engineering schools, schools of education, and even medical schools have been much more receptive, not only allowing but also encouraging other disciplines in their programs.

Legal education, to be sure, is changing, although mainly in the leading schools. In the more prominent law schools, subjects in economics, sociology, and anthropology have appeared, and faculty have been added whose main specialty is in one of these disciplines. Various governmental and professional society devices have aided the process of change. The American Bar Association has a Committee on Law and Technology that encourages this kind of activity, and that association also sponsors the *Jurimetrics Journal,* which provides a forum for discussion and research in these subjects. The National Science Foundation has been helpful through its sponsorship of the Institute for Social Science Methodology in Legal Education (SMILE) at the University of Denver. It has also sponsored summer institutes for law librarians on the social, behavioral, and natural sciences.

The use of social science methodology in legal research requires a good understanding of statistics, yet training in this subject does not seem to have received the same encouragement by government and the American Bar Association. Moreover, the notion of appointing a statistician to a law faculty has not yet permeated those strongholds, even though statisticians are now tolerated and even welcomed on faculties in the other professional schools. Another factor that may inhibit the use of statistics in legal research or the appointment of statisticians to law faculties is that the leading scholars in the field have not yet given their approval to the incorporation of this subject matter in their professional work.

Thus we find lawyers in the federal agencies running into issues and problems for which they have received no training at all. This

(Footnote 1 continued)
of the Committee on Science and Public Policy, the Committee on Problems and Policy, National Academy of Sciences, Social Science Research Council, Englewood Cliffs, New Jersey: Prentice-Hall, Inc., 1969.

includes training in the general sense, namely, some prior experience or some knowledge of specialties that can be helpful in law in addition to specific training in a formal subject matter. What is even worse, lawyers do not recognize that a number of issues are statistical or probabilistic in nature. Therefore they run the risk of not doing as good a job as could have been done or of running head on, in an adversary proceeding, into an opponent who has successfully recognized that an issue at hand does have such elements.

Law school curricula will change slowly in this direction unless the case for this kind of thinking and training is presented with some urgency. If the federal agencies wish a supply of lawyers acquainted with such matters, they must take the lead in programs that provide some updating in law school curricula to include work in statistics and probability for a number of students achieving a law degree. Beginning as far back as the Morrill Act of the 1860's, which provided training for those in agriculture and the mechanic arts, the federal government has stimulated changes in college curricula in other fields.

RECENT PERTINENCY OF STATISTICS

One may ask why this issue seems to be so pertinent at this time. One factor is that statistics is a rather modern discipline. In fact, it originated and developed almost wholly within the 20th century. This suggests one reason why government attorneys as well as others could go for a long time without recourse to this knowledge. In addition, there is always a natural time lag between the development of a discipline and its widespread acceptance.

The same case cannot be made for knowledge of probability, which is older than statistical theory. In fact, we find a flourishing school of probabilists in the late 18th and early 19th centuries, some of whose main efforts were devoted to issues in the legal process. These scholars contributed a number of papers on this subject, and in the period 1835 - 1845 two important books [2] appeared.

---

2   *Recherches sur la Probabilite des Jugements en Matiere Criminelle et en Matiere Civile,* S.D. Poisson, Bachelier, Paris Imprimeur Libraire, 1837. *Exposition de la Theorie des Chances et des Probabilities,* A. A. Cournot, Paris: Librairie de L. Hachette, 1834.

Both books introduce the reader to the calculus of probabilities and give an exposition of its application to questions arising in judgments and decisions made in the civil and criminal law. Questions of jury size, credibility of jurors, and the impact of these factors on judicial decisions are discussed in great detail. It is odd that a period of more than one hundred years ensued in which no attention was paid to these efforts, and that we find only recently that some of these questions are with us again for solution. For example, the U.S. Supreme Court decision on June 22, 1970 that each state can determine the size of the jury in a criminal trial should cause some investigations into that subject matter. There are also a number of current issues related to discrimination in the selection of jurors in which statistical and probabilistic thinking is important in determining whether discrimination exists. This is true in challenges for cause, in peremptory challenges, and in the preparation of lists of jurors.

The use of probability theory has also been employed dramatically in two recent decisions, the Sneed case [3] in New Mexico in 1966, and the Collins case[4] in California in 1968. The Supreme Court in each state ruled that the probability model employed by the prosecutor either had been developed incorrectly or permitted other interpretations which led to reasonable doubt. In the former case, the court overturned a conviction of murder, and in the latter a conviction of second-degree robbery because no other substantive evidence remained. These recent decisions have led to a spate of articles on "trial by mathematics" in several law review journals and other legal journals. In fact, of late there has been an outcry by legal scholars that an unhappy marriage has occurred between mathematics and law, for which an immediate divorce should be granted. Even here a fundamental mistake is made by lawyers who equate mathematics and mathematical thinking with statistical and probabilistic thinking. By suggesting mathematics and law as estranged partners, a disservice is rendered because this is not the issue at all.

---

[3] Supreme Court of New Mexico: *State of New Mexico v. Joe E. Sneed,* No. 7996, May 31, 1966.

[4] California Supreme Court: in the case of *People v. Malcolm Ricardo Collins,* Crime No. 11176, March 11, 1968.

504

Naturally no one, especially those in statistics and probability, is arguing that any judicial judgment or legal decision should be rendered by mathematical formula. Those who claim that this is the wish of mathematicians are as much in error as those who do not see the usefulness of statistical thinking in some legal contexts. What is at issue here is an understanding of when statistical and probabilistic thinking is either central or helpful to the resolution of an issue before a regulatory agency or a judicial body. This may not occur too often but it is wasteful and wrong to ignore it when it does apply. Moreover, this is not a static situation, and one could venture to say that it will increase as engineering technology increases and measurement in the social and behavioral sciences develops new precision. For example, it would have been impossible to consider exclusion in paternity cases before a court until the genetic and probabilistic model for blood group factors had been worked out. Right now, even though in non-exclusion situations it is possible to evaluate probabilities of paternity for the putative father, such evidence is usually not admissible because it is considered prejudicial to a judge or a jury because of its complexity. Even this may change as a good level of statistical and probabilistic know-how invades the judicial arena.

OCCURRENCE OF STATISTICS IN FEDERAL LAWS

We may, then, ask ourselves where attorneys in government should be primed to consider the uses of statistical and probabilistic thinking. There is a wide spectrum of possibilities in the legal work of federal agencies. For example, it is apparent that such thinking is consonant in a number of cases in rate-making, trademark registration, and consumer opinions before regulatory agencies, and that issues brought before such bodies would be and are contested through the use of statistical procedures. It should be apparent that the Internal Revenue Service, in challenging some returns, would have to provide a reconstruction of income and that in such cases statistical and probabilistic thinking could be necessary. It is apparent that in a number of criminal cases faced by attorneys in the Department of Justice, the evaluation of evidence would in a number of situations require statistical and probabilistic thinking. This is especially true because of the large num-

505

ber of non-violent felony cases that are social or political in nature, e.g., violations of our dangerous drug and narcotics law. Statistical thinking is not only appropriate in some cases in connection with the evaluation of evidence, but it also looms in connection with sentencing after conviction. This would be the situation if the judge in meting out a sentence considered the amount of contraband seized as a factor and decided the amount was excessive. Would government chemists have to examine every shred of evidence to ascertain the exact amount, or would the judge accept an estimate based on a sampling of the seized materials?

Thus, while litigation provides one broad arena in which statistics is becoming important, there are other areas in which statistical knowledge would be useful to federal lawyers. Legislative drafting is such an area. In proposed legislation of traffic regulations, in various aspects of commercial law, in the criminal law in connection with gaming statutes, and in legislation on the establishment of venire for juries — in all these, a knowledge of statistics would be very useful.

Negotiation is another area in which statistical knowledge would be useful. For most lawyers, more time is spent in negotiation than in trial. Knowledge of statistics would be very useful in the preparation of contracts so that subsequent litigation would be avoided or minimized. In some contracts a clause could be inserted relating to the use of a sample survey and its data to settle a difference, or in other cases the use of some experimental data and its analysis could be formalized as a way of resolving conflict. For example, in some Department of Defense contracts, the amount payable is associated with the satisfying of statistical criteria that measure the performance of a weapons system.

The foregoing discussion has not attempted to delimit the ways in which federal agencies may engage in problem areas that subsume statistical thinking. In this way it is incomplete. Moreover, it should not convey the thought that all federal agencies are only just beginning to apply statistics in legal settings. In the next section there is a brief history and a listing of survey data as evidence that should dispel that idea. However, it should be clear that we are entering an era in which such statistical activity will multiply many fold, both in number of cases and types of situations. This has strong implications for the kind of federal attorney the government will seek in the future.

BRIEF HISTORY OF SURVEY DATA AS EVIDENCE

It is possible to get some idea of how survey evidence is received in legal settings by examining the records where this issue has been in contention. In the literature one finds only those cases where one of the contestants has brought either the acceptance or denial of sample survey data as evidence to a higher authority for an appellate-type hearing or review. This provides a limited but still illuminating way of viewing what has been going on in this subject. Thus, it is only by inference that one can gain some knowledge of the status of sample survey evidence in litigation.

The three tables that follow give a brief account of activity by providing decisions on admissibility of sample survey data as evidence. In Table 1, this is presented for civil cases and is categorized by year and by legal setting. The legal setting is divided into federal court, state court, and federal regulatory agencies. Table 2 gives the same information in condensed form by depicting activity over five-year periods. Table 3 is very brief and demonstrates the status of sample survey evidence in criminal cases.

In Table 2, we list five-year periods beginning in 1925 and ending in 1969. There is little activity until 1950 – in fact, only twelve cases from 1928 on. However, in the period 1950-59, there is a peak of thirty-four cases and then lessening to twenty-one cases in 1955-59, fourteen cases in 1960-64, and only six in the period 1965-69.

Sample survey methodology did not develop until the early 1920's and so in the early days sample surveys were few in number. As a result, there are very few cases in which they are presented as evidence and are in contention. However, in the 1950's sample survey evidence seems to be presented many times and in fact receives some kind of appellate review fifty-four times in this ten-year period. Then we note in the decade of the 1960's only twenty cases in contention, suggesting that sample survey evidence is not as frequently in contention, although it is probably presented many more times than in the past. Thus, we probably have an increase in the number of sample surveys offered as evidence and a dramatic decrease in the number of times there is any contention about the methodology or the results. While we may expect these subjects to continue in contention, the number in any one year should be rather small. On the other hand, the number of times federal attorneys will have to evaluate sample survey data or call in experts to do this should increase many fold.

Sample Survey Data Accepted or Rejected as Evidence in Civil Cases by Legal Setting and by Year

Year	Decision	Federal Court	State Court	Regulatory Agency	Total	
1928	Accepted	0	0	0	0	1
	Rejected	1	0	0	1	
1929	A	1	0	0	1	1
	R	0	0	0	0	
1939	A	1	1	0	2	2
	R	0	0	0	0	
1940	A	0	1	1	2	
	R	0	0	0	0	
1943	A	0	0	0	0	1
	R	1	0	0	1	
1945	A	0	0	1	1	1
	R	0	0	0	0	
1947	A	1	0	0	1	1
	R	0	0	0	0	
1948	A	2	0	0	2	2
	R	0	0	0	0	
1949	A	1	0	0	1	1
	R	0	0	0	0	
1950	A	3	1	2	6	8
	R	2	0	0	2	
1951	A	3	1	1	5	5
	R	0	0	0	0	
1952	A	3	1	0	4	5
	R	0	1	0	1	
1953	A	5	2	1	8	9
	R	0	0	1	1	
1954	A	2	1	2	5	7
	R	1	0	1	2	
1955	A	2	1	2	5	7
	R	1	0	1	2	
1956	A	0	0	2	2	3
	R	1	0	0	1	
1957	A	1	0	0	1	2
	R	1	0	0	1	
1958	A	2	3	0	5	7
	R	0	1	1	2	
1959	A	1	0	1	2	2
	R	0	0	0	0	

1960	A	1	0	0	1	1
	R	0	0	0	0	
1961	A	3	0	0	3	4
	R	0	0	1	1	
1962	A	0	1	0	1	1
	R	0	0	0	0	
1963	A	2	11	1	4	6
	R	0	0	2	2	
1964	A	2	0	0	2	2
	R	0	0	0	0	
1965	A	1	0	0	1	2
	R	0	0	1	1	
1966	A	2	0	0	2	3
	R	0	0	1	1	
1967	A	0	0	1	1	1
	R	0	0	0	0	
1969	A	0	0	0	0	1
	R	1	0	0	1	

Sample Survey Data Accepted or Rejected as Evidence in Civil Cases by Legal Setting and by Year in Five-Year Intervals: 1925-1969

Years	Decision	Federal Court	State State Court	Regulatory Agency	Total	
1925-29	A	1	0	0	1	2
	R	1	0	0	1	
1930-34	A	0	0	0	0	0
	R	0	0	0	0	
1935-39	A	1	1	0	2	2
	R	0	0	0	0	
1940-44	A	0	1	1	2	3
	R	1	0	0	1	
1945-49	A	4	0	1	5	5
	R	0	0	0	0	
1950-54	A	16	6	6	28	34
	R	3	1	2	6	
1955-59	A	6	4	5	15	21
	R	3	1	2	6	
1960-64	A	8	2	1	11	14
	R	0	0	3	3	
1965-69	A	3	0	1	4	7
	R	1	0	2	3	

509

Sample Survey Data Accepted or Rejected as Evidence
In Criminal Cases by Legal Setting and by Year

Year	Decision	Federal Court	State Court	Total	
1950	A	0	0	0	
	R	1	0	1	1
1951	A	1	0	1	
	R	0	0	0	1
1953	A	0	0	0	
	R	0	1	1	1
1954	A	0	1	1	
	R	0	0	0	1
1969	A	0	0	0	
	R	1	0	1	1

STATISTICAL THINKING AND LAW

Despite the fact that there are any number of situations where statistics and probability are important or are at the core of legal issues, there is a major obstacle to the employment of statistical and probabilistic thinking by lawyers. It stems from the institutionalized manner in which their profession handles uncertainty. One may with interest note that the measurement of uncertainty is the bread and butter of statisticians and probabilists, as well as the central theme in law. Attorneys and statisticians are both concerned with decisions or judgments made in the face of uncertainty. This may be one reason why statistics has found a more comfortable haven in other professional schools such as engineering, education, and medicine. The backbone of thinking and methodology in those areas does not depend as much on uncertainty as it does in the law. Perhaps this lack of competition made it easier for those schools to accept statisticians as companions or at least aides in the development of their subject matter.

As in any other two disciplines that may merge, each, of course, must learn from the other. One of the themes or topics common to statistician and lawyer is the notion of variability. A lawyer is usually operating implicitly with notions of variability. The statistician, on the other hand, is one who considers how to measure variability in some quantitative way; in fact, in a way that is not only quantitative but which also produces some meaning in an operational context. In effect, the statistician, in measuring variability, tries to construct a yardstick that can be applied in the particular situation from whence the variability derives. The application of this yardstick then suggests whether the evidence at hand is anomalous or is within some acceptable norms.

Much of what lawyers do in the measurement of evidence has a great deal to do with the notion of variability. There are a few occasions when variability should be taken into account in some explicit way, and in fact, the only possible enlightenment for these situations is where this can be and is done. For these situations, knowledge of some statistical thinking and statistical technique is essential. The lawyer himself need not be an expert in these matters, but recognition of these situations is paramount. Thus, for example, in many legal situations we note the use of data from sample surveys. (Below we will discuss an actual sample survey data situation in a courtroom context to highlight some interesting points.) In each such setting, an estimate of interest to both parties is made from a sample culled from a universe in a very special probabilistic way. It is the design of the sample survey that permits one not only to provide estimates of interest, but also to measure the variability or precision of these estimates. What is of importance to us in this exposition is how the measurement of precision is accepted and employed in a legal context.

There is another way in which data can arise and be used as evidence; that is, it does not have to arise from a sample survey. In this situation, data has been observed for one reason or another not related to the legal issue that has now made it a contender for evidence. Nevertheless, it is important to analyze it so as to gather some idea as to what has been going on in the issue to be resolved. For example, the data could have been collected in connection with some engineering operation and thus be available because some issues have arisen in connection with the situation. These circumstances occur less frequently than situations involving sample survey data, at least in a recorded sense. This may be due to the fact that quite often the data is not admissible as evidence or the data comes about in situations where resolution is attained before any formal judicial hearing takes place. There is no doubt, however, that in the future we will see more and more such observational data and supporting analysis admitted into evidence because it sheds light on the situation before the court. Later, we will list and discuss some situations that occurred in a legal context to bring out this particular point. Once again, not only will estimates be of interest, but the variability or precision of these estimates will be important in helping both parties arrive at a decision.

To this point, we have discussed notions of estimates and measuring the variability of such estimates. These estimates can be averages, and in most situations they are. On the other hand, they can be other indexes of interest. For example, they may be sample correlation coefficients or sample regression coefficients employed in prediction equations. Obviously, one would like to have some idea of the variability of measures of association or prediction statements. Thus, whatever the estimate, be it average, measure of association, prediction, or another pertinent index, it is the variability of such estimates that should play a large role in proceedings.

Perhaps it is best to digress here and note once again that nowhere in a law school curriculum is this subject matter considered. Thus, if one is to establish a course for students in law schools, it obviously should contain material usually found in statistics courses - various averages and how to compute them, various measures of association and how to compute them, and other indexes that arise that serve to represent data. This should be followed by a comprehensive examination of the variability of such estimates, how to compute them, and how to view their operational meaning. For example, the notion of confidence intervals for estimating true values of a population is learned by those in elementary statistics courses, and obviously plays an important role in legal situations where estimation and variability are at issue. Yet the law student after three or four years at law school is totally unaware of this concept or its meaning. This is in contrast to the other professional schools where statistics is a required course for a number of programs. A number of medical schools require statistics courses for their first-year students.

Much of what appears above can be enhanced and sharpened by looking at special cases and tying the thoughts made previously to actual situations. In addition, this permits us to learn from the past and be prepared for departures in future investigations. We have talked about those uncertainty situations in which variability can be measured and, in fact, where it is important that it be measured. This occurs in situations in which estimates have been made for presentation to a hearing board or court and some idea of the variability of these estimates is desired. The estimates come about in one of two principal ways: an estimate from data collected in connection with a sample survey design or an estimate that is made from data that have come about through observation.

In the final section of this report, three specific situations are discussed and analyzed. In one case, the contest between the retail

513

store chain and the City of Inglewood in California, the use of sample survey evidence is paramount and there are questions related to its admissibility and probative value. In two other cases, the Pacific Gas and Electric Company versus Sacramento Municipal Utilities District case, observed data became central to the questions before the California Public Utilities Commission. Once again questions of admissibility and probative value of this observed data as evidence came to the fore. In the second matter before the California Public Utilities Commission, we have once again the use of observed data, giving rise to questions of its admissibility and probative value in a situation where the statistical interpretation was essential for resolution of the case.

In the sample survey case we analyze, there is no doubt that it was recognized from the beginning as an issue. However, in the two observed data situations before the California Public Utilities Commission it was only after the cases were under way that the statistical aspects of the contest were recognized. The tradition in electric power data and telephone circuitry data suggested engineer expert witnesses. It did not seem likely at first to either side that statistical expertise was necessary or required. Lawyers with training in statistics (or training in the *uses* of statistics) could have recognized this at the outset. In each case a statistical analysis and subsequent interpretation of the data was fundamental.

At this point we must ask whether statistical interpretation of evidence will be allowed as a matter of course in a courtroom setting or in hearings before a regulatory agency. The author can vividly remember his statistical testimony based on experimental data being thrown out in a criminal misdemeanor case by the trial judge who considered it evasive and prejudicial. Yet it was permitted in evidence by several other trial judges in similar cases. Because of the use of general hearsay evidence in administrative agencies hearings, and because their conclusions cannot usually be so damaging to the civil rights of one individual, we can expect quite a bit of tolerance in allowing sample survey data and observed data as admissible evidence in hearings before regulatory agencies. Then, too, one can pay full attention to the probative value of the data. Yet even here there will be questions as to whether the evidence tends to confuse or prejudice a trier of fact in such a way as to outweigh the probative value for the case. This will certainly be more of an issue in civil law and criminal law contexts. A legal fraternity more sophisticated in the uses and understandings of statistics can minimize the situation when an analysis confuses or prejudices the judge or jurors.

JUDICIAL NOTICE OF STATISTICS

We are probably a long way from the time when judicial notice will be taken of the validity of statistical investigations and statistical interpretations from data. For example, there is no problem now in regarding blood tests as necessary to determine issues of degree of intoxication and non-paternity. On the other hand, the association between degrees of intoxication as measured by the weight of alcohol in the blood and its effect on visual acuity and driving behavior is not as deterministic as the courts make it out to be. There is no doubt that for any specific value of the weight of alcohol in the blood, say, for example, the usual standard of .15 of one percent, there will be variability in driving behavior over a population of individuals conditioned on the same .15 level. This is usually ignored, and in fact many state laws on driving under the influence are written so as to make it necessary for the defendant in what is usually a criminal misdemeanor case to prove beyond a reasonable doubt that he is not guilty. There is also no doubt that where non-paternity cannot be established, the probability that the putative father is the father can be computed exactly, yet this assertion is not permitted as evidence because of its prejudicial nature. This is probably more a phenomenon of ignorance of statistics and its usage.

Statistics seems to be in a state which has befallen many other disciplines now recognized in the courts. Medical experts and engineering experts were probably at one time in the same position in which statisticians tend to find themselves today. It would appear, however, that if we can extrapolate from what has happened in other disciplines, the time between regarding a statistician as someone who practices witchcraft to the time when his expertise will be regarded as meeting judicial notice may be short. If this is so, we will require a rapid readjustment in law school training and in fact training for those already practicing law.

We will probably see more of the following in the way judges or hearing examiners listen to statistical evidence. In a recent murder case, the judge made the following statement:

> "The tests by which the medical examiner sought to determine whether death was caused by some specific drug were novel and devised specifically for this case. This does not render the evidence inadmissible. Society need not tolerate homicide until there develops a body of medical literature about some particular lethal agent. The expert witnesses were examined and cross-examined at great length and the jury could either believe or doubt the prosecution's testimony as it chose."

It is obvious that this could be paraphrased in terms of statistical evidence, and the time span in which this will occur is not too large.

TRAINING IN STATISTICS FOR LAWYERS

A major purpose of this paper is to look into and discuss how federal lawyers can be educated in the employment of statistics where appropriate in their responsibilities. To accomplish this, it is obvious that training is required by those already discharging those responsibilities and also by those studying in law schools, whether they enter federal service or go into other kinds of practice. Mention was made early in this paper about the way in which the federal government has assisted training in areas considered to be in the national interest in the past. During World War II, training was provided in quality control of mass produced items. The Defense Department, the Atomic Energy Commission, the National Science Foundation, the Department of Agriculture, and other federal agencies, at one time or another, have had training programs so that the expertise they require will be made available.

It would seem that the Department of Justice is a likely agency to look into the training of lawyers in statistics and probability. The Law Enforcement and Assistance Administration, through its Institute for Law Enforcement and Criminal Justice, could be instrumental in accomplishing this. That agency is already engaged in making grants to universities. Certainly, under some of the responsibilities stated in its charter, LEAA could look into the financing of such training programs in coordination with the federal regulatory agencies. If this is not practical or possible, other devices can be sought through the Department of Justice and the federal regulatory agencies. It might be a good idea for the LEAA to develop a university research program in statistics in the law. This would also provide for training of practicing lawyers and law students.

Support to law schools, of course, does nothing for those who have already graduated and are in practice. However, there are established continuing legal education programs. The two largest are offered by the Practicing Law Institute of New York and the Joint Committee on Continuing Legal Education of the American Bar Association. These and similar organizations should be encouraged and supported to conduct short courses on statistics for lawyers.

SPECIAL AND SPECIFIC ILLUSTRATIONS OF STATISTICS IN LAW

There are a number of cases in the records in which sample survey data have been employed in legal situations. Let us now consider one that helps illustrate my fundamental points. In any such situation there are two questions to be resolved: 1) the admissibility of the sample data, and 2) the probative value of the sample data. In connection with admissibility, one runs into the problem of hearsay evidence. This has been treated in different ways and seems to be a function of the kind of legal setting in which the data is introduced. Because of their differing responsibilities, regulatory agencies, civil courts, and criminal courts would treat the admissibility question differently. One can easily say that this, of course, is true for other kinds of evidence produced in legal settings. Another question that arises in the presentation as evidence of data from sample surveys or observations is the best evidence rule. For example, the fact that sample survey data is available for evidence does not necessarily make it important for the case at hand unless, as is true in some situations, it is the best evidence available. Now let us look at the points we have mentioned in the following case reported in the literature.[5]

5   R. Clay Sprowls, "The Admissibility of Sample Data Into a Court of Law: A Case History", *UCLA Law Review,* 1962 (p.222).

SAMPLE SURVEY EVIDENCE IN A CIVIL COURT

A large retail chain sought a sales tax refund from the City of Inglewood in California. Sales made by its store in the city to residents living outside the city limits were not subject to a one-half of one percent sales tax. The store in question did a substantial volume of business with out-of-city residents. Taxes were paid on a quarterly basis. An error in measuring the extent of out-of-city sales resulted in an overpayment to the City which was discovered by the accounting department of the retail chain.

A pilot study based on sample days indicated an overpayment of $27,000. It was necessary to institute a court suit for its recovery. Obviously a complete audit may have mitigated the necessity for a court review. The store presented to a court as supporting evidence results from a probability sample that independently estimated the refund at approximately the same amount. This probability sample, based on a random selection of 33 out of 826 working days, yielded a ratio of out-of-city to total sales 36.69%. The sampling error in this case turned out to be approximately 1.5%. A 95% confidence interval for the true value that would result from a complete audit is therefore the interval 33.7% to 39.7%, that is, 36.69% plus or minus 3%. Translated into dollar amounts, these ratios become $28,250 plus or minus $4,200, or approximately $24,000 to $32,400. They tend to support the claim of a tax refund of $27,000. A $24,000 refund could have resolved the case for the retail chain might have accepted this to avoid further litigation and the City could show its taxpayers that it was offering a minimal amount.

Let us digress at this point to suggest that this case probably should not even have reached the courts if both sides were willing to accept the results of the sample survey, plus or minus a few percent, under the assumption that the probability sampling was done efficiently and was well managed. Naturally both sides should have complete access to the data and the procedures. Unfortunately, this access does not occur in a number of cases. Thus, in this case an amount around $27,000 could have been agreed upon without recourse to the courts. However, one must also recognize that the City would not like to be in a position of presenting such a substantial tax refund on the basis of a study prepared solely by the large retail chain itself. Moreover, the thought of doing this on the basis of less than 5% of the total number of business days might be unacceptable to the City. Because of these political considerations, and probably a prudent business practice of never returning funds paid into the City unless required to do so, we now find this particular situation in the courts. Now a judge must make the decision as to what amount is owed, if any, by the City to the retail chain.

The judge ruled against the introduction of these sampling results as evidence. It is significant but typical that the counsel for the City asked the statistician appearing as an expert witness for the retail chain only one question, namely: "Do you know exactly that the ratio of out-of-city to totals sales is 36.69%?" Obviously, the statistician had to reply that he did not. He did make the statement about the confidence interval, already calculated and mentioned above, for the true proportion of out-of-city to total sales. Here the question becomes not one of admissibility alone but also one of best evidence. (This is a point to consider here and as counterpoint to the next situation to be described below. Before we get to that, let us complete the story for this particular case.) The judge asked for a complete audit before he ruled on the case if the retail chain were willing to undergo this expense. Note that there are two particular points of interest here: 1) the complete population of data is available and accessible, and 2) the retail chain probably does have the resources to take a 100% sample or in other words look at the total universe of sales. The retail chain elected to do this, and the complete audit yielded a figure of $26,750, just a bit short of the claim of $27,000. Thus in this situation the court was in effect giving zero weight to an estimate, namely, the sample estimate of 36.69%, as a piece of evidence and giving total weight to the value achieved by a complete audit, the equivalent of 100% sampling. In other words, it was not allowing any statistical inference.

This may seem a bit demanding, and yet it does make some sense. An affluent company was required to spend its own funds to provide a value with zero variability, and in this case it was possible to do so. It would be an entirely different matter if funds were not available to the complainant to accomplish this, or if, as is frequently the case, it is impossible to reconstitute all the original observations. We will now look into an actual illustration where this situation occurs. It concerns a matter brought before a regulatory agency by a utility district against a public utility. The evidence consists of observational data rather than sample survey data.

OBSERVED DATA AS EVIDENCE, I

The case in question, presented before a state regulatory agency,[6] centered about metering error in the measurement of electrical power demand and its implication for billing purposes. Although the major point of controversy was statistical in nature, this was not recognized at first by either party. The statistical aspects of the situation seeped into the hearings only because one of the engineers who appeared as an expert witness employed statistics in his testimony and was somewhat knowledgeable in the subject. A description of this problem follows, and we will highlight general points as we proceed.

In 1955, the Pacific Gas and Electric Company (hereafter PG&E) entered into an agreement with the Sacramento Municipal Utilities District (hereafter SMUD) wherein PG&E would furnish electric power to SMUD in accordance with a listed monthly rate schedule. The monthly charge was based on the maximum half-hour load placed by SMUD on PG&E facilities. According to the schedule, the billing for electrical power demand each month was obtained by a rate per kilowatt applied to the power demand on PG&E, provided that the demand in any half-hour period did not reach or exceed 50 megawatts. If the maximum demand in any such period in one month reached or exceeded 50 mw., the same rate applied, except that thereafter the minimum billing was for 50 mw. and demands in excess of 50 mw. were payable at the same basic rate. The utility district also purchased power from the US Bureau of Reclamation, and it was the joint demand by SMUD on both agencies that determined the billing. Since the Bureau of Reclamation could supply at most 290 mw., it was deemed that a total demand of 340 mw. or more by SMUD on the two agencies

---

6   California Public Utilities Commission, Case 7127, 1962

was equivalent to a demand on PG&E of 50 mw. or more. Herein were several elements that might cause complications in the future, yet no attention was paid to any administrative accommodation relating to errors in billing. Moreover, the agreement left the metering of this demand to the joint approval of PG&E, SMUD, and the Bureau.

On July 21, 1960, in the half-hour period between 2:30 and 3:00 p.m. the meter readings depicted a demand of 342.274 mw., that is 2.274 mw. above the critical billing value. On that particular day there were four meters measuring the total demand. Thus, beginning August 1, 1960, a minimum charge for 50 mw. was in order and was billed monthly by PG&E. SMUD paid this minimum charge for several months and then instituted litigation on the basis that one of the meters was in error on July 21, 1960. In addition, SMUD claimed that the magnitude of the error was such that this reading indicated a demand above the true situation by an amount that caused the total reading to exceed the critical value of 340 mw. It was SMUD's allegation that the faulty meter was reading on the high side by about 2 mw. on the average, and that therefore a total value of less than 340 mw. might be the true situation for the half-hour period in question.

Here we have a situation where the reading of total demand obviously has some variability. In fact, the total reading variability is a compound of the variability inherent in each of the four meters, since it is based on an algebraic sum over the four meters. Moreover, each meter has built-in variability because it records only a fixed amount of electrical power after it is expended, and thus there is always a quantizing error between registered demand and actual demand. Thus, to act as if an average error in one meter, even though agreed to by both parties, is to be subtracted from the total demand is to ignore the whole variability framework inherent in the measurement scheme. This exact point occurs again in the next actual illustration to be discussed.

If both sides had taken into account the natural variability in measurement of demand for each of the four meters in their agreement and then provided some basis for an accommodation, there would have been no need for litigation to arise. For example, a 2% error rule is traditional in the electrical power industry. Naturally

521

the onset of litigation is also influenced by political matters, in this case a quasi-public utility district versus a giant in the private power industry. Since there are enough variables that can cause conflict between two such bodies, it would seem better if litigious factors could be eliminated as much as possible. However, this was not done.

At stake here, then, are the meanings of these facts: obviously some observations do appear in the records, each is subject to some kind of measurement error, and from this compound one desires to get an estimate of the total demand that did occur on that day and the variability connected with this estimate. Armed with this kind of yardstick measuring total error, once again, one can see whether the differences at issue between observed value and the contract value are anomalous or fall within previously acceptable norms. This need not provide immediate closure but obviously should help in providing a means by which closure can be attained.

Note that here we are in a situtation unlike that of the retail chain store. We do not have access to the original data and it is impossible ever to reproduce the conditions that led to the readings on record. Could a judge or an arbiter then say that because any estimate produced has some variability, it should not be admitted as evidence in the proceedings? Because what is recorded is the best evidence, if not the only evidence, it is obvious that this at least would have to be admissible or else there would be no substantive basis on which to reach a decision. In other words, an estimate with some uncertainty attached to it, which of course could be measured by computing its variability in this case, would have to stand as is. The major issue then is the probative value of the evidence presented. From this point on, a number of statistical techniques would be required to examine the probative value of the evidence. It is easy to see how this kind of analysis could be ruled prejudicial because it could easily be confusing and yet there would not seem to be any other way out that relates to the evidence. Naturally, of course, an agreement could be reached for other reasons and this was the outcome of the case.

The State Public Utilities Commission was spared the necessity for a decision on their part because both parties came to closure and resolved their differences successfully. It is apparent that had the case been completed and presented for decision, the Commission would have to assess the statistical analyses presented by each side in terms of admissibility and probative value. It is also quite possible that an accommodation was reached between the two parties because of the force of the statistical presentations by each side. In fact, this is one of the ways in which some proficiency in statistics can lead to a resolution of a contentious issue in litigious matters which would please regulatory agencies or the courts.

OBSERVED DATA AS EVIDENCE, II

Another case before the same State Public Utilities Commission also had an interesting twist insofar as the concept of variability is concerned. This, in brief, was the situation. As in many states, it is necessary to get permission to affix a foreign device to a telephone or to obtain a tariff for its use from the appropriate state commission. A company in northern California had manufactured a call diverter for use on phones in California. This device accepts an incoming call on one telephone and then, through the use of a second telephone, transfers the call to a number which has already been set in the call diverter. At the time, the Pacific Telephone Company did not wish to attach the device to phones in its system even for customers who desired it, on the basis that it was not yet commercially acceptable.

An experiment was decided upon to test this claim. In the experiment, a number of diverter devices were used on telephones and tests were made on the engineering performance of the call diverter. According to several indexes of performance computed from the experimental data, the Pacific Telephone Company decided that the call diverter was not yet satisfactory for commercial usage.

In the tests, however, any lack of successful performance was ascribed wholly to the call diverter device itself. No evidence was presented as to what the operating performance of the telephone system was in general when the call diverter was not attached. If service were absolutely perfect, then of course any deviation from that could be ascribed to the call diverter. In other words, there was an implicit assumption that there was zero variability in the

523

performance of the equipment of the Pacific Telephone Company.

From what we know of telephone service or any kind of similar system in communications, it would appear that there must be some conditions under which service is not absolutely perfect. If one could quantify the deviation from perfection in the system itself, then one could get an estimate of the variability of performance when the call diverter was not used. This, then, could be subtracted from the variability in performance when the call diverter was attached, and thus an estimate could be obtained of the effect of the call diverter on telephone performance. Here again, we have an example of how the concept and measurement of variability is important in a legal situation. Its appropriate use probably could have eliminated litigation.

An appreciation of this very important statistical concept by each side could help prepare them to enlighten the hearing examiner or the commissioners. This could provide a more equitable decision should that point in the proceedings be reached, or it could lead to a termination of the hearings with both parties arriving at an accommodation because of the substance of the analyses presented. In this particular example, one side paid no attention at all to the statistical aspects of the situation, namely the concept of variability in performance by a system based on unreliable components. The Public Utilities Commission ruled for the call diverter company. One can venture the statement that the lack of any appreciation for sorting out the unreliability due to the call diverter from the unreliability of the remainder of the telephone system played a large role in the Commission's decision.

RECENT ARTICLES ON "TRIAL BY MATHEMATICS"

Broun, K.S. and Kelly, D.G.
"Playing the Percentages and the Law of Evidence,'" *The University of Illinois Law Forum,* Volume 1970, No. 1, pp. 23.

Cullison, A.D.
"Identification by Probabilities and Trial by Arithmetic (A Lesson for Beginners in How to be Wrong with Greater Precision)," *Houston Law Review,* Volume 6, Number 3, January, 1969, pp. 471-518.

Cullison, A.D.
"Probability Analysis of Judicial Fact-Finding: A Preliminary Outline of the Subjective Approach," *The University of Toledo Law Review,* Volume 1969, Number 3, Summer, pp. 538-598.

Finkelstein, M.O.
"The Application of Statistical Decision Theory to the Jury Discrimination Cases," *Harvard Law Review,* Volume 80:338, 1966, pp. 338-376.

Finkelstein, M.O. and Fairley, W.B.
"A Bayesian Approach to Identification Evidence," *Harvard Law Review,* Volume 83, Number 3, January, 1970.

Tribe, L.H.
"Trial by Mathematics: Precision and Ritual in the Legal Process," *Harvard Law Review,* Volume 84, April, 1971, No. 6, pp. 1329-1393.

Unsigned Student Note
"Evidence: Admission of Mathematical Probability Statistics Held Erroneous for Want of Demonstration of Validity," *Duke Law Journal,* Number 3, June, 1967, pp. 665-685 .

CHAPTER 12

THE FUTURE OF LAW ENFORCEMENT STATISTICS: A SUMMARY VIEW

By

Hans Zeisel

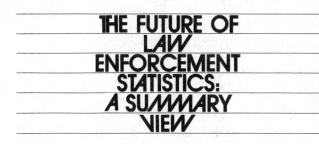

THE FUTURE OF LAW ENFORCEMENT STATISTICS: A SUMMARY VIEW

TABLE OF CONTENTS

SUMMARY OF FINDINGS

The crucial event, now in its development stage, is the advent of longitudinal statistics in which the data base of all law enforcement statistics will be formed by the individual records of those involved in the criminal process. If successful, it will have a profound effect on our ability to understand crime and the law enforcement process. At this early stage, it is not possible to foresee all the consequences and problems that will emerge from the new statistics. Nevertheless an effort has been made in this chapter to deal with some of the recommendations for their solution.

There is one question, however, that transcends all the others in importance and urgency: the question of who should be the custodian of the new statistics. The last section of this chapter discusses that problem.

NEW LONGITUDINAL RECORDS

If, as I believe, our ultimate task is to cooperate in bringing about the reduction of a crime rate that far exceeds that of other developed countries, then the presently available crime and law enforcement statistics are almost useless.

In the main, these statistics give us a one-at-a-time overview of the many separate layers of the process, allowing only loose connections between them. None of them allows us to understand the totality of the law enforcement process and to judge the effects of what is being done by the police, the courts, the prisons, or the rehabilitation offices.

The pioneering project SEARCH seeks to replace the lateral agency reporting with longitudinal data on individual offender histories. If successful, this system will bring about a radical change. By being able to trace different "treatments," or changes in policy to their ultimate goal — the reduction of crime among the "treated" ones — we will have a genuine chance of learning what we do wrong, what we do right, and the direction in which improvement lies. If successful, we will be the first country to have such statistics, and such insights.

These longitudinal statistics will force us to see and analyze the crime and law enforcement process as the complicated system it is in fact: the flow from crime through the police, through the courts, through the prisons, through probation and parole, and at each point, various forms of release into society; and every so often, the return to the cycle.

What Should be Recorded?

The development of individual offender histories and their storage in national computer centers with push-button retrieval possibilities provides the proper opportunity for reconsidering what these individual offender histories, commonly called criminal records, ought and ought not to contain. Two crucial points deserve attention: whether arrests should in any way be part of these individual records; and for how long a time period an item should stay on the record.

At present, the arrest is the only firmly established part of the criminal record; and with minor exceptions, the record is for all practical purposes permanent. Yet there are important reasons for not allowing arrest to become part of the record initially, and for allowing automatic expunction of items from the record after appropriate time intervals.

The reasons for the elimination of arrest figures from the record are briefly these:

1. An arrest, if not followed by a court conviction, is far from being a proof of guilt, however convinced the arresting policeman may be of the contrary.

2. Roughly 2 out of every 4 adults arrested for a felony are subsequently not found guilty of *any* crime; roughly 1 out of every 4 individuals charged with and prosecuted for a felony are subsequently not found guilty of any crime. [See Appendix I].

3. An arrest record, even when not followed by a conviction, is a serious obstacle in a man's efforts to compete for jobs. [See Appendix II].

4. In this interpretation of an arrest record we have been led by the FBI terminology of long standing which calls any man arrested an "offender" and any man arrested twice a "multiple offender," even if he has never been convicted of a crime. [See Appendix III].

5. Under these circumstances it may come as a surprise that no other country allows the arrest to become part of the criminal record. In all other countries a man has a criminal record only if he has been found guilty of a crime. [See Appendix IV].

Right now we have the record backward. What we do have is the police record, the certain fact of an arrest; what we too often do not have is the subsequent disposition.

It is however, precisely the court disposition that should be the cornerstone of the record, reducing the preceding arrest to the auxiliary position it occupies in fact. What is long overdue is the changeover from the "police record" to the "court record."[1]

None of this goes to the usefulness of arrest data for evaluating performance within the police system, or for evaluating the role of the police as a whole. Arrests should therefore remain part of the data system, but should not be part of the criminal record. In the following pages, we discuss the usefulness of arrest ratios.

---

1 In an obvious effort to buttress the present anomalous situation, the Uniform Crime Reports produce a set of data that carries the implication that those arrested by the police but not convicted by the courts are, if anything, more involved in crime than those that have been convicted. [See Appendix V].

How Long Should The Record Be Preserved?

An indelible, permanent record of a conviction of a crime, is likely to be counterproductive. By now we know that at the point where man "has paid his debt to society," he begins to pay his second installment — by having to live the life of a marked ex-convict. But there should come a time, after which, if he has not committed another crime, all traces of his conviction should be eliminated. Some of our states allow such expunction, and most European countries have such statutes. [See for an example Appendix VI].

The establishment of computer based criminal records in a central system requires a set of rules, centrally applied, which would allow under specified conditions, the automatic expunction of a record-item. The automatic element is essential, because experience has shown that the mere right to expunction remains almost ineffective; worse, it discriminates against the lowest socio-economic strata who will know least about how to pursue such a right.

MAJOR STATISTICS FROM INDIVIDUAL RECORDS

Offhand, it would seem that longitudinal crime statistics demand an all embracing unitary system. The realities of law enforcement, however, suggest for a variety of reasons a dichotomy: there should be the crime count, a measure of the extent and quality of the committed crime; and there should be a tracing of individual offender histories. It makes little sense to connect these two phases, except on the aggregate level, by establishing certain general ratios with the crimes known to the police as base.

Otherwise, the two statistics should remain operationally separate: the one concerns a crime, the other concerns a human being involved in crime and law enforcement. Even where the link to a crime is established by a conviction, the recorded link is of dubious value. In the course of the plea bargaining process, our law is too often satisfied with *any* conviction, and does not insist on the one for the crime that has actually been committed.

534

Clearance Rates

At present, the link between the two segments of our crime statistics, the number of committed crimes and the number of men involved in crime, is the so called clearance rate. It is the proportion of crimes which the police consider as cleared, either by an arrest and subsequent charge, or in certain situations, where they believe they have identified the perpetrator of the crime but for reasons beyond their control are unable to make an arrest. (E.g., a hold-up man has been killed in the attempt.) The problems with clearance figures are manifold.

First, they substitute the judgment of the police for the judgment of the courts. Whenever the police arrest and charge a man for a crime, and turn him over to the courts for prosecution — the crime is considered cleared, irrespective of what the court found. Second, there is the judgment of the policeman in those cases where there is no arrest. The greatest difficulty, however, stems from the fact that one arrested man may, through multiple confessions, "clear" more than one crime and, as a Rand Corporation study convincingly showed, the variations from precinct to precinct in obtaining such multiple confessions were found to be disturbingly great, in at least the one city in which they were studied. [See Appendix VII].

There is no easy cure for the problem. But for many purposes, it will be preferable to use simply the arrest rate, the ratio of arrests to crimes known to the police. To be sure, that index too has its shortcomings, but at least it avoids some of the ambiguities of the clearance rate. It would be what its name indicates, and in many situations, is likely to have greater operational significance for the quality of police performance than the clearance figures which can be manipulated by those whose performance is to be evaluated.

The difference, incidentally, between arrest figures and clearance figures turns out to be small, apparently because the number of multiple arrests for one crime (counted as *one* clearance), is approximately balanced by the multiple clearance from one arrest. The exact nature of the "mix" is never disclosed in the routine reports of clearances. [See Appendix VIII].

There will be, of course, also other ratios, so that on the aggre-

535

gate level a total profile emerges that looks roughly as follows for
any particular crime category:

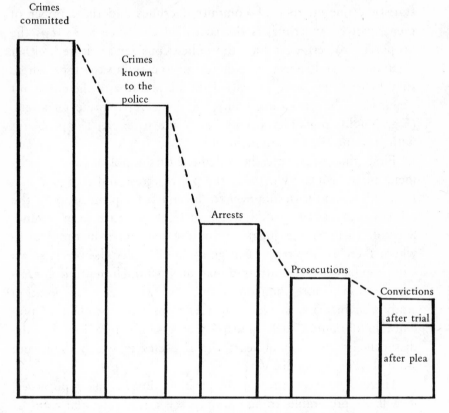

This graph represents a summary view of the "old" aggregate,
lateral statistics; it will be only an incidental by-product of the
new longitudinal statistics.

Victim Surveys

It has always been realized that the number of "crimes known
to the police" is smaller than the number of committed crimes. A
first inkling of the quality and magnitude of the deviation came
from two pilot studies made for the President's Commission on
Crime and Delinquency. At present, the Law Enforcement Assistance Administration (LEAA) is preparing careful studies of these
discrepancies by surveying the victims of crime, in the general
population, as well as among business establishments and public
agencies. These studies will reveal new dimensions of the crime

problem. They will provide estimates of the crimes not reported to the police and, incidentally, also of the crimes reported to the police that were not reported by the police. As a by-product of these surveys we should also learn a good deal about what crime and law-enforcement mean and do not mean to the affected public. It cannot be said with certainty at this point whether these victim surveys should become permanent features of our statistical inventory. Perhaps their greatest value will consist of providing ratio-estimates that can be applied as correctives to the "crimes known to the police." But it is also possible that the periodic continuation of these surveys will yield important insights, especially if they can provide longitudinal victim histories, through the panel method.

In any event, victim surveys are an important, path breaking innovation that will make major contributions to our criminological knowledge.

USES OF LAW ENFORCEMENT STATISTICS

With the foreseeably great increase in the amount of data there is also the increased danger of not asking: Statistics for what? There is a need for seeing law enforcement statistics not only as a means of elucidating the law enforcement field, but also as a system by itself. What statistics ought to be collected and presented depends on the uses to be made of them. In view of the considerable new costs the system will bring about, it would seem worthwhile to survey what present and future uses the various parts of the system, police, courts, prisons, rehabilitation agencies, as well as higher levels of administration, are now making and are likely to make in the future of the data. As a matter of fact, some of the suggestions in this memorandum might either gain or lose in value if we knew more about what use is made of the data. As an example, one might take the issue of carrying arrests in the criminal records. Even the courts are reluctant to disallow the procedure, on the grounds that the individual must not mind some infringement on his privacy if it helps to maintain a safe society. The word of the police is accepted that publication of arrest records performs this function. It would be relevant to learn just what specific uses are made of the arrest records, and what would, in fact, change if arrest records were replaced by conviction records.

The Data Base

Perhaps the most serious problem of our count of "crimes known to the police" is the unknown reliability of the underlying collection procedure.

As one observer has put it, some 8,000 police departments, operating essentially independently of each other in "different criminal jurisdictions, each varying from the other in definitions of crime, in organization of law enforcement operations, and in methods of maintaining basic records, raises a real question as to how homogeneous and accurate the facts collected and published in this series may be." [2]

The FBI has performed a major educational function by attempting to improve the collection methods through the issuing of manuals, through correspondence, and through personal contacts by its agents. But in spite of improvements, the data base remains a major problem.

In the years gone by, some startling statistics drew attention to the difficulties. Thus in 1948 New York City reported 2,726 burglaries, in 1952 it reported 42,491; in 1951 Philadelphia reported 16,776 Index Crime Offenses, in 1953 it reported 28,560, an increase of over 70 percent in two years. But the more recent past, too, is filled with jumps in the data that do not occur in systems whose collection methods are standardized and under consistent quality control. [See Appendix IX].

A variety of reasons have been found to bias the data collection process. First, of course, there is lack of appropriate procedural discipline. Secondly, there is occasionally true bias where the statistics are manipulated to support political goals. Occasionally, it is to demonstrate by higher crime rates, the need for additional police appropriations; occasionally, the bias will be in the opposite direction. As a distinguished criminologist put it: "Police have an obligation to protect the reputations of their cities, and when this cannot be done efficiently under existing legal and administrative

2 Ronald H. Beattie, "Problems of Criminal Statistics in the United States," *Journal of Criminal Law,* Volume 46 (1955), pages 178 and 183.

machinery, it is sometimes accomplished statistically."[3]

Paradoxically, part of the trouble comes from constant efforts to improve collection methods. Increasing care in the recording of committed crimes, unless properly handled, leads to biased year-to-year comparisons.

Part of the answer could come from better disclosure of such changes. At present, few if any of the difficulties or uncertainties are disclosed. At best they are treated as an internal police issue, at worst they are disregarded.

In the long run, the solution, as part of the continuing education process, must come from systematic auditing by the respective state bureaus of criminal statistics. At present an audit is performed only when the local police organization requests it.

The Opportunity for Experimentation

The usefulness of the new longitudinal statistics will be multiplied if we make proper use of the opportunities they offer. The Constitution has left the primary burden of law enforcement on the states, not on the federal government. In some respects this diversified responsibility has created many difficulties for the collectors and keepers of statistics. But in another, more important way, this regional diversification could enrich our knowledge of what to do about crime. Now that we will have the statistical tools with which to measure the effects of changes in our law enforcement policies, the states should earnestly and systematically plan changes and reforms as parts of controlled experiments. In this fashion all states could begin to learn which law enforcement measures are effective and which are not.

Needless to say, the usefulness of such experimentation could be even further enhanced, if the states were to cooperate in this enterprise, so that all may learn from the experience of each.

The larger vision is that of the law enforcement system as an entity, whose purpose it is to obtain a maximum reduction in crime at minimum costs. If properly implemented and used, the new statistics might teach us gradually how to achieve this goal by properly allocating our resources.

---

3   Donald Cressey, "The State of Criminal Statistics," 3 *National Probation and Parole Association Journal*, Volume 3 (1957), page 232.

WHO IS TO BE THE CUSTODIAN OF
THE NEW DATA?

The advent of a new era in law enforcement statistics should also be the occasion for reconsidering who should be the custodian of the new data.

In September 1930, maintenance of uniform crime reporting was assigned to the FBI by an act of Congress. And now, a short while ago, the FBI was also assigned responsibility for SEARCH, the pilot study that is to usher in the longitudinal statistics. A review of the FBI stewardship is therefore in order.

The first observation is an acknowledgement of the FBI's formidable achievement. To forge even a modicum of uniformity on the reports from some 8000 independent police forces is an extraordinary accomplishment, and there can be no doubt that, as time goes on, the performance would improve further.

But a second observation is also in order: through presentation and emphasis, the FBI has used the statistics it collected for the documentation of its viewpoints. For this they have been harshly criticized by some authors.[4]

The criticism turned, of course, on technical points. For example, the FBI was advised by its own committee of consultants to differentiate, within the index crime category "auto theft," between permanent appropriation, sale or stripping – and joy riding. The FBI has never heeded the advice, on the grounds, as Dr. Lejins reports:

> "that separating the offense of joyriding from auto theft would diminish the deterrent effect on the potential violators." [5]

The FBI never responded to the advice that the index crime category "larceny $50 and over" has a built-in inflationary effect on the amount of crime. Nor have they removed the "Crime Clock," which shows how many seconds or minutes elapse, on the

---

4   Sophia M. Robison, "A Critical View of the Uniform Crime Reports," *University of Michigan Law Rev.,* Volume 64 (1966), pages 1031 ff. Marvin Wolfgang, "Uniform Crime Reports: A Critical Appraisal," *Pennsylvania Law Review* Volume III (1963), page 708 ff.

5   Peter P. Lejins, "Uniform Crime Reports," *University of Michigan Law Review,* Volume 64 (1966), page 1024.

average, between every two murders, two auto thefts, and so forth, in spite of the advice that the shortening of that interval is as much a function of the increase in population as it is of the rise in criminality.

The criticized procedures have a common denominator: they tend to increase the reported volume of crime, and the FBI, for reasons they know best, seems to believe that the nation is best served by this emphasis.[6]

At times the thrust goes to a more complicated point, namely, to show or at least to suggest that the courts by their misapplied leniency might be responsible for a portion of the increase of crime. In the 1967 Uniform Crime Report we can read:

"There appears to be a similarity between the burglar and the bogus check offender in that 63% of the latter [and 65% of the former] were granted the above forms of leniency [probation, suspended sentence or parole] and both of these criminal types have a high rate of recidivism in the same type of offense."[7]

The hint that this type of crude parallelism even suggests a causal connection is, of course, far fetched. The attempt can be understood only in the context of other efforts to show that the courts do not always do what is needed, for instance, when they fail to convict men who turn out to have the highest recidivism rate.

To appraise the whole situation fairly, we cite here the defender of the FBI against its critics, Dr. Lejins, who in 1957 was asked by the FBI to chair the three-man consultant committee on Uniform Crime Reporting. He discerned the problem with precision and objectivity:

...These *Reports* are intended to be a statistical house organ of the police in the United States....most critics disregard this aspect of the *Reports* and confuse the perspective by criticizing them for not being something which they never intended to be.[8]

---

6   Recently the FBI, on this tendency, was found to be in disagreement with its own Department of Justice. (See *New York Times*, September 8, 1971.)

7   *Uniform Crime Reports — 1967*, page 36.

8   Peter P. Lejins, "Uniform Crime Reports," *University of Michigan Law Review*, Volume 64 (1966), page 1011 and 1016.

What happened was that the temptation to use the statistics they collect for purposes of arguing the law enforcement positions they hold, has proved too strong for the FBI. All through the years they have kept presenting some of their statistics for a purpose — whether a good or a bad one need not be discussed here. Nobody denies the FBI the right if not the duty to fight for its convictions. But such partisan spirit is not compatible with the impartiality and objectivity required of an agency responsible for a most crucial part of our statistical system, involving the measurement of part of our national health.

This view is not new. As far back as 1931 the Wickersham Commission called for independent agencies as custodians of crime statistics. The 1946 Uniform Criminal Statistics Act held to that position.[9] With respect to the national level, Dr. Lejins himself concluded:

> This analysis suggests the need for a specialized collecting and processing agency, either in the Department of Justice or, perhaps, the Bureau of Census, which would deal with the total crime picture on a national scale.[10]

It is indeed the natural position to take.

One of the functions of statistics is to provide performance indicators, and it is never sound policy to let the performer be its own uncontrolled statistician, especially when it is as powerful and spirited an organization as the FBI.

But there is also a larger issue. The broader danger lies in the prospect that the police view may exert an inappropriately large influence on our law enforcement philosophy.

There is nothing wrong with the police view. It is born out of the harsh realities of the police function. The police — as the statistics of killed policemen show — encounter crime as the enemy not only in the figurative sense. It also derives from the too frequent experience of the policeman finding the man he has

---

9   Should a Bureau of Criminal Statistics be an independent agency . . . devoting its entire effort to criminal statistics? That is from many points of view the best solution. (Comment to Section 1).

10 Peter P. Lejins, "Uniform Crime Reports," *University of Michigan Law Review,* Volume 64 (1966), page 1019.

turned over to the courts only a short while ago, back at his business. In spite of occasional lip service to the need for rehabilitation, the police appear to feel the courts are releasing too many criminals, and if they sentence them, they sentence them too leniently. And whenever a law enforcement policy is up for debate, be it the matter of recording arrests or of capital punishment — the police position is predictable.

Yet the police phase is but part of the law enforcement process and we would be ill served if, by allowing them to dominate the statistics, their voice would have more resonance than it deserves.

On all these grounds it would seem advisable to award the stewardship of law enforcement statistics to independent statistical bureaus both in the states and at the federal center. There is a distinguished precedent for such a move: the Bureau of Labor Statistics in the Department of Labor.

APPENDIX I
DISPOSITION AFTER FELONY ARREST

Ronald H. Beattie, Chief of the Bureau of Criminal Statistics, California Department of Justice has developed the following statistics:[1]

DISPOSITIONS OF DEFENDANTS ARRESTED AND BOOKED ON FELONY CHARGES: 1965-1969*

State of California

Type of disposition

	Total Defendants (667,763) Per Cent	
Released by Police	33.3	
Released or dismissed prior to superior court filing	7.2	
Dismissed by Superior Court	2.5	
Acquitted by Superior Court	2.4	
Total Released		45.4
Prosecuted as misdemeanant or Juvenile, or in lower court		26.2
Convicted in Superior Court		28.4
	Total	100.0

* The original table gives the data for each year separately; this is a summary which I made of all five years.

---

1   "Developing Integrated Criminal Records," *Proceedings of the National Symposium on Criminal Justice Information and Statistics Systems,* Sponsored by Project SEARCH, November 1970, Pages 279 and 286.

Of the 26.2 percent of the cases whose disposition was not directly available for this table, Beattie estimates that another 5.9 percent were released so that the total percentage of those released after an original felony arrest is 45.4 plus 5.9, or 51.3 percent. The remainder, 48.7 percent or not quite one-half, were convicted.

What figures we have on this topic in the F.B.I.'s *Uniform Crime Report* compare well with Beattie's more detailed, if less comprehensive, statistics:[2]

DISPOSITIONS OF PERSONS FORMALLY CHARGED BY THE POLICE

(2,640 cities; 1969 estimated population 66,155,000: Sub totals for criminal homicide, forcible rape, robbery, aggravated assault, burglary — breaking or entering, larceny — theft, auto theft)

Number charged (held for prosecution)	(396,291)
	Per Cent
Guilty	39.4
Acquitted or dismissed	15.1
Referred to Juvenile Court	45.5
	100.0

If we recompute the State of California percentages on the basis of all felony defendants not released (charged) by the police, that is on the basis of $(100.0 - 33.3) = 66.7$ percent multiplied by 100.0/66.7 or 3/2 of all cases, we obtain the following comparison:

COMPARING UNIFORM CRIME REPORT WITH CALIFORNIA (I)

	UCR 1969	California 1965-69
	%	%
Guilty	39.4	42.5
Acquitted or dismissed	15.1	18.1
Referred to Juvenile Court	45.5	39.3
	100.0	100.0

Since the UCR statistics contain not only felony arrests (*all* larceny), the higher referral rate to the Juvenile Court is understandable. If we apply Beattie's estimate of the proportion of releases of these referrals also to the UCR figures, we obtain the following

---

2 *Uniform Crime Reports — 1969,* page 102.

estimates for the total percentage of those charged by the police but ultimately released.

COMPARING UNIFORM CRIME REPORT
WITH CALIFORNIA (II)

	UCR 1969	California 1965-69
	%	%
Acquitted or released as recorded	15.1	18.1
Acquitted or released by the court to which referral was made	10.3*	8.9**
Total not guilty	25.4	27.0

*26.2/5.9 = 45.5/10.3
**26.2/5.9 = 39.3/8.9

The Uniform Crime Report provides us with still another set of figures, namely the disposition by the court of *adult* offenders charged with an index crime type felony[3] which allows differentiation by type of crime.[4]

PROSECUTED ADULTS AND THEIR
DISPOSITION IN 1969

(2,344 cities; 1969 estimated population 59,267,000)

	Violent Crime	Property Crime	Total
	%	%	%
Guilty as charged	43.1	66.8	61.8
Guilty of lesser offenses	18.0	8.6	10.6
Acquitted or dismissed	38.9	24.6	27.6
Total	100.0	100.0	100.0
Number of Dispositions	(39,420)	(150,541)	(189,961)

APPENDIX II

THE ARREST STIGMA AND EMPLOYMENT

Experts agree, as matters now stand, that a record of an arrest—irrespective of whether or not it was followed by a conviction — is a most serious handicap for any man seeking a job.

"The practical effects of arrest . . . on the job hunting

---

3 Murder and non-negligent manslaughter, forcible rape, robbery, aggravated assult, burglary — breaking or entering, larceny — theft, auto theft.

4 *Uniform Crime Reports — 1969*, Table 17, lower half of columns 1, 2, and 3.

problem are virtually the same as the consequences of a conviction."[1]

"Those of us who deal with the practicalities . . . find that, in the main, irreparable injury is done a defendant acquitted after a trial; the fact of his arrest is very often sufficient to rule him out of consideration for employment."[2]

The operational reasons for this stigma are easily traced. First, the crucial question in the employment questionnaires goes not to convictions for a crime but to arrest. Here, for instance, is the procedure followed by the Post Office in California: applicants who answered the question on arrest affirmatively are

"automatically disqualified because it is simpler and cheaper to hire an applicant without any record whatever than to investigate the circumstances of an arrest."[3]

It is unlikely that other employers, public or private, act much differently, unless they are confronted with a labor shortage. According to a study of New York City area employment agencies by the New York Civil Liberties Union, 75 percent of the agencies sampled do not even make a referral of an applicant who has an arrest record.[4]

An applicant who lists a previous arrest faces at best a "second trial" in which, without procedural safeguards, he must prove his innocence — at worst the listing of the arrest disqualifies him *per se*.[5] The arrest record is the first of a series of "status degradation ceremonies" in the criminal law process.[6]

---

1 Albert G. Hess & Fre Le Poole, "Abuse of the Record of Arrest Not Leading to Conviction," *Journal of Research on Crime and Delinquency* (1967).

2 Judge Irving Ben Cooper, U.S. District Court, Southern District of N.Y., cited in Hess and Le Poole, p. 497.

3 *California Assembly Interim Committee on Criminal Procedure, 1959-61 Report,* (Sacramento, California: California Assembly, 1961), page 68.

4 Hess and Le Poole, *Op.cit.*, page 495.

5 *Ibid.* p. 497.

6 Joseph Goldstein, "Police Discretion not to Invoke the Criminal Process," *Yale Law Journal,* (1960) page 590.

It is argued that information of an arrest helps employers and bonding companies, at least on the average, to reduce the chances of loss, a point we discuss elsewhere. Here, it is merely necessary to stress the countervailing danger that results from the publication of a record of an arrest without conviction: the degree to which the ensuing employment difficulties may drive these applicants into crime.

APPENDIX III

FROM "OFFENDER" TO "REPEATER"

The policy of considering a man who has been arrested a criminal ("offender" is the more polite term used in the Uniform Crime Reports), reaches a new plateau when a man who has been arrested once is arrested a second time. He then becomes, in the language of the Uniform Crime Reports, a "repeater."

For the last few years, the Uniform Crime Reports have included a new section called "Careers in Crime." Its primary purpose is "to document the extent to which criminal repeating over time contributes to annual crime counts."[1] It is based upon the "offenders" released by the federal judicial system to the community either: (1) after a finding of guilty that did not involve prison, such as fine or suspended sentence; (2) those released from prison, either through parole or after serving their full term; and (3), those whose case the court either dismissed or who were acquitted after trial.

The UCR then reports for each of these groups the proportion of "offenders" released in the base year 1963 who in the intervening years have become "repeaters,"[2] the immodest label for having been rearrested. Thus a man graduates from being an "offender" to becoming a "repeater," simply by having been arrested a second time — even though he may not have been convicted of a crime even once.[3]

---

1 *Uniform Crime Reports — 1968.*

2 *Ibid.,* p. 38, 39.

3 That the identification of "arrest" with "offender" is by no means accidental can be seen from the more recent FBI instructions for operators of the SEARCH which requests that a man arrested (!) in two different states be called a "multiple offender."

THE "CRIMINAL RECORD" ABROAD[1]

In November 1966, the Information Center of the National Council on Crime and Delinquency mailed questionnaires to its foreign correspondents, asking them to describe their countries' laws and practices with respect to the nature and uses of criminal records.[2] Thirty-nine replies were received: twelve from common law countries, twenty-two from civil countries, four from socialist countries, and one from Interpol.[3]

The "criminal record" in these thirty-nine countries lists only convictions, and often only those for serious crimes. No country lists arrests that have not led to convictions. On this point, the reply from Interpol, the international police organization, is of interest:

> Arrest, detention prior to official arrest, and police questioning are only initial phases . . . and . . . their justification . . . can be overruled by the Judge's decision in cases where such measures were taken on the sole initiative of the police. Even when arrest or detention prior to arrest has been ordered by the judicial authorities, the trial and verdict of the court can also declare the innocence of the accused and show that the arrest or detention prior to arrest were not justified.

> Thus, in our opinion, arrest, detention, or cross-examination by the police cannot be taken into account to the detriment of an individual without prejudging the outcome of the trial and should be completely disregarded.

The report on the international inquiry of the NCCD discusses

---

1 Hess and Le Poole, *Op. cit.,* pages 494 and 497.

2 *Ibid.,* p. 500 ff.

3 Argentina, Australia, Belgium, Bulgaria, Ceylon, China (Taiwan), Colombia, Czechoslovakia, Denmark, Ethiopia, Finland, France, West Germany, East Germany, Iceland, India, Israel, Jamaica, Japan, Kenya, Lebanon, Luxembourg, Malaysia, Morocco, Netherlands, New Zealand, Nigeria, Norway, Portugal, Spain Sweden, Switzerland, Tanzania, Uganda, United Arab Republic, United Kingdom, U.S.S.R.

also the use of arrest data. The summary states: "Disclosure of arrest is generally restricted to law-enforcement agencies, chiefly for identification purposes in criminal cases. . . . Only a few countries released arrest data to (other) government agencies . . . . Even where this is the case, the release . . . is on a discriminative basis."[4] In at least one country, Belgium, disclosure of information on arrests and pretrial detentions, either to a public or private agency or to an individual, constitutes a criminal offense.[5]

APPENDIX V

ARRESTS *NOT* FOLLOWED BY CONVICTION

In its section on "Careers in Crime," the follow-up of "offenders" released from the judicial system, there is one column in a chart to which the Uniform Crime Reports attach special significance. The chart shows that of the various subgroups, arranged by the type of release in 1963, the one that shows the highest rate of rearrests are the men who, although arrested by the police, had been released by the courts.

PERCENT OF PERSONS REARRESTED WITHIN 5 YEARS

By Type of Release in 1963

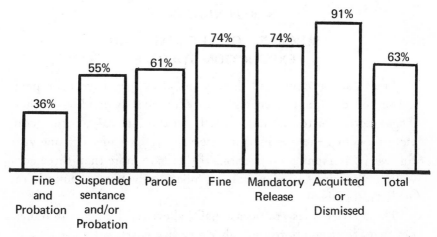

The FBI leaves no doubt as to the importance it attaches to the result. It is the one they cite first in the "Five Year Follow-Up"

---

4   Hess and Le Poole, *Op. cit.,* page 50.

5   *Ibid.,* page 50.

section, after giving the average of 63 percent rearrests for *all* offenders by the end of the fifth calendar year after release: "Of those persons acquitted or who had their cases dismissed in 1963, 91 percent were re-arrested for new offenses."

The statistics suggest that the men whom the FBI arrests but whom the courts acquit or dismiss are, from society's point of view, an even greater danger than all the rest of the released men.

An interesting result, if true. But since it is so obviously a self serving statistic one would wish some clarifications and assurances. At a minimum, one would wish to know the aftermath of these second arrests of men who, as far as the statistics go, have not yet been found guilty of any crime. One also would want to know for what crimes they had been arrested in the first place and rearrested the second time. The point that might be more difficult to establish is that certain persons, such as those arrested by the FBI but released by the courts, remain perhaps more visible to the police. The point to be established here is not that the suggested inference is necessarily incorrect; for all we know it may be true. But since it is a highly self-serving statistic from the FBI's point of view, on a controversial point, its presentation and analysis merit somewhat more care.

APPENDIX VI

SUMMARY OF THE AUSTRIAN EXPUNCTION STATUTE

Fines can be expunged three years after they have been paid, jail sentences after five years, prison sentences, depending on their length, after ten to twenty years. If, in the interval, another conviction occurs, the expunction intervals are extended by one year for every intervening conviction. If there are more than three convictions for crimes of identical or similar motivation, expunction is denied altogether.

These strict rules are occasionally alleviated by general amnesties that are given approximately every five years.

At present the Austrian Parliament is deliberating on a proposal submitted by the Minister of Justice which would provide automatic expunctions, no longer requiring any initiative on the part of the ex-convict. The bill also proposes that jail or prison sentences under six months not be included in the criminal record.

550

APPENDIX VII

FROM: AN ANALYSIS OF THE APPREHENSION ACTIVITIES OF THE NEW YORK CITY POLICE DEPARTMENT

Peter W. Greenwood
The New York City
Rand Institute

Clearance Rate: A Traditional Measure

The "clearance rate" is the traditional measure of effectiveness invoked by writers on police affairs.[1] Simply stated, the clearance rate is the fraction of crimes reported to the police that the police claim to have solved.

According to the definition of "clearance" in the FBI *Uniform Crime Reporting Handbook*, a crime is cleared by arrest when a suspect is arrested, charged with the offense, and turned over to the court for prosecution. Certain "exceptional clearances" are granted when the police have sufficient information to support an arrest, to charge, locate, and turn the suspect over to the court, but are prevented from making an arrest by circumstances beyond their control, e.g., when the suspect is dead or in prison. The definition of clearance specifically allows multiple clearances for one arrest if the suspect can be established as the offender for each case cleared. The prevalence of multiple clearances is the chief cause for disputing clearance figures.

Clearance rates are one of the few indices which are routinely collected and relate directly to the performance of professional police administrators. Therefore, it is not surprising that some administrators may be concerned with achieving a high clearance rate. Unfortunately, a high clearance rate does not necessarily reflect high performance. It may only indicate that the detectives in that unit are extremely thorough in connecting an arrestee to several of his past crimes. As a hypothetical example, one squad may receive 1000 crime reports during a month and make 100 arrests but claim no multiple clearances, thereby achieving a 10-percent clearance rate. Another squad with 1000 reported

---

1   O. W. Wilson, *Police Planning*, Charles C. Thomas, Springfield, Ill., 1962; John Griffin, *Statistics Essential for Police Efficiency*, Charles C. Thomas, Springfield, Ill., 1958.

crimes may make only 50 arrests but succeed in linking each suspect to two additional cases, thereby achieving a 15-percent clearance rate. But it is questionable whether the second squad is really superior in performance.

The dilemma is that the small gain to society for substantiating multiple clearances, after a suspect has been arrested, does not appear to justify the considerable effort which may be required of the detectives concerned.

In some cases a suspect possesses stolen property from past crimes, and this will be used as evidence that he was the offender and that the case is cleared. The large majority of cases cleared that meet the FBI definition rely on the suspect's admission of guilt. This leads to the question of what induces an offender, arrested for one crime, to admit several, maybe hundreds, of others. For some crimes against the person, such as rape, robbery, or assault, there is a good chance that the victim can identify the offender. Recognizing this probability, an offender may be willing to confess to other crimes rather than wait for identification by the victim, hoping to receive a lighter sentence in return for his cooperation. Even when he cannot be connected to other crimes by hard evidence, a suspect may be willing to confess to these crimes if he believes he will receive more lenient treatment from the police and courts for his cooperation in clearing cases. Jerome Skolnick found this to be true in his studies of a Western police department.[2] In one case, a burgler who confessed to and cleared over 400 cases was allowed to serve out a previous sentence and was released within thirty days, while his codefendants, who had no similar favors to offer the police, received substantial sentences.

Many police units do not rely exclusively on hard evidence and confessions to clear additional cases. They may also claim clearances on the basis of M.O. (modus operandi). When an offender is arrested, the Detective Squad Commanding Officer can compare the offender's M.O., place of operation, and other known characteristics with the known facts in unsolved cases. If in his judgment the crimes were committed by the same offender, he might claim a clearance. Since the decision as to when multiple cases have been cleared is a matter of judgment, it is likely that the decision to

---

2   J. H. Skolnick, *Justice Without Trial*, John Wiley and Sons, New York, 1966.

clear is not consistently applied across police units. In fact, the number of cases cleared by an arrest in any unit is probably influenced by how important the unit commander feels his clearance rate is.

In an attempt to examine the consistency in claiming clearances among individual commands within New York City, the author computed the ratio of cases cleared to cases in which arrests were made for different crime types in each precinct. The distribution of these ratios for burglary is presented in the histogram of Fig. 3. It is most unlikely that the wide variance in these ratios can be explained by differences among the population or police tactics of individual precincts or by simple chance variation. A more likely explanation is that individual commanders define clearances differently.

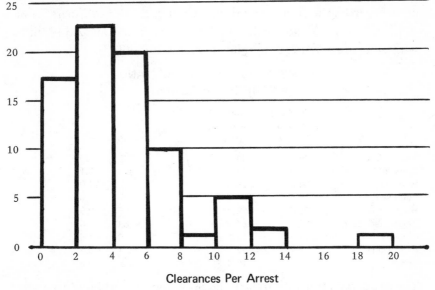

Clearances Per Arrest

Figure 3 — Distribution of the average number of clearances per burglary arrest for the 79 precincts of New York City, January 1 - June 30, 1967.

APPENDIX VIII

CLEARANCE RATES

Traditionally, police statistics carry figures on "Crimes Cleared by Arrest." The label is a slight misnomer, since there are some situations where the crime may be noted as cleared even if no arrest has occurred. E.g.: a juvenile cited to appear in Juvenile

Court; suicide of the alleged offender; his having been killed by the police; extradition is denied, etc.

The great bulk of "clearances" are likely to be based on arrests of a single person for a single crime. But variations may occur:

1. One arrest may clear several crimes, for instance, if an arrested burgler confesses several burglaries. Here one arrest causes several clearances.

2. One crime may involve several arrests, for instance, if one robbery was committed by several men. Here several arrests cause one clearance.

The two deviations from the one-to-one relationship will have a tendency to balance each other. It will therefore not come as a surprise that the number of clearances and the number of arrests are as a rule not far apart. Here, for instance, are the pertinent excerpts from the summary tabulation of the 1969 *Uniform Crime Reports* for 2,497,957 offenses known, representing 2,344 cities with an estimated 1969 population of 59,267,000.[1]

COMPARING "CLEARANCE" AND "ARREST" FIGURES

	Per Cent Offenses Cleared	Ratio of Arrests to Offenses known	Difference	
Violent Crimes	46.6	41.3	-5.3	-5.3
Property Crimes	17.5	17.6	+0.1	+0.1
Homicide	84.8	98.8	+14.0	+14.0
Forcible rape	55.7	53.7	-2.0	-2.0
Robbery	25.8	28.7	+2.9	+2.9
Aggravated Assault	67.0	51.0	-16.0	-16.0
Burglary	17.1	18.1	+1.0	+1.0
Auto Theft	17.2	17.3	+0.1	+0.1
Total	19.7	19.4	-0.3	-0.3

The property crimes (burglary, larceny and auto theft) show relatively small differences; the violent crimes somewhat larger ones. At some point it might be worthwhile to study the various "mixes" that go into these crime categories. Judging merely from the marginal differences between clearance and arrest ratio, it would seem that auto theft is the crime likely to have more cases

---

1 Table 17, page 103.

of "one arrest – one clearance" than the other crimes. Burglars confess occasionally to more than one crime, and larceny results more often in more than one arrest for one crime.[2]

APPENDIX IX

JUMPING CRIME RATES

For the metropolitan area of the following cities the development of the FBI Index crimes per 100,000 population is recorded as follows:

Pittsburgh		Denver	
Date	Average Annual Rate of Change in %	Date	Average Annual Rate of Change in %
1960-67 (7 years)	+ 7	1960-67 (7 years)	+ 6
1965-66 (1 year)	+ 1	1965-66 (1 year)	+ 8
1966-67 (1 year)	+19	1966-67 (1 year)	+13
1967-68 (1 year)	+35	1967-68 (1 year)	+35
1968-69 (1 year)	+ 1	1968-69 (1 year)	+31
New Orleans		Milwaukee	
1965-66 (1 year)	+40	1965-66 (1 year)	+20
1966-67 (1 year)	+13	1966-67 (1 year)	+33
1967-68 (1 year)	+ 2	1967-68 (1 year)	+ 7
1968-69 (1 year)	+12	1968-69 (1 year)	+12

---

2   Incidentally, the arrest figure for homicide comes close enough to the 100.0 percent level to suggest, since this is an average, that in many situations the ratio will transcend that level.

U.S. GOVERNMENT PRINTING OFFICE: 1971   O—448-559